The Chemistry and Mechanism of Art Materials

The Chemistry and Mechanism of Art Materials

Unsuspected Properties and Outcomes

Michael J. Malin, Ph.D.

CRC Press

Taylor & Francis Group

Boca Raton London New York

CRC Press is an imprint of the
Taylor & Francis Group, an **informa** business

A PXRF instrument mounted on a camera studio stand during analysis of 'The Lady Eating Oysters' (James Ensore, 1882) in the Koninklijk Museum voor Schone Kunsten Antwerpen, Antwerp, Belgium (please see Chapter 1, Figure 1.5).

First edition published 2022
by CRC Press
6000 Broken Sound Parkway NW, Suite 300, Boca Raton, FL 33487-2742

and by CRC Press
2 Park Square, Milton Park, Abingdon, Oxon, OX14 4RN

© 2022 Michael J. Malin

CRC Press is an imprint of Taylor & Francis Group, LLC

ISBN: 978-0-367-49075-1 (hbk)
ISBN: 978-0-367-51345-0 (pbk)
ISBN: 978-1-003-05345-3 (ebk)

DOI: 10.1201/9781003053453

Typeset in Times
by codeMantra

Contents

List of Figures

List of Schemes

List of Tables

Preface

Welcome. This book deals with the many chemical processes related to art materials. Subjects covered in the book include synthesis of inorganic pigments used by artists, silica and silicates, deterioration of pigments in paintings, toxicity of art materials, and aging of oil paint and wall paintings. There is an introductory chapter which reviews basic material such as chemical bonding, oxidation/reduction, mechanism writing, hard and soft acids and bases, and analytical methods used by art conservation scientists. A non-mathematical approach is taken throughout. The material has been written assuming that readers would have one year each of general chemistry and organic chemistry.

This book comes from my experience teaching a course on the chemistry of art materials at Sarah Lawrence College. Mechanisms "break down" complex chemical phenomena into a series of steps which allow the reader to logically follow the developing reaction. There was no book of this type available at the time I taught the course.

Mechanisms are the common language of chemistry. Most of the reactions in the book have been presented with mechanisms. These have been constructed from the composition and structures of reactants and products and mole ratios of reactants. This approach is superior to the presentation of net reactions, "black boxes", which usually do not engage the reader. Included are mechanisms for syntheses, discoloration of pigments, toxicity and aging of oil binder in paint and sulfation of wall paintings. Mechanisms must be consistent with reaction conditions and electronegativity differences of atoms which in turn are responsible for reactivity. Further, mechanisms are based on a limited list of possible "moves" (e.g., electron pairs moving toward the more electronegative atom which usually has a positive formal charge). The net effect is that the large and diverse universe of reactions can be understood to occur with a small set of mechanistic "moves".

Chapter 1 presents essential concepts such as bonding, oxidation numbers, mechanism writing and methods used by art conservationists. Much of this work is associated with the analysis of artworks facilitated by Synchrotron Radiation-based spectroscopies. These methods depend on very narrow beams of radiation focused with a microscope on tiny areas of paintings. Instruments can be programmed to scan across a painting to provide elemental-composition "maps", oxidation states and other types of information.

Chapter 2 deals with the synthesis of inorganic pigments used by artists. Organic pigments have been excluded. Most of the inorganic pigments contain transition-metal chromophores, e.g., mercury, vermilion; chromium, chrome yellow; lead, white lead and red lead, and so forth. There are some notable exceptions. For example, ultramarine originally was a rare material, mined in Afghanistan, refined from lapis lazuli, and shipped "over the sea" (hence "ultramarine"). Ultramarine consists of a cage-like aluminosilicate skeleton which houses di- and tri-polysulfide radical ions which are the chromophores. This pigment is now produced synthetically. The yellow and orange arsenic sulfide pigments, realgar and orpiment, are polycyclic compounds in which arsenic atoms are covalently bonded to sulfur atoms. There are many fascinating things to learn about these pigments. Chapter 3 presents the chemistry of silicates and aluminosilicates. These substances are the structural components of some pigments, ceramic glaze and ceramics.

Chapter 4 consists of chemical processes associated with discoloration of specific pigments in paintings. These vignettes are based on published materials in which the authors not only pursued and documented the color changes but also went further to investigate a plausible chemical mechanism. In the Cultural Heritage field, art conservation scientists first determine the nature of chemical change, and this is followed by restoration of the artwork by art restoration specialists. In this chapter, examples include explanations for the fading of chrome yellow in van Gogh's yellow "Sunflower" paintings, the blackening of red vermilion in the "Adoration of the Magi" painting by Rubens, the blue to gray discoloration of smalt and the photo-induced degradation/isomerization of α-realgar.

In Chapter 5, toxicity aspects of art materials are considered, focusing on solvents and pigments. The chemistry takes on a biochemical flavor. Exposure to art materials without the benefit of adequate safety measures and ventilation has long been associated with toxic consequences to the artist. Ironically, chemists and artists often use similar materials in their work. Yet, artists often ignore the toxicological properties of their materials. Chapter 6 is concerned with the aging of the binder in oil paint. Pigments often contribute to the deterioration of the oil binder and this, in turn, leads to cracks and surface eruptions. Chapter 7 presents some issues involved with aging of wall paintings.

I sincerely hope that the reader enjoys and learns from the material in the book.

Michael Malin

Acknowledgments

First, I would like to acknowledge my editor, Barbara Knott, for her support during the review phase and throughout the writing phase. Special thanks to Danielle Zarfati, my editorial assistant, who patiently answered my emails and advised me about permissions and images for the book. Thanks also to Tara Mawhinney, science librarian at McGill University, who helped me get started with literature searches during my summer visits to Montreal. Finally, thank you to the many authors who shared information about their published works.

Author

Michael Malin received a BS from City College of New York and a Ph.D. from Rutgers (biochemistry). This was followed by postdoctorals at Rutgers (organic) and then Brandeis (bio-organic). He taught chemistry at Western Connecticut State College/University (16 years) and at Sarah Lawrence College (SLC) (2 years). He covered courses in general, organic and biochemistry. At SLC, he taught a course in the chemistry of art materials, and this book came out of that experience. He was employed by Technicon Instruments Corporation/Bayer Diagnostics for 23 years. His time in industry was spent between two multi-year periods of teaching. His role was generally to solve stability problems related to both liquid reagent formulations and machine hardware in the development of automated blood analyzers. The scope of these problems varied widely, from the instability of a photo-polymerizable acrylic adhesive to the erosion of alumina shear valves. After he left industry, he resumed thinking about art materials and found common chemical/mechanistic themes related to stability problems. Eventually, this book was the result. His hobbies include international travel, playing double bass in jazz groups, salsa dancing, and cycling.

List of Abbreviations

BBB	blood–brain barrier
CB	conductance band
cm^{-1}	reciprocal cm
CYP450	cytochrome P450
CySH	cysteine
ETC	electron transport chain
FA	fatty acid
FTIR	Fourier Transform Infrared Spectroscopy
GC/MS	Gas Chromatography/Mass Spectrometry
GSH	glutathione
h$^+$	positively charged hole
IARC	International Agency for Research on Cancer
μ-XRF	micro-X-ray fluorescence
NMP	N-methylpyrrolidone
[O]	oxidation
ON	oxidation number
PB	Prussian blue
PXRF	portable X-ray fluorescence
[R]	reduction
RH	relative humidity
ROS	reactive oxygen species
SOD	superoxide dismutase
SR	synchrotron radiation
XAS	X-ray absorption spectroscopy
UM	ultramarine
VB	valence band
XRD	X-ray diffraction
XRF	X-ray fluorescence

1 Essential Concepts

1.1 CHEMICAL BONDING

Art materials are generally solids (including pigments, metals, ceramics and enamels, which are covered in this book) and also solvents, polymerizable liquid binders, including wax, egg yolk, (linseed) oil and acrylic polymers (which are organic materials) [1]. Of the organic materials, the toxicity of solvents and the aging of oil binders are covered in the book. The focus will be inorganic materials, particularly pigments whose discolorations have been investigated by contemporary analytical techniques and described in detail. Some space is also allotted to ceramics and glazes to provide a chemical foundation.

There are four types of inorganic solids: metallic, ionic, molecular, and network. These are distinguished by the lattice-point particles (i.e., the type of particle, atom or ion), which occupy the lattice points of the respective crystal, and physical properties such as melting point, electrical conductivity, hardness and solubility, see Table 1.1.

Solubility is defined as the number of grams of substance which will dissolve in 100 mL of a liquid solvent at a specified temperature. Inorganic pigments are generally ionic compounds with low solubility in water and even lower solubility in organic liquids, e.g., linseed oil, or egg yolk. In oil painting, linseed oil is used as a "binder", a spreadable liquid in which pigment particles are suspended.

Metallic solids include pure metals (elements) and also alloys in which the two or more species of metal atoms have similar size and are therefore able to co-crystallize. The "sea of electrons" model for metallic bonding consists of a three-dimensional stacked array of cations which are surrounded by loosely bound valence electrons which

TABLE 1.1
Solids and Associated Physical Properties [1]

Solid/property	Metallic	Ionic	Molecular	Network
Particle	Atoms	Ions	Molecules	Atoms
Bonding	Metallic	Ionic	Covalent	Covalent
Melting point	Low to high	High	Low	High
Elec. Conductivity	High	Solid: nil	Nil	Nil
		Melt: high		
		Solution: high		
Hardness	Hard	Hard	Soft	Hard
Solubility	Insol	Depends on ionic charge	Like dissolves like	Insoluble
Examples	Ag, Cu, Pb	$CaCO_3$	Arsenic sulfides	Diamond
		Prussian blue	Orpiment, realgar	Silica

DOI: 10.1201/9781003053453-1

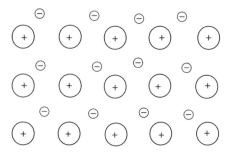

FIGURE 1.1   Electron-sea model for metal bonding.

are shared by all of the cations, see Figure 1.1. The mobility of the valence electrons is consistent with the high electrical conductivity and thermal conductivity of metals.

Ionic solids are held together by Coulombic forces between anions and cations according to Coulomb's Law:

$$\text{Force of ionic attraction} = \left[k \left| q^+ q^- \right| \right] / d^2,$$

where q^+ and q^- are the respective ionic charges, d is the inter-nuclear distance and k is a proportionality constant. Hence, ionic bond strength is directly proportional to the absolute value of the product of the ionic charges and inversely proportional to the inter-nuclear distance. This accounts for the wide range in water solubility of salts, e.g., $Na^+ Cl^-$ (very soluble) and $Ca^{2+} S^{2-}$ (poorly soluble). Further, ionic compounds conduct electricity in the molten state and also when dissolved in a solvent because the ions are mobile. In the solid state, ionic compounds do not conduct because the ions are locked up in a crystalline lattice. When salts dissolve in water, the aquated ions carry electrical current through the solution. Figure 1.2 shows a representation of the NaCl crystal matrix in which the smaller spheres are the sodium cations and the larger spheres are the chloride anions [2].

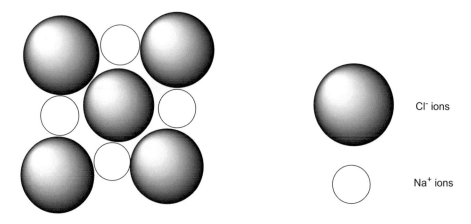

Cl^- ions

Na^+ ions

FIGURE 1.2   NaCl crystal lattice.

In *molecular* solids, the atoms are held together by covalent bonds. Melting points of molecular compounds are low, generally < 200°C, because the crystal lattice is stabilized by weak attractive forces between molecules (e.g., dispersion forces, dipole–dipole interactions and hydrogen bonds), all of which are considerably weaker than either covalent or ionic bonds. When a molecular crystal is heated to its melting point, the weak *intermolecular* forces are broken but not the strong *intramolecular* covalent bonds unless decomposition occurs. This class of compounds does not conduct electricity because there are no ions present. Covalent bonds are "directional" in the sense that they form because of the overlap of hybridized orbitals and as a consequence, specific molecular geometries result which manifest in characteristic bond angles. In contrast, ionic bonds are not directional, and characteristic crystal unit cells are formed because of favorable energetics due to stacking of ions (in ionic compounds) or atoms (in metals).

In discussions of chemical bonding, it is convenient to present three types of bonds. See Figure 1.3, where "I" represents a covalent bond between two identical atoms (e.g., I_2 or H_2). In this case, the electron pair which comprises a single bond must be equally shared between the bonding partners, and therefore, this type of bond is said to be non-polar. The other extreme situation, "III", can be represented by the ionic bond between Na^+ and Cl^-, in which there is little or no sharing of a pair of electrons. In pictorial terms, the pair of electrons in the bond resides very close to the chlorine and far away from the sodium, so that effectively an *ion-pair* is formed. In the intermediate situation, II, a pair of electrons is unequally shared between the bonding partners. The more unequal the sharing, the more polarized the bond will be. In this situation, partial positive and negative charges are assigned to the bonding pair, and a bond dipole can be drawn over the bond (with the arrow facing the negative end of the dipole). The concept of electronegativity (EN) was developed to account for the varying tendency of different atoms to attract electrons. The qualitative concept of EN is universally accepted and is very useful in predicting electrophilic or nucleophilic reactive sites in molecules. However, the assignment of numerical values in an EN scale is more difficult because this tendency cannot be measured directly. Pauling and others developed numerical EN scales in which fluorine is the most electronegative atom. In these systems, metals are given positive values, and non-metals are given negative values, consistent with the tendency to be either electron donors or receptors.

This diagram shows three archetypical bonding situations. Pauling and others proposed "dividing lines" which separated polar from non-polar bonds and polar from

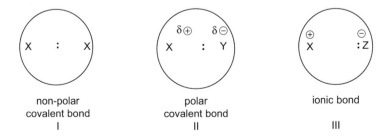

FIGURE 1.3 Bond archetypes based on electronegativity differences.

ionic bonds. Therefore, it is reasonable to state that a covalent bond between two identical atoms would have to be non-polar, and bonds between two non-identical atoms would have both a covalent and an ionic component. As ΔEN increases, the ionic component increases until the bond is ionic.

1.2 OXIDATION–REDUCTION, OXIDATION NUMBERS

Oxidation numbers are assigned to atoms in ions or molecules which are undergoing the gain or loss of electrons (reduction or oxidation). Elements are assigned the oxidation number zero. If an elemental atom accepts two electrons, then its ON would be −2. For example, if one molecule of dioxygen *accepts* a total of 4 e⁻, the products would be two oxide ions:

> 1 O_2 + 4 e⁻ [R] → 2 O^{2-}, chemical reduction, reactant gains electrons. And conversely, if a Group 1A atom *loses* one electron, then its ON would be +1. An example would be:
> Na· [O] → Na^+ + 1 e⁻, chemical oxidation (oxidation, reactant loses electrons).

A complete set of rules for calculating the ON for any atom in a chemical compound are as follows:

1. ON for any element if zero.
2. ON for any monoatomic ion equals the ionic charge.
3. For polyatomic compounds, the sum of ON's is zero; and for polyatomic ions, the sum of ON's equals the ionic charge.
4. In compounds, the more-electronegative element (usually a non-metal) has the more negative ON. The more-electropositive element (usually H or a metal) has the more positive ON.
5. The ON for oxygen is usually −2; except in peroxides, where it is −1.
6. The ON for hydrogen is usually +1; except in metallic hydrides, such as NaH, where hydrogen has ON of −1.
7. Since there is only one As atom in O=As(OH)$_3^-$, its ON is +5.

The oxidation numbers for various atoms are based on the atom's reactivity. In this system, the oxidation numbers for H and O are +1 and −2, respectively. For H, +1 indicates that the neutral atom's reactivity is to lose one electron and become a positively charged proton. For oxygen, its reactivity would be for a neutral atom with six valence electrons to gain two electrons and become O^{2-}, a negatively charged oxide anion. In this accounting method, the sum of all oxidation numbers for the molecule or ion in question must be zero.

This allows us to calculate the oxidation number of arsenic in O=As(OH)$_3$, see Table 1.2. In this neutral molecular compound, the total net charge must be zero. The total negative charge contributed by the four oxygen atoms is $[4 \times (-2) = -8]$. The total charge attributed to the three hydrogen atoms is $[3 \times (+1) = +3]$. Therefore the total charge contributed by arsenic must be +5. And since there is only one arsenic atom, its ON is +5.

TABLE 1.2

Calculation of Oxidation Number of As in O=As(OH)$_3$

Atom	Number of Atoms	x	ON	= Total Charge
H	3		+1	+3
O	4		−2	−8
As	1		?	+5

1.3 HARD AND SOFT ACID BASE THEORY

The preference of Group 12 cations (Zn^{2+}, Cd^{2+} and Hg^{2+}) for ions and covalently bonded atoms of sulfur and selenium is satisfactorily explained by the Theory of Hard and Soft Acids and Bases (HSAB) [3,4]. Accordingly, bond formation between electron acceptors (Lewis acids) and electron donors (Lewis bases) in solution is driven by polarizability (transient polarity caused by momentary distortion of the electron clouds) of the bonding partners. The very polarizable species are classified as "*soft*" acids and bases, and the poorly polarizable species are then "*hard*" acids and bases – all in the Lewis concept of acidity/basicity, which is based on sharing of *electrons*. [Recall that the Bronsted concept of acidity/basicity depends on the sharing of *protons*.] Hard Lewis acids prefer to bond with hard Lewis bases (Na^+ and F^-), and soft acids with soft bases (Hg^{2+} and S^{2-}). The pairing preferences are analogous to the solubility rule, "like dissolves like". For example,

$$Hg^{2+} + H:SR \rightarrow Hg^+:SR + H^+.$$

Note that the coordinate bond formed from sulfur or selenium uses a lone pair from the Group 16 atom. Further, the new bond has a partial covalent character. The HSAB concept has been applied to geochemistry, which explains why specific ion pairs formed during the formation of the Earth's crust, thus accounting for the occurrence of minerals such as $CaCO_3$, $CaSO_4 \ 2H_2O$, $BaSO_4$, Al_2O_3, Fe_2O_3 (hard acid–hard base), and Ag_2S, HgS, ZnS, PbS, As_4S_6 and FeS_2 (soft or borderline acid–soft base), see Table 1.3 [3,4].

TABLE 1.3

Hard and Soft (Lewis) Acids and (Lewis) Bases [3]

Lewis Acids (metal centers)

Hard: Li^+, Na^+, K^+, Ca^{2+}, Sr^{2+}, Ba^{2+}, Cu^{2+}, Al^{3+}, Cr^{3+}, Co^{3+}, Fe^{3+}, Ti^{4+}, Zr^{4+}, Sn^{4+}, VO^{2+}

Borderline: Fe^{2+}, Co^{2+}, Zn^{2+}, Pb^{2+}, Sn^{2+}, Sb^{3+}, Bi^{3+}

Soft: Cu^+, Ag^+, Au^+, Hg^+, Cd^{2+}, Hg^{2+}, CH_3Hg^+

Lewis Bases (ligands)

Hard: H_2O, O^{2-}, HO^-, F^-, $CH_3CO_2^-$, $[PO_4]^{3-}$, $[SO_4]^{2-}$, Cl^-, $[CO_3]^{2-}$, $[NO_3]^-$, NH_3, RNH_2, H_2NNH_2

Borderline: $[N_3]^-$, Br^-, $[NO_2]^-$, $[SO_3]^{2-}$

Soft: H_2S, I^-, RS^-, S^{2-}, SCN^-, R_3As, CN^-, CO

1.4   WRITING CHEMICAL REACTION MECHANISMS

Throughout the book, reactions are presented first as a balanced net equation and then in the mechanistic form [5]. The purpose of the mechanisms is to illustrate that complex reactions which seem to have little commonality, often share common features. The power of the mechanistic approach is that it allows the reader to reason through a reaction as long as the structures and mole ratio of the reactants and products are known. This also engages the reader and avoids the presentation of a list of reactions to be memorized or to be accepted as a "black box".

As an example, consider the acid-catalyzed hydrolysis of a carboxylic acid ester presented in Scheme 1.1.

This mechanism presented in Scheme 1.2 illustrates the hydrolysis of an ester in acidic aqueous solution. The reaction is acid-catalyzed, and in aqueous solution, protons are attached to water forming the hydronium ion, H_3O^+. [I] and [Ia] represent resonance forms of the ester starting material. Resonance (the movement of valence electrons within valence-bond structures) is facilitated by the EN difference between carbon and oxygen, which is inherent in the polarized C=O bond. Species [Ia] has a negative formal charge on oxygen and a positive formal charge on carbon. *The general rule in mechanisms is that the curved arrow always shows the direction of electron flow toward the more positively charged atom.* In step 1, the carbonyl oxygen is protonated by addition of H^+, resulting in the positive charge being formally transferred to the carbon atom and a carbocation [II] is formed. The electropositive (electrophilic) carbon atom is a "magnet" which is attacked in step 2 by a lone pair of electrons on the oxygen atom of water (the nucleophilic agent) to form onium ion, [III]. In [IV], the positive charge has been transferred to the oxygen atom which formerly belonged to water. In step 3, the "extra" proton is transferred to a molecule of water, and then, the alkoxy oxygen is protonated by H_3O^+ to form an onium cation [V]. In the final step, one of the OH groups is deprotonated by transfer of H^+ to water, and electrons flow toward the carbon to form a C=O bond, which then forces the alcohol product, HOR, to leave. The reaction generates two products, the carboxylic acid, $R'CO_2H$ and the alcohol, ROH. Additionally, the catalyst H_3O^+ is regenerated. If all of the intermediates are removed, the net process is equivalent to the balanced equation. And, significantly, both charge and mass are conserved. In mechanism construction, the formal charge on atoms is a concern. The formal charge can be calculated with the formal charge rule, whereby

$$\text{Charge on an atom} = \text{group number} - \text{number of covalent bonds}$$

$$- \text{number of non} - \text{bonded electrons}$$

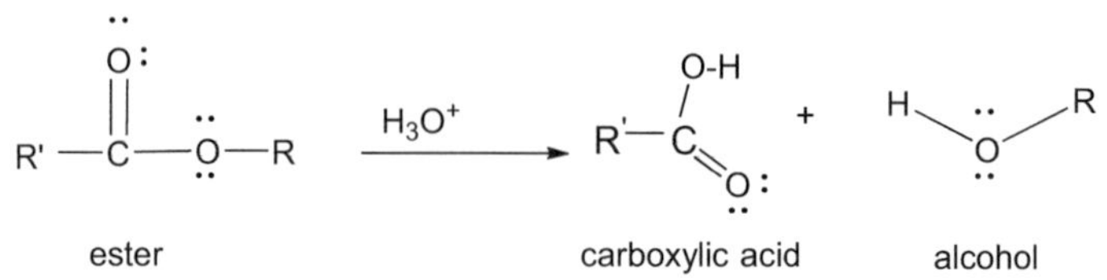

SCHEME 1.1   Ester hydrolysis net reaction.

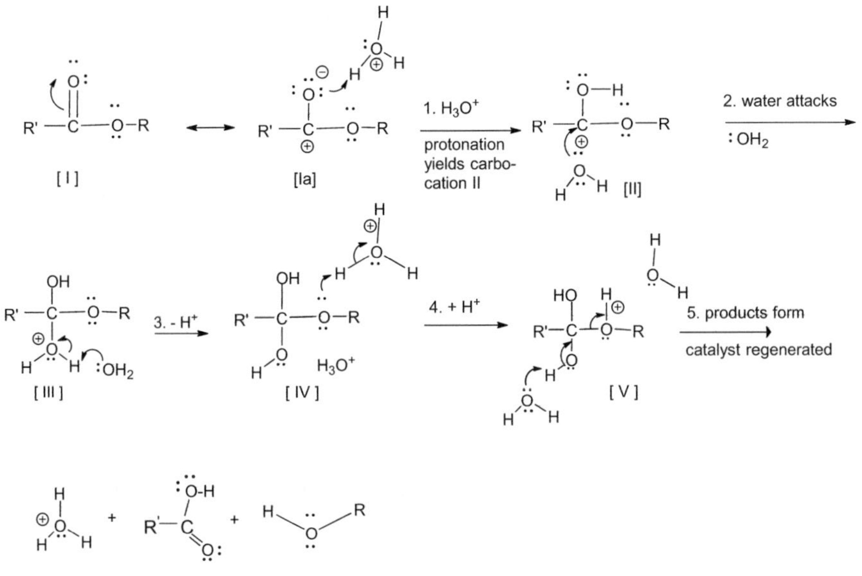

SCHEME 1.2 Ester hydrolysis mechanism.

In general, the formal charge on covalently bonded atoms usually does not exceed ± 2. Also, if there is choice on where to place a formal charge, the more-electronegative atom would receive the negative charge, and the less-electronegative atom would receive the positive charge.

1.5 EXPERIMENTAL METHODS USED TO CHARACTERIZE WORKS OF ART

How do art conservation scientists characterize works of art? Visual inspection may indicate that a pigment is fading, and this would be the first step in defining the nature of the chemical change (or "alteration") of the pigment. Conservation scientists analyze art works for three main reasons: to diagnose alterations, to establish authenticity and to investigate the artist's motivations for particular works.

Until about the 1990s, alteration problems were analyzed by physically removing tiny samples from the artwork. This approach was undesirable because it has a destructive effect on the artwork. Fortunately, the analytical process has been dramatically improved by recent developments in instrumentation, which allow the specimen to be examined in a non-destructive manner. The keys to this improvement include synchrotron radiation (SR)-based spectroscopy, lasers and micro-spectroscopy. Some of the methods used in contemporary art conservation work may not be familiar to students. In this section, the reader will be introduced to these methods.

1.5.1 X-RAY SPECTROSCOPIC METHODS

Synchrotrons are large-ring particle accelerators which were constructed to study high-energy particle physics. The diameter of synchrotrons ranges from 180 to

460 m. In the mid-1990s, art conservation-minded chemists became acquainted with physicists with SR expertise; the rest is history. Consequently, high-energy electrons (X-rays) can be focused on tiny areas of a painting, and samples need not be physically removed from the original artwork. In principle, synchrotrons can generate frequencies from the entire electromagnetic spectrum. There are several types of SR-based X-ray-based spectroscopic method: X-ray fluorescence (XRF) and X-ray absorption spectroscopy (XAS) {X-ray absorption near edge spectroscopy (XANES) and extended absorbance fine structure (EXAFS)} and X-ray diffraction (XRD). In addition, SR-based FTIR spectroscopy is also widely available. These methods optionally can include a microscope which narrows the focus to a tiny area. The advantages of SR-based spectroscopies include non-invasive, low detection limits, high lateral resolution and high chemical sensitivity [6,7]. Each methodology reveals different information about the sample, see Table 1.4.

XRF results from X-ray radiation of the sample which excites a core electron to either an unoccupied orbital or ejects the electron from the atom. Loss of the core electron creates a positively charged hole ("h$^+$"). A short time later, an electron from a higher energy level drops down to occupy the hole, and this is accompanied by *emission* of energy (as fluorescence). Each element has a characteristic emission energy, thereby facilitating elemental analysis. XRF is illustrated for a generic atom, as shown in Figure 1.4. The utility of XRF is illustrated in Table 1.5, which relates pigments, color and elements detected by XRF [8,9]. The development of *portable* spectrometers has facilitated data collection in the art conservation field. For example, a portable X-ray fluorescence spectrometry (*PXRF*) was used to determine the characteristics of pigments used by the painter, James Ensore, see Figure 1.5 [10].

TABLE 1.4

SR-Based Spectroscopic Methods and Information Characteristics

Method	Information Obtained
XRF[a]	Elemental analysis, qualitative and semi-quantitative
XAS[b]	
XANES[c]	Chemical oxidation state, coordination number
EXAFS[d]	Number and type of neighboring atoms, bond distances
XRD[e]	Structure of crystalline phases
FTIR[f]	Qualitative presence of functional groups, organic and inorganic

[a] X-Ray Fluorescence.

[b] X-Ray Absorption Spectroscopy.

[c] X-Ray Absorption Near Edge Structure.

[d] Extended X-Ray Extended Fine Structure.

[e] X-Ray Diffraction.

[f] Fourier Transform Infrared.

Modified and reprinted with permission of M. Cotte, J. Susini, J. Dik, K. Janssens, (2010) *Acc. Chem. Res.* 43: 705–714.

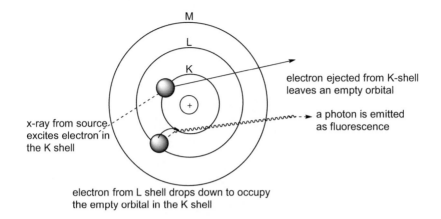

FIGURE 1.4 X-Ray fluorescence atomic model.

TABLE 1.5
Elements in Paintings Detectable by XRF [7,8]

Color	Key Element	Pigment	or	Chemical Formula
Yellow, brown, green, red	Fe	Ochres, earths		Iron oxides and silicates
Blue green	Cu	Cu pigments		Natural: azurite, malachite, atacamite artificial: acetates, resinates, chlorides
White	Pb	Lead white		$2PbCO_3 \cdot Pb(OH)_2$
Blue	Co	Smalt		SiO_2, K_2O, Al_2O_3, CoO
Red	Hg	Cinnabar		HgS
Red	Pb	Red lead		Pb_3O_4
Yellow	As	Orpiment		As_4O_6
Dark brown	Mn	Manganese brown		MnO_2
Yellow	Cd	Cadmium yellow		CdS
White	Ti	Titanium dioxide		TiO_2
Yellow	Pb + Sn	Lead-tin yellow		Pb_2SnO_4 and $PbSnO_3$
Yellow	Pb + Sb	Naples yellow		$Pb_3(SbO_4)_2$
Brown	Fe + Mn	Umber		MnO_2 + Fe hydroxide
Yellow	Pb + Cr	Chrome yellow		$PbCrO_4$
Red	Pb + Cr	Chrome red		$PbCrO_4 \cdot Pb(OH)_2$
Green	As + Cu	Emerald green		$Cu(CH_3CO_2)_2 \cdot 3Cu(AsO_2)_2$
White	Zn + Ba	Lithopone		$ZnS + BaSO_4$

XAS is also triggered by irradiation of the sample by X-rays, which promote an inner-core electron to a higher energy level. A detector tracks the *absorption* of energy as the strength of exciting energy is increased, see Figure 1.6. There are several features of interest. The XANES region provides information about the oxidation state and coordination number. EXAFS is sensitive to the type and number of neighboring atoms and bond lengths.

FIGURE 1.5 A PXRF instrument mounted on a camera studio stand during analysis of *The Lady Eating Oysters* (James Ensore, 1882) in the Koninklijk Museum voor Schone Kunsten Antwerpen, Antwerp, Belgium. (Reprinted with permission of G. Van der Snickt, K. Janssens, O. Schalm, C. Albeo, H. Kloust, M. Alfeld, *X-Ray Spectrom* (2010) 39: 103–111. Copyright 2009, John Wiley and Sons.)

The XAS spectrum is generated by varying the voltage of incident X-rays and measuring the energy absorbance of the sample. The applied voltage is proportional to the frequency of the associated wavelength of incident X-rays. For example, Figure 1.6 shows the XAS of chromium in $K_2Cr_2O_7$ [6]. As the voltage is increased, the XANES region appears, encompassing the range: about ± 150 eV to either side of the absorption *edge*. The edge is the step-rising region marked by "E_0". In the spectrum of $K_2Cr_2O_7$, there is a strong *pre-edge* peak at 5.993 keV which is diagnostic for Cr^{6+} and tetrahedral geometry. In the pre-edge region, the energy absorbed by the absorbing atom promotes a core electron (K, L or M shell) to an unoccupied orbital of higher energy. This transition is strongly dependent on the cationic charge of the metal. At the edge, the incident energy is strong enough to cause the excited electron to ionize (escape from the atom). Practically, the signals in the XANES region are useful in "fingerprinting" i.e. comparing an unknown to pure standard compounds. The degradation of chrome yellow pigment ($PbCrO_4 \rightarrow Cr_2O_3$), ($Cr^{6+} \rightarrow Cr^{3+}$) was based on XANES data, see Figure 4.11 [11]. Beyond the XANES region is the EX**AFS** region in which oscillating peaks and valleys (**fine structure**) are often very weak compared to the XANES signals. The oscillations arise from electron waves emanating from the absorbing atom. These waves interact with neighboring atoms, and some of the energy is reflected back to the absorbing atom. The interaction of the

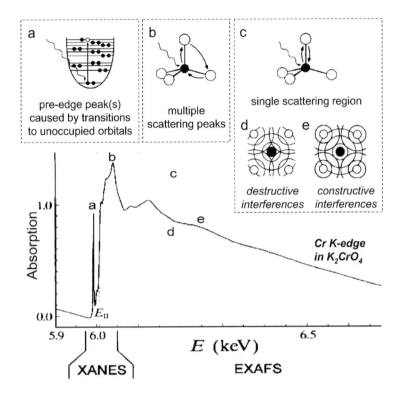

FIGURE 1.6 X-Ray absorption spectrum of $K_2Cr_2O_7$. XANES, X-ray absorption near edge spectroscopy; EXAFS, extended absorbance fine structure. (Reprinted with permission of M. Cotte, J. Susini, K. Janssens, *Acc. Chem. Res.* (2010) 43: 705–714. Copyright 2010, American Chemical Society.)

backscattered waves results in both constructive and destructive interferences. These interferences result in the oscillating pattern [7].

XRD yields the structure of crystalline phases in the sample. The sample is irradiated with monochromatic X-rays which are reflected by atoms in the repeating crystal lattice and yield a diffraction pattern. The structure is deduced from the pattern of dots with the use of Bragg's Law and sophisticated calculations. The underlying principle of XRD is that the wavelengths of X-rays are about the same length as the distance between atoms in a crystal ($\sim 10^{-10}$m). The crystal acts like a diffraction grating for the X-rays. Further, each crystalline substance generates a unique diffraction pattern. For X-ray crystallography, it is usual to use an X-ray vacuum tube equipped with a copper anode. In this tube, electrons emitted by the cathode are accelerated under high voltage and collide with the anode, which produces X-rays. K_α X-rays arise from anodic electronic transitions when an electron in the L (2p) shell falls to the K (1s) shell.

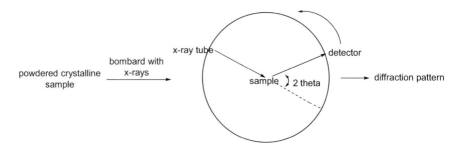

FIGURE 1.7   Schematic for X-Ray diffraction.

The purpose of XRD is to determine the structure of the crystalline phase(s) in the sample. Bear in mind that a single chemical substance may have more than one crystalline form. A powdered crystalline sample is irradiated with X-rays of a defined wavelength, λ. Ideal crystals are repeating arrays of atoms, ions or molecules which are arranged in lattice planes, which are in turn separated by a regular repeating distance, d. Actual crystals also contain defects which cause difficulties in the analysis. The detector is rotated around the sample, and at each setting of the angle of incident rays, $\ominus$, reflected rays are collected, see Figure 1.7.

Bragg's Law, $n\lambda = 2d\sin\theta$, is the key relationship used to decipher diffraction patterns; n is an integer which can have the value of 1, 2, or 3; λ, d and $\ominus$ as defined. The diffraction pattern is a series of lines (due to constructive interference or "in-phase" reflected rays) separated by spaces (destructive interference or "out-of-phase" reflected rays). The pattern is deconvolved through computerized calculations to give the size and shape of a crystal unit cell [8,13].

1.5.2 ELECTRON MICROSCOPY

Electron microscopy (EM) is used to characterize the structure, crystal shape and elemental composition of solids. The underlying principle for this technique is analogous to light microscopy except that a beam of accelerated electrons replaces a beam of visible light. Electrons behave both as particles and as waves. For a beam of high-energy electrons, the associated wavelengths are very small. For example, for an accelerating voltage of 100 kV, the associated wavelength is 0.0123 nm (0.123 Å). In SEM (scanning electron microscopy), the incident electron beam collides with an atom near the surface of the sample and causes a K-level electron to be ejected from the atom. This results in a positively charged hole, h^+ which is filled by a L-level electron which drops down. The excess energy results in the emission of a "characteristic" X-ray (i.e., unique for different types of atoms in the sample). The detection of these characteristic X-rays constitutes SEM-EDX (scanning electron microscopy-energy dispersed analysis by X-rays) and thereby facilitates qualitative and quantitative elemental analysis of the sample [7]. EDX is based on the same principle as XRF. The difference between the methods is the type of radiation used to impact the sample. In EDX, an electron beam is used, while in XRF, an X-ray beam is used. Further, XRF is more sensitive than EDX [12]. SEM-EDX was used to detect changes in the elemental composition of smalt which caused color change from blue to gray, see Figure 4.15.

In transmission electron microscopy (TEM), a very thin sample is exposed to an electron beam such that electrons pass through the sample. By combining scans taken at different angles, a three-dimensional structure is obtained. A scanning transmission electron microscope (STEM) combines the scanning feature of SEM with high resolution of TEM. Electron energy loss spectroscopy (EELS) data is obtained with STEM. The thin sample is exposed to a high-energy electron beam, and some of the incident energy is transferred to electrons in the sample by inelastic collisions. The energy loss yields the following information: chemical elements, stoichiometry and bonding. For an example of the application of EELS in the degradation of the pigment chrome yellow, see Figure 4.12 [7].

1.5.3 VIBRATIONAL SPECTROSCOPY

Infrared spectroscopy (IR) is based on bond vibrations in which there is a change in bond dipole. It is used to identify bond types and functional groups. Samples can be crystalline or amorphous. Raman spectroscopy is a complimentary method also based on bond vibrations. In Raman spectroscopy, a laser excites the sample and characteristic non-elastic vibration bands are detected. In Raman spectroscopy, lasers provide a highly concentrated beam of radiant energy somewhat analogous to synchrotrons. Raman frequencies are detected provided that there is a distortion of the electron cloud of specific bonds (i.e., polarizability) when they vibrate. Consideration of the symmetry of the molecule allows for prediction of which vibrations will be detected by IR or Raman [13–16]. For colored compounds (including pigments), there is greatly enhanced sensitivity when the laser excitation wavelength coincides with absorption maxima in the visible spectrum; this is known as Resonance Raman Spectroscopy.

1.5.4 ELECTROCHEMICAL METHODS

Electrochemical methods have been used to investigate photo-semiconductor pigments which are susceptible to redox. Such studies are advantageous because data can be collected quickly, and results show a progression of products which result from discrete redox reactions. Examples of pigments studied with this analytical modality include the photo-semiconductors: red lead, cadmium yellow and cinnabar/vermilion. In a typical three-electrode experimental setup, a water-insoluble pigment is deposited on a graphite electrode which is then exposed to laser irradiation. The electrodes are immersed in a pH-controlled buffered aqueous solution, see Figure 1.8. Reaction products are determined by spectroscopic analysis of the solid material adhering to the irradiated electrode [17–20].

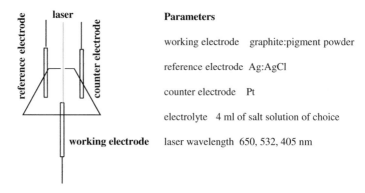

Parameters

working electrode   graphite:pigment powder

reference electrode   Ag:AgCl

counter electrode   Pt

electrolyte   4 ml of salt solution of choice

laser wavelength   650, 532, 405 nm

FIGURE 1.8   Electrochemical setup of pigment-modified electrode with irradiation possibility. (Adapted and reprinted with permission of W. Anaf, S. Trashin, O. Schalm, D. van Dorp, K. Janssens, K. DeWael (2014) *Anal. Chem.* 86:9742–9748. Copyright 2014, American Chemical Society.)

REFERENCES

1. Tro NJ (2017) *Chemistry A Molecular Approach*, 4th ed: 382–472, 532–556 Pearson, Boston.
2. Pietrovito A, Davies P (2007) Ionic crystal structures, http://www.seas.upenn.edu. Accessed 27 Dec 2017.
3. Raynor-Canham G, Overton T (2006) *Descriptive Inorganic Chemistry*, 4th ed: 148–154, Freeman, New York.
4. Hancock RD, Martell AE (1996) Hard and soft acid-base behavior in solution. *J Chem Ed* 73:654–661
5. Wade LG, Jr (2006) *Organic Chemistry*, 6th ed: 1007, Pearson, Upper Saddle River, NJ.
6. Cotte M, Susini J, Dik J, Janssens K (2010) Synchrotron-based X-ray absorption spectroscopy for art conservation: looking back and looking forward. *Acc Chem Res* 43:705–714.
7. Smart LE, Moore EA (2012) *Solid State Chemistry An Introduction*, 4th ed: 75–89, 101–111, 116–124. CRC Press, Taylor and Francis Group, Boca Raton, London, New York.
8. Canova C, Ferretti M (2000) XRF spectrometers for non-destructive investigations in art and archeology: the cost of portability. *15th World Conference on Non-Destructive Testing*, 15–21 October, 2000.
9. Howard DL, de Jonge MD, Lau D, Hay D, Varcoe-Cocks M, Ryan CG, Kirkham R, Moorhead G, Paterson D, Thurrowgood D (2012) High definition X-ray fluorescence mapping of paintings. *Anal Chem* 84:3278–3286.
10. Van der Snickt G, Janssens K, Schalm O, Albeo C, Kloust H, Alfeld M (2010) James Ensore's pigment use: artistic and material evolution studied by means of portable X-ray spectrometry. *X-Ray Spectrom* 39:103–111.
11. Monico, L, Janssens K, Miliani C, et al. (2013) Degradation of lead chromate in paintings by Vincent van Gogh studied by means of spectroscopic methods. 4. Artificial ageing of model samples of co-precipitates of lead chromate and lead sulfate. *Anal Chem* 85:860–867.
12. Scanning Electron Microscope, SEM, Yale University, West Campus Materials Characterization Core, https:// ywcmatsci.yale.edu/sem, downloaded May 8, 2021.

13. Skoog DA, Holler FJ, Nieman TA (1998) *Principles of Instrumental Analysis*, 5th ed: 278–281, 429–443. Harcourt Brace, Philadelphia, PA.
14. Housecroft CE, Sharp AG (2008) *Inorganic Chemistry*, 3rd ed: 100–101, Pearson/ Prentice Hall, Harlow.
15. Bell IM, Clark RJH, Gibbs PJ (1997) Raman spectroscopic library of natural and synthetic pigments (pre~1850 AD). *Spectrochim Acta Part A* 53:2159–2179.
16. Caggiano MC, Cosentino A, Mangone A (2016) Pigments Checker version 3.0, a handy set for conservation scientists: A free online Raman spectra database. *Microchem J* 129:123–132.
17. Anaf W, Trashin S, Schalm O, van Dorp D, Janssens K, DeWael K (2014) Electrochemical photodegradation study of semiconductor pigments: influence of environmental parameters. *Anal Chem* 86:9742–9748.
18. Anaf W, Janssens K, DeWael K (2013) Formation of metallic mercury during photodegradation/photodarkening of α-HgS: electrochemical evidence. *Angew Chem Int Ed* 52:12568–12571.
19. Ayalew E, Janssens K, DeWael K (2016) Unraveling the reactivity of minium toward bicarbonate and the role of lead oxides therein. *Anal Chem* 88:1564–1569.
20. Janssens K, Van der Snickt G, Vanmeert F, Legrand S, et al. (2016). Non-invasive and non-destructive examination of artistic pigments, paints, and paintings by means of x-ray methods. *Top Curr Chem* (Z) Doi: 10.1007/s41061-016-0079-2.

2 Preparation of Inorganic Pigments Used by Artists

The preparation of inorganic pigments used by artists is grouped by color in this order: black, blue, brown, green, red, violet, white, and yellow. Key references are noted which cover aspects of synthesis, manufacture, properties and uses of many inorganic pigments [1–3].

2.1 BLACK PIGMENTS

Antimony Black, Sb_2S_3, antimony trisulfide can be prepared by treatment of an aqueous solution of Sb^{3+} with H_2S [3]. Current uses include pyrotechnics and ruby glass. The chemical structure consists of $(Sb_4S_6)_n$ units which form infinite parallel chains, see Figure 2.1 [4–6]. In this structure, there are two types of Sb atoms and three types of S atoms. With respect to Sb, one type is covalently bonded to three S. The second type of Sb is bonded to five S atoms; three by covalent bonds and the remaining by van der Waal's forces to the neighboring parallel chain. This substance can be synthesized as follows:

$$2\,SbCl_{3\,(aq)} \;+\; 3\,H_2S_{(aq)} \;\rightarrow\; Sb_2S_{3\,(s)} \;+\; 6\,HCl_{(aq)}$$

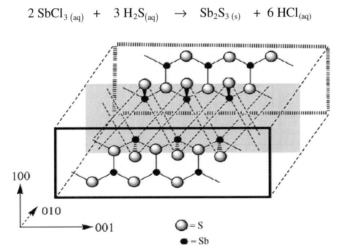

FIGURE 2.1 Antimony Black. Parallel chain structure of Sb_2S_3 viewed along the [010] direction. The dashed lines (---) indicate weak van der Waal's bonds and the cleavage trace is defined by the brown shadow. The numbers 100, 010, 001 and the axes located at the lower left corner of the figure are Miller Indices. Miller Indices are a notation system in crystallography relating planes in crystal lattices [6]. (Reprinted with permission of N. Maiti, S.H. Im, Y.H. Lee, S.I. Seok (2012) *ACS Appl. Mater. Interfaces* 4: 4787–4791. Copyright 2012, American Chemical Society).

DOI: 10.1201/9781003053453-2

Carbon Black is a generic name for a family of products that are used principally to strengthen rubber. It is also used as a pigment and as an electrically conductive material. There are many types of carbon black and their names often are associated with the carbon source (e.g., lampblack, boneblack or acetylene black) or with a specific process (furnace black). The worldwide production of carbon black in 2005 was >10 billion tons [1]. In the most widely used process, hydrocarbon feedstocks are partially oxidized at high temperature. The pyrolysis reaction is very fast. The overall reaction can be represented as follows:

$$C_xH_y + y/4\ O_2\ (1,200°C - 1,900°C) \rightarrow x\ C + y/2\ H_2O$$

$$\text{If } x = 2 \text{ and } y = 6, \text{ then, } C_2H_6 + 1.5\ O_2 \rightarrow 2\ C + 3\ H_2O.$$

Several theories have been presented to account for the formation of carbon black, but no single mechanism is consistent with all of the experimental data. There is agreement that carbon black formation involves three stages.

Stage 1: Nucleation, in which carbon atoms liberated from bonding with hydrogen combine covalently to form nanometer-sized particles;

Stage 2: Aggregation, in which nanometer-sized particles combine to form spherical particles which are 10–50 nm in diameter, and

Stage 3: Agglomeration, in which spherical particles form chains up to ~1 mm in length.

The form of carbon black known as lampblack is still produced by a process which is similar to that used by the ancient Chinese and Egyptians. Liquid hydrocarbons are combusted in a restricted air supply. The resulting smoke passes through settling chambers or filters, and the black solid material is collected. This process is probably familiar to most of us who have observed soot formation when a candle flame touches a metal surface.

When the words are switched, we have "black carbon", a term which refers to the collection of carbonaceous particles which are formed mostly from kerosene stoves, which collect in the atmosphere and prevent some of the sun's radiation from reaching the Earth's surface. Inhalation of black carbon is a recognized cause of respiratory issues [7].

Cobalt Black, Co_3O_4, cobalt (II, III) oxide. This compound contains Co^{2+} and Co^{3+}. It can be prepared by heating $Co_2O_3H_2O$ in the presence of air [8]. This material is not used as a pigment, but is used in ceramic glaze, and develops a deep blue color after firing. It is also used as an oxidation catalyst for fast drying paints and varnishes and was incorporated into potassium silicate glass to form the blue pigment, smalt.

$$CoO\ (300°C, air) \rightarrow Co_3O_4$$

Magnetite, Fe_3O_4, iron (II, III) oxide. This compound contains Fe^{2+} and Fe^{3+}. It occurs naturally as the mineral magnetite. One of several synthetic routes is presented in which Fe_2O_3 is reduced by carbon monoxide. The redox nature of this

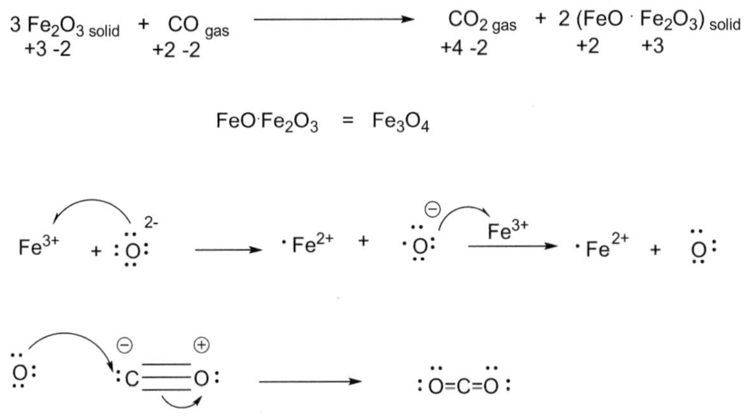

$$3 \, \underset{+3 \, -2}{Fe_2O_3 \, solid} + \underset{+2 \, -2}{CO \, gas} \longrightarrow \underset{+4 \, -2}{CO_2 \, gas} + 2 \, (\underset{+2 \quad +3}{FeO \cdot Fe_2O_3}) \, solid$$

$$FeO \cdot Fe_2O_3 = Fe_3O_4$$

SCHEME 2.1 Synthesis of magnetite, Fe_3O_4 [10].

reaction is flagged by the corresponding changes in the oxidation numbers of Fe and C. The mechanism shows two successive 1 e⁻ transfers from oxide anion (−2) to Fe^{3+} to generate two Fe^{2+} ions and one oxygen atom. The latter is attacked by the electron-dense carbon atom of carbon monoxide in a 2e⁻ transfer to give carbon dioxide, see Scheme 2.1. The other pieces are spectators which go along for the ride. Magnetite is a versatile compound with many applications, including environmental, biomedical, microfluidics, and mechano-electrical [9,10].

Manganese Black, MnO_2, manganese (IV) oxide. This substance is used for making amethyst glass, decolorizing glass, painting on porcelain, faience (earthenware) and majolica (glazed pottery) and as a drier for oil paints. It occurs naturally as the major manganese ore, pyrolusite. It can be synthesized by the following reaction [11]:

$$Mn_3O_4 + 2 \, H_2SO_4 \rightarrow 2 \, MnSO_4 + MnO_2 + 2 \, H_2O.$$

2.2 BLUE PIGMENTS

Azurite and Malachite, these two copper minerals, basic copper (II) carbonates, are usually found together in a piece of rock. Both pigments can be prepared synthetically [2]. Azurite [2 $CuCO_3 \cdot Cu(OH)_2$, blue] can be converted to malachite [$CuCO_3 \cdot Cu(OH)_2$, green] by hydration. However, the prevalent cause for the greening of azurite in paintings is the aging of varnish and or polymerized oil overlaying the painting [3].

The interconversion of these pigments is reversible. Azurite is unstable when exposed to water (as might occur with exterior paint or in an aquarium). Azurite is stable under dry storage conditions. Water reacts with carbonate in an acid-base reaction, see Scheme 2.2. The carbonate anion abstracts a proton from water to form a bicarbonate ion, and this decomposes to carbon dioxide and hydroxide. Release of CO_2 gas to the air drives the "forward" reaction by increasing the overall entropy. Increasing atmospheric CO_2 levels have increased from 318 ppm in 1960 to 390 ppm in 2010 [12] and this favors the "reverse" reaction.

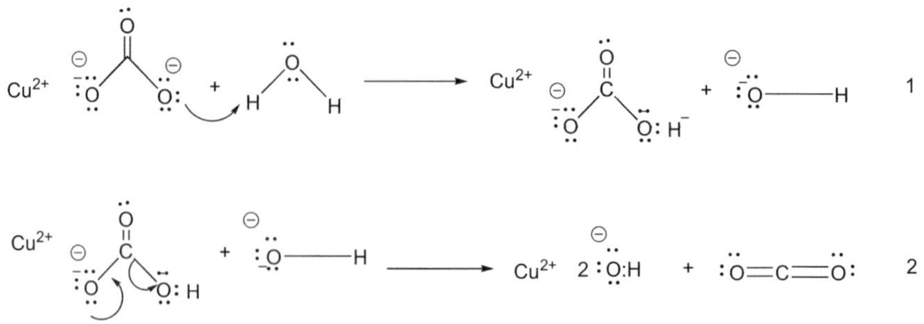

$$2\,[CuCO_3 \cdot CuC(OH)_2]_{solid} + H_2O_{liquid} \underset{}{\overset{slow}{\rightleftharpoons}} 3\,[Cu_2(CO_3)(OH)_2]_{solid} + CO_{2\,gas}$$

Azurite Malachite

SCHEME 2.2 Conversion of azurite to malachite.

Cerulean Blue is a pigment which has been used in painting (oil, watercolor and acrylic), porcelain decoration and also as a ceramic glaze. In addition, it has been used as a material in battery electrodes, gas and humidity sensors and thermally stable capacitors. The commercial pigment obtained from Kremer Pigmente (GmbH and Company, Aichstetten/Allgau, Germany) was analyzed by several methods and contains Co_2SnO_4, [cobalt (II) stannate] as the principle phase along with Co_3O_4 [cobalt (II, III) oxide] and SnO_2 [tin (IV) oxide] as minor phases [13]. Co_2SnO_4 is blue, Co_3O_4 is black and SnO_2 is white. Consequently, the color of the pigment depends on the quantitative composition of the mixture.

Cerulean blue is prepared by the co-precipitation method and gave $CoSnO_4$ as the only product [14]. In this synthesis, cobalt (II) chloride hexahydrate and tin (IV) chloride pentahydrate were each dissolved in water and then combined in the presence of a capping agent (oleic acid), with a Co/Sn mole ratio of 2/1. The capping agent adsorbs to tiny nanocrystals and prevents the formation of large crystals. The pH was adjusted to 10, causing the formation of a precipitate. The solid was washed with water, then ethanol, and then dried at 120°C and then the solid was calcined in the presence of air to yield nano-sized particles of the spinel. $CoSnO_4$ is a spinel. Spinels have the general formula, AB_2O_4 and take their name from $MgAl_2O_4$, the mineral spinel. The process may be represented by the steps in Scheme 2.3.

Egyptian Blue is the oldest of the blue pigments dating back to about 2575 BC. It is made by calcining a mixture of a copper (II) salt (e.g., malachite or azurite) with silica and calcium carbonate in the presence of air. A *flux* (e.g., NaCl, Na_2CO_3 or Na_2SO_4) is used to lower the melting point of silica.

$$2\,Co^{2+}_{aq} + Sn^{4+}_{aq} + 4\,HO^{-}_{aq} \xrightarrow{pH\ 10} 2\,Co(OH)_{2\,s} + Sn(OH)_{4\,s}$$

$$2\,Co(OH)_{2\,s} + Sn(OH)_{4\,s} \xrightarrow{heat} Co_2SnO_4 \cdot 4H_2O_s \xrightarrow{heat} Co_2SnO_{4\,s} + 4\,H_2O_g$$

SCHEME 2.3 Synthesis of cerulean blue [14].

$$Cu_2(CO_3)(OH)_2 + 8\,SiO_2 + 2\,CaCO_3 \ (800°C - 900°C, \text{air})$$

$$\rightarrow 2\,CaCuSi_4O_{10} + 3\,CO_2 + H_2O$$

Three equivalents of carbonate decompose to gaseous carbon dioxide and oxide anion.

$$CO_3^{2-} \rightarrow CO_2 + O^{2-}$$

Two equivalents of hydroxide ion yield water and oxide anion.

$$2\,HO^- \rightarrow H_2O + O^{2-}$$

The presence of O_2 in the reaction atmosphere is necessary to prevent the reductive formation of the red compound, copper (I) oxide, Cu_2O.

$$Cu^{2+} + 1\,e^- \rightarrow Cu^+$$

$$4\,Cu^+ + O_2 + 4\,e^- \rightarrow 4\,Cu^{2+} + 2\,O^{2-} = 2\,Cu_2O$$

A related pigment, known as Chinese blue or Han blue, was produced during the late Zhou period (1207–771 BC) by a process analogous to that used to prepare Egyptian blue.

$$Cu_2(CO_3)_2(OH)_2 + 8\,SiO_2 + BaCO_3 \xrightarrow{\text{Pb Additive, 900–1000C}} 2\,BaCuSi_4O_{10}$$

$$+ 3\,CO_{2\,g} + H_2O_g$$

In this process, a lead salt (carbonate or oxide) has two roles: (1) catalyst in the decomposition of the barium starting material and (2) flux to lower the reaction temperature [15].

In the structure of Egyptian blue, Cu^{2+} ions are coordinated in a square-planar arrangement [16]. The four ligands are oxygen atoms belonging to SiO_4 tetrahedra. The structure of the silicate network can be explained by a model of progressive silicate condensation which starts with SiO_4^{4-} (orthosilica) which dimerizes to $Si_2O_7^{6-}$ (disilicate) [17]. The process continues to form $Si_4O_{12}^{8-}$ (cyclotetrasilicate) and finally ends as the network, which can be expressed as $Si_4O_{10}^{4-}$. The progression can is illustrated by the following steps:

$$2\,SiO_4^{4-} \rightarrow Si_2O_7^{6-} + O^{2-}$$

$$2\,Si_2O_7^{6-} \rightarrow Si_4O_{12}^{8-} + 2\,O^{2-}$$

$$n\left(Si_4O_{12}^{8-}\right) \rightarrow \left(Si_4O_{10}^{4-}\right)_n + 2n\,O^{2-}$$

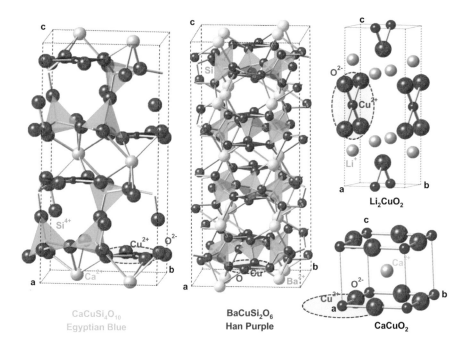

FIGURE 2.2 Unit cells corresponding to Egyptian Blue $CaCuSi_4O_{10}$ (and Han Blue $BaCuSi_4O_{10}$) pigment, Han Purple $BaCuSi_2O_6$ pigment, $CaCuO_2$ and Li_2CuO_2 compounds. Cu^{2+} ions involved in square-planar CuO_4^{6-} complexes (yellow dotted circles) are depicted in dark blue, while SiO_4^{4-} tetrahedra are in green. (Reprinted with permission of P. Garcia-Fernandez, M. Moreno, J.A. Aramburu (2016) *J. Chem. Ed.* 93: 111–117. Copyright 2015, American Chemical Society.)

Egyptian blue is classified as a phyllosilicate (phyllo=layered). The structure can crudely be described as containing: Ca^{2+} ions, square-planar Cu^{2+} ions and a SiO_4 tetrahedral network (Figure 2.2).

Prussian Blue, PB. Cyanide iron blues include a family of compounds based on the anion, $\left\{ Fe^{2+} \left[Fe^{3+} \left(CN^- \right)_6 \right] y\ H_2O,\ \text{where } y = 1\text{–}5 \right\}$, balanced by Na^+, K^+, or NH_4^+ ("M^+"). These compounds are known as "soluble Prussian blue", SPB. In addition, another form of the pigment is known; the "insoluble Prussian blue", IPB, Fe^{3+}_4 $[Fe^{2+} (CN^-)_6]$ x H_2O, (x = 14–16). These pigments were named according to the place where they were produced or after their original inventor. Hence, the family includes PB, Berlin blue, Milon's blue, Paris blue, Turnbull blue and others. PB was used to dye the uniforms of Prussian soldiers in the 19th century. Cyanotyping, a process based on PB, was used to create photographs and blueprints [18].

PB is usually prepared by a two-step process, also known as the "indirect" method. In the first step, aqueous solutions of an iron (II) water soluble salt and M_4 ferrocyanide (hexacyanoferrate (II)) are combined. Conversely , the reactants can be an iron II salt and M_3 ferricyanide (hexacyanoferrate (III)). A white solid, $\left[M_2Fe^{2+} \left[Fe^{2+} \left(CN \right)_6 \right] \right]$,

Berlin white, precipitates and is filtered away from the soluble M_2SO_4. An oxidizing agent such as sodium chlorate ($NaClO_3$) or sodium dichromate (Na_2CrO_4), oxidizes one of the Fe^{II} ions to Fe^{III}. This change results in the formation of the blue pigment. If the iron salt is in excess, the so-called "insoluble" PB is formed, $Fe^{3+}_4\left[Fe^{2+}(CN)_6\right]_3 \cdot xH_2O$, where x is 14–16. On the other hand, if the hexacyanoferrate is in excess, the product is the so-called "soluble" PB, $KFe^{3+}\left[Fe^{2+}(CN)_6\right] \cdot xH_2O$. Both the "soluble" and "insoluble" forms of PB are actually insoluble. The soluble form results in colloidal suspensions.

Alternatively, PB can also be synthesized by adding a solution of an Fe^{2+} salt to a solution of hexacyanoferrate (III). Conversely, the reactants can be an iron (III) salt and hexacyanoferrate (II). This approach, also known as the "direct" method, was the historical route to Turnbull's blue, which now is known to be identical to PB. Additional factors that influence the properties of the product are the formation rate of Berlin white, incubation of Berlin white prior to oxidation and the atmosphere above the solution [19]. The synthesis of PB by the indirect method is presented in Scheme 2.4. The relationship of the direct and indirect methods is illustrated in Scheme 2.5.

PB is used mainly in the printing industry. It is sensitive to base, and therefore cannot be used in frescoes (which are based on lime, CaO, a base). Reaction with NaOH provides a rapid qualitative identification. A drop of NaOH solution on Prussian blue will yield the red-brown color of $Fe(OH)_3$.

$$Fe_4\left[Fe(CN)_6\right]_3 + 18\ NaOH \rightarrow 4\ Fe(OH)_3 + 18\ NaCN + 3\ Fe(OH)_2$$

2.2.1 Prussian Blue as Antidote

The density of PB is unusually low for an iron salt, see Table 2.1. This is explained by the crystal structure which contains large cavities. The centers of these cavities can be occupied by ions or molecules up 182 pm (1 pm $= 10^{-12}$ m) radius. PB has been used as an antidote for thallium poisoning. The radius of Tl^+ is 164 pm and can replace K^+ with a radius of 152 pm. PB is non-toxic, unreactive and can be eaten in

$$FeSO_{4\ (aq)} + M_4\ [Fe(CN)_6]_{(aq)} \rightarrow M_2\ Fe^{2+}\ [Fe^{2+}\ (CN)_6]_{(s)} + M_2SO_{4\ (aq)}, \qquad (1)$$

Where M = Na^+, K^+, or NH_4^+.

$$6\ Na_2\ Fe^{2+}\ [Fe^{2+}\ (CN)_6]_{(aq)} + NaClO_{3\ (aq)} \rightarrow$$

$$NaCl_{(aq)} + 6\ NaFe^{3+}\ [Fe^{2+}\ (CN)_6]_{(s)} + 3\ H_2O_{(l)} \qquad (2)$$

The net ionic equation is :

$$ClO_3^-{}_{(aq)} + 6\ Fe^{2+}{}_{(aq)} + 6\ H^+{}_{(aq)} \rightarrow Cl^-{}_{(aq)} + 6\ Fe^{3+}{}_{(aq)} + 3\ H_2O_{(l)} \qquad (3)$$

SCHEME 2.4 Synthesis of Prussian blue by the indirect method [19].

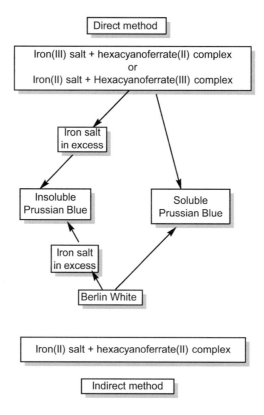

SCHEME 2.5 Schematic representation of the direct and indirect methods to produce Prussian blue pigments. (Adapted and reprinted with permission of L. Samain, G.J. Long, P. Martinetto, P. Bordet, D. Stivray (2013) *J. Phys. Chem.* 117: 9693–9712. Copyright 2013, American Chemical Society.)

TABLE 2.1
Densities of Various Iron Salts

Salt	Density, g/cm³	Salt	Density, g/cm³
Prussian blue	1.80	$FeCl_2$	3.16
FeF_3	3.87	Fe_2O_3	5.24
$FeCl_3$	2.90	Fe_3O_4	5.1
$Fe(OH)_3$	3.4–3.9	$Fe(OH)$	4.28
$FePO_4$	2.87	FeO	5.7

gram amounts. The thallium-PB complex is eliminated from the body. PB was fed to sheep in England after the Chernobyl nuclear accident in 1986. The nuclear explosion released radioactive $^{137}Cs^+$ into the atmosphere. Eventually, cesium ions were brought to the Earth's surface with rain. The cesium ions were trapped by PB, and thereby prevented a calamity [18].

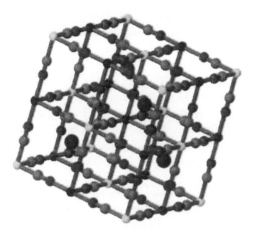

FIGURE 2.3 Prussian blue unit cell. Fe^{2+} yellow; Fe^{3+} red; C gray. N blue. K^+, purple occupy the centers of half of the cubic cells. (Reprinted with permission of M. Ware (2008) *J. Chem. Ed.* 85: 612–621. Copyright 2008, American Chemical Society.)

The crystal structure of PB can be described as a simple cubic lattice with alternating Fe^{3+} and Fe^{2+} with CN^- groups placed so that carbon atoms face Fe^{3+} and nitrogen atoms face Fe^{2+}, see Figure 2.3. PB is a prototype MOF (metal organic framework compound). MOFs typically are formed by polyvalent transition metal ions which interact with double headed organic ligands. MOFs have many applications, particularly for gas storage.

The blue color of the pigment is due to absorption of light at ~640 nm which causes the transfer of one electron from Fe^{II} to Fe^{III}. The process is known as *intervalence charge transfer* [19]:

$$\left[Fe^{3+} - C \equiv N - Fe^{2+} \right], \text{ light absorption } \leftrightarrow$$

$$\left[Fe^{2+} - C \equiv N - Fe^{3+} \right]^*, \text{ excited state}$$

Smalt is a blue pigment which is described as azzuro di smalto (blue enamel in *Italian*). Smalt is not a naturally occurring substance. It is synthesized by heating a mixture of silica (SiO_2), potash (K_2O) and a cobalt mineral, such as cobalt (II) oxide (CoO). This produces a potassium silicate network with Co^{2+} cations coordinated by oxygens form the network. A typical formula consists of 65–71 g of silica, 16–21 g of potash and 6–7 g of cobalt (II) oxide. The mixture is heated to melt the silica into a glass into which the other components dissolve. Upon cooling, a blue glass was obtained. If the hot glass is plunged into cold water, it shatters into particles. These were then ground into small particles which were used by artists. Smalt was used with various binders including oil, wax and fresco [3].

Ultramarine, UM, was first obtained from the precious blue stone, lapis lazuli. UM is remarkable because it is one of the few inorganic pigments with a *non-metallic chromophore*. [The other non-metallic inorganic pigments are the carbon blacks, and the arsenic sulfides, realgar and orpiment.] UM was extracted by kneading a paste of wax, pine resin, linseed oil and gum mastic (the "dough") with powdered lapis which was suspended in a weak solution of lye (aqueous NaOH solution). The blue pigment remained suspended in the lye solution while various impurities in the stone (including silica, SiO_2, calcium carbonate ($CaCO_3$), pyrite (FeS_2) and others) were taken up by the "dough". Particles of UM settled from the solution and were washed. From this traditional procedure, therefore UM is stable to base, and this property allows its use in wall paintings. In contrast, UM is quickly and irreversibly decolorized by aqueous acid solutions to yield a gray solid and H_2S gas. The name "ultramarine" arose because the pigment was originally brought to the West from "beyond the sea" in Asia [3,20].

Lapis lazuli contains lazurite, a blue compound, and other colorless compounds. The characteristics of a sample of lapis lazuli pigment obtained from Kremer Pigmente are shown in Figure 2.4 including Raman spectra and elemental analysis [21]. Note that the blue ultramarine particles "b", contain Al, Si, S, O and Na consistent with the chemical characterization as sodium aluminosilicate containing a polysulfide chromophore, and with the chemical formula ($Na_8[Al_6Si_6O_{24}]S_n$). This sample also contains colorless particles. One of the colorless particles, "a", contains Mg, Ca, Si and O which is consistent with diopside ($CaMgSi_2O_6$).

The scarcity of lapis lazuli limited the use of UM. However, its strong, distinctive color and stability encouraged Europeans to search for synthetic routes. In 1828, the Societe' d'Encouragement pour l'Industre Nationale (France) awarded a prize of six thousand Francs to Jean-Baptiste Guimet of Toulouse for the synthesis of UM. UM pigments are currently or have been used in inks, textiles, rubber, artists' colors, cosmetics, roofing granules and laundry blueing.

The basic two-step synthesis of UM used for manufacture of UM follows [22–24]:

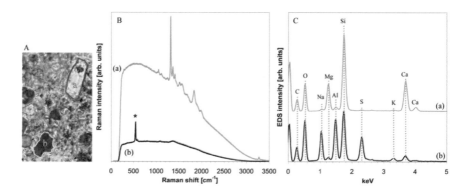

FIGURE 2.4 (A) Optical photograph, representative colorless (a) and blue (b) particles from Kremer *lapis lazuli* pigment (sample no. 2), (B) Raman spectra, and (C) elemental analysis (SEM-EDS) of particles marked in panel A. In both panels (B) and (C), the gray upper trace corresponds to colorless particle (a), and the black lower trace corresponds to blue particle (b). Raman spectra were collected using 785 nm excitation, ~0.3 mW/μm^2, and a 10 s acquisition. (Reprinted with permission of C.M. Schmidt, M.S. Walton, K. Trentelman (2009) *Anal. Chem.* 81: 8513–8518. Copyright American Chemical Society, 2009.)

a-1. China Clay (kaolin) is heated to ~700°C to "activate" or dehydrate the clay forming metakaolinate,

$$Al_2Si_2O_5(OH)_4 - Al_2O_3 \cdot 2\,SiO_2 \cdot 2\,H_2O_{(s)} \rightarrow Al_2O_3 \cdot 2\,SiO_{2\,(s)} + 2\,H_2O_{(g)}$$

a-2. Metakaolinate is dry-blended with Na_2CO_3, elemental sulfur (cyclic S_8) and pitch (a reducing agent), and formed into bricks under pressure. Pitch is a mixture of hydrocarbons obtained from the processing of coal tar. This reductive step typically requires 4–5 days at ~800°C. At this stage, sodium polysulfides form.

The boiling point of cyclic S_8 is 445°C, hence at 700°C, S_8 volatilizes and fragments into short polysulfide di-radicals, S_2, S_3, S_4. At the same time, sodium carbonate decomposes to form sodium oxide (a strong base) and a source of sodium ions which are incorporated into the pigment. Carbon dioxide escapes from the system. The di-radicals are *reduced* to disulfide dianions either by the oxide anion or by the reductant [22a], see Scheme 2.6.

The di-radicals are reduced by transfer of two hydrogen atoms from the reducing agent to the unpaired electrons of the di-radicals to form species known as *sulfanes*. Sulfanes, $HS(S)_nSH$, are analogous to alkanes, $H_3C(CH_2)_n$ CH_3. The sulfanes undergo an acid-base reaction with oxide anion to form a mixture of poly-disulfides, $Na^+S^-(S)_n\,S^-Na^+$.

Along with these changes, the aluminosilicate framework is also changing. The original kaolin structure is converted to *sodalite* (see Figure 2.5) [24,25]. The sodium poly-disulfides are contained within β-cages of sodalite. Gobeltz et al. also reported the synthesis of ultramarine starting with sodalite, sodium sulfide and sulfur. This demonstrated the possibility that the S_3 and S_2 radical anions diffused into sodalite, and has been confirmed [22b].

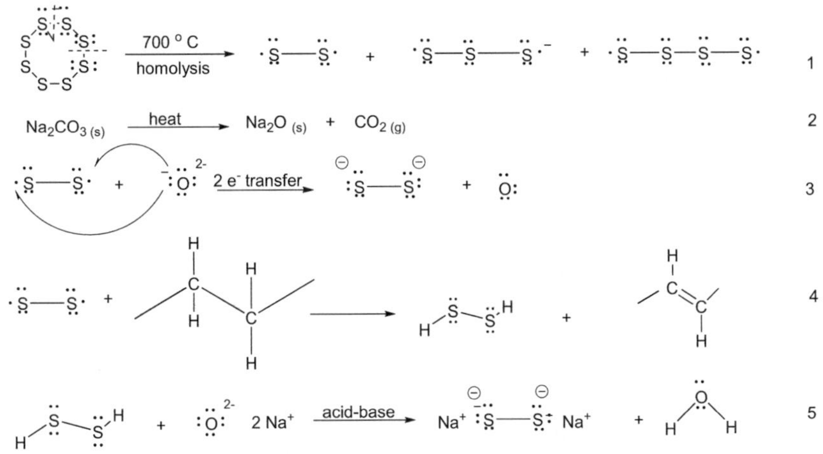

SCHEME 2.6 Ultramarine chromophore formation.

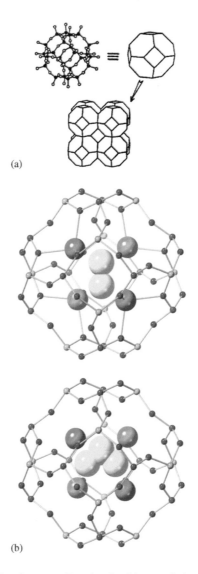

(a)

(b)

FIGURE 2.5 (a) Sodalite β-cages. (Reprinted with permission of N. Gobeltz-Hauteur, A. Demortier, B. Lede, C. Duhayon (2002) *Inorg. Chem.* 41: 2848–2854. Copyright 2002, American Chemical Society.) (b) Ultramarine yellow S_2 chromophore and blue S_3 chromophore inside sodalite cage. Sulfur atoms are yellow, sodium ions, magenta; oxygen, red; Si, dark blue; Al, cyan. M.T. Weller (2000) *J. Chem. Soc., Dalton Trans.* 4227–4240. (Copyright 2000, Royal Society of Chemistry.)

b. In the next stage of manufacture of UM, the oven is cooled to ~500°C, and an oxidizing gas (either air or SO_2) is admitted. The action of the oxidant converts the disulfide anions to the corresponding radical anions by the *transfer of one electron*. In this example, O_2 is reduced to the superoxide anion radical. In UM, the chromophores are radical anion species; S_3^-

(blue), S_2^- (yellow) and S_4^- (red). UM is stable toward base but unstable toward acid. Acid causes the aluminosilicate cages to open, and then the exposed chromophores are destroyed (see: Section 4.9 in Chapter 4).

$$[S_2]^{2-} + O_2 \quad (1 \ e^- \text{transfer}) \rightarrow [S_2]^- + [O_2]^-$$

The synthetic process has been modified to produce UM-like pigments with a wider color range (yellow, blue, green, pink, red and violet). This has been accomplished by various means including cation exchange [26,27], and substitution of Se and Te for S [28].

Verdigris, Vert de Grice or Green of Greece (also known as Spanish Green or Greenspan), refers to a family of blue to blue-green compounds obtained by the oxidation of metallic copper. Contemporary production processes are based on an ancient process in which copper metal is exposed to the vapors of fermenting grape skins which contain acetic acid [2]. The crude pigment was recovered by washing and was recrystallized from acetic acid [3].

In the French Process, sheets of copper are rubbed (seeded) with verdigris placed in earthen pots which are filled with pressed grape skins, and kept at constant temperature. In the German Process, copper plates are wrapped in flannel which has been soaked in acetic acid. The flannel is renewed weekly for eight weeks. These processes are somewhat similar to the process for making white lead, $Pb(OAc)_2$ $PbCO_3$.

How does verdigris form in this process? In the absence of O_2, copper metal does not react with aqueous non-oxidizing acid (H+) in a redox reaction, based on the respective positions of these substances in the table of standard reduction potentials. However, in the presence of O_2, copper metal does react with acetic acid to produce CuO [29]. A peroxide intermediate species is involved [30,31]. In Scheme 2.7, elemental copper is represented as Cu: since the most stable oxidation state for copper is +2.

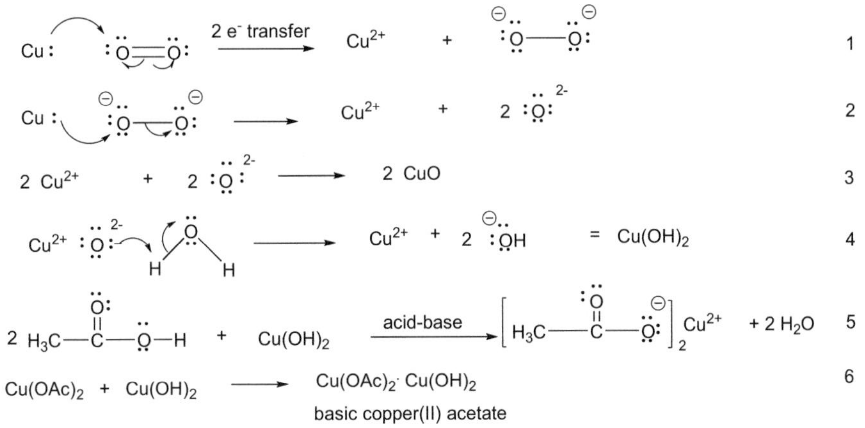

SCHEME 2.7   Formation of basic copper (II) acetate.

$$x\,Cu(OAc)_2 + y\,Cu(OH)_2 + n\,H_2O \rightarrow [Cu(OAc)_2]_x\,[Cu(OH)_2]_y\,nH_2O$$

$$x\,CuCl_2 + y\,Cu(OH)_2 + n\,H_2O \rightarrow [CuCl_2]_x\,[Cu(OH)_2]_y\,nH_2O$$

SCHEME 2.8 Stoichiometry for formation of verdigris variants [31].

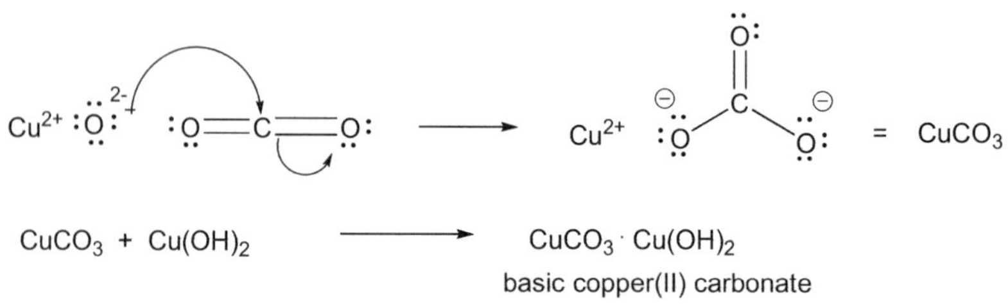

CuCO₃ + Cu(OH)₂ ⟶ CuCO₃ · Cu(OH)₂
basic copper(II) carbonate

SCHEME 2.9 Formation of basic copper (II) carbonate.

Depending on the concentrations of the reactants, copper (II) acetate and copper (II) hydroxide can combine to form a series of compounds. Verdigris has been classified with respect to composition: neutral verdigris, $Cu(OAc)_2 \cdot H_2O$; basic verdigris, $x\,Cu(CH_3CO_2)_2 \cdot y\,Cu(OH)_2 \cdot n\,H_2O$, and the so-called green salt, $x\,CuCl_2 y \cdot Cu(OH)_2 \cdot n\,H_2O$, [25]. There are four types of basic verdigris: blue, $2\left[Cu\,(OAc)_2\right] \cdot 1\left[Cu\,(OH)_2\right] \cdot 5\,H_2O$; blue, $1\left[Cu\,(OAc)_2\right] \cdot 1\left[Cu\,(OH)_2\right] \cdot 5\,H_2O$; blue, $1\left[Cu\,(OAc)_2\right] \cdot 2\left[Cu\,(OH)_2\right]$; and green, $1\left[Cu\,(OAc)_2\right] \cdot 3\left[Cu\,(OH)_2\right] \cdot 2\,H_2O$. If chloride is present in the synthesis, basic Cu (II) chlorides also form, see Scheme 2.8 [32].

Further, to add to the general confusion, verdigris is sometimes used to describe basic copper (II) carbonate, $CuCO_3 \cdot Cu(OH)_2$, which is also known as the pigment verditer (vert de terre), see Scheme 2.9. This substance develops as the green *patina* on copper, brass or bronze objects. Basic copper carbonate occurs as the mineral malachite.

2.3 BROWN PIGMENTS

2.3.1 BROWN IRON (III) OXIDE PIGMENTS

Siennas and umbers are naturally occurring materials. Siennas consist of Fe_2O_3 (~50%) and MnO_2 (<1%). Raw sienna is yellow-brown; after calcination, the color is red-brown. Umbers contain Fe_2O_3 (45%–70%) and MnO_2 (5%–20%); the color is deep brown to greenish brown [43].

Lead Dioxide, PbO_2, is a chocolate-brown compound. It occurs naturally as the mineral, plattnerite. It can be synthesized by reaction of lead acetate and calcium hypochlorite [11]. Even though PbO_2 is not used as a pigment, it is included in the discussion because it is a raw material used in the synthesis of lead pigments and is also a degradation product in discolored paintings.

The highlights of PbO_2 synthesis are: formation of insoluble $Pb(OH)_2$ by single displacement which is followed by $2e^-$ oxidation of Pb^{2+} to Pb^{4+} by Cl_2. The product, PbO_2, is purified by removing the soluble bi-products with water, see Scheme 2.10.

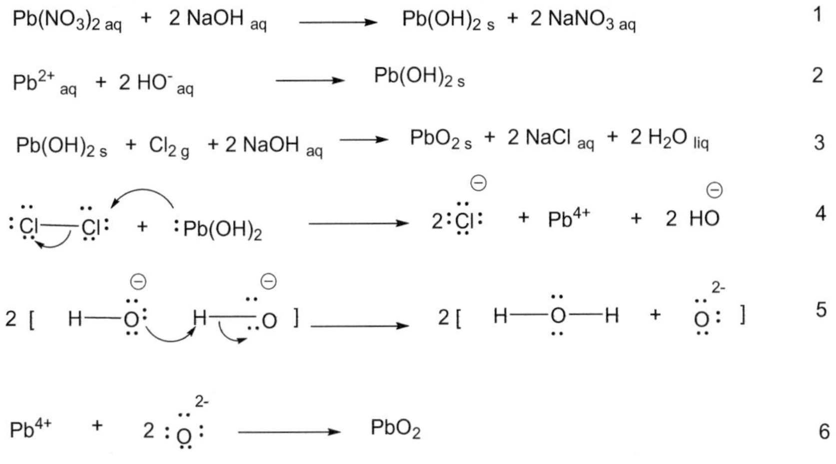

$$Pb(NO_3)_{2\,aq} + 2\,NaOH_{aq} \longrightarrow Pb(OH)_{2\,s} + 2\,NaNO_{3\,aq} \qquad 1$$

$$Pb^{2+}_{\,aq} + 2\,HO^-_{\,aq} \longrightarrow Pb(OH)_{2\,s} \qquad 2$$

$$Pb(OH)_{2\,s} + Cl_{2\,g} + 2\,NaOH_{aq} \longrightarrow PbO_{2\,s} + 2\,NaCl_{aq} + 2\,H_2O_{liq} \qquad 3$$

$$:\!\overset{..}{\underset{..}{Cl}}\!\!-\!\!\overset{..}{\underset{..}{Cl}}\!: \;+\; :Pb(OH)_2 \longrightarrow 2:\!\overset{..}{\underset{..}{Cl}}\!:^{\ominus} + Pb^{4+} + 2\,\overset{\ominus}{HO} \qquad 4$$

$$2\,[\;\; H\!\!-\!\!\overset{..}{\underset{..}{O}}\!:^{\ominus} \quad H\!\!-\!\!\overset{..}{\underset{..}{O}}\!:^{\ominus}\;] \longrightarrow 2\,[\;\; H\!\!-\!\!\overset{..}{\underset{..}{O}}\!\!-\!\!H \;+\; \overset{..}{\underset{..}{O}}\!:^{2-}\;] \qquad 5$$

$$Pb^{4+} + 2:\!\overset{..}{\underset{..}{O}}\!:^{2-} \longrightarrow PbO_2 \qquad 6$$

SCHEME 2.10   Synthesis of lead (IV) oxide.

2.4   GREEN PIGMENTS

Chromium (III) Oxide. There are two green chromium (III) pigments. They are the anhydrous and the hydrated chromium (III) oxides, respectively, Cr_2O_3 and $Cr_2O_3 \cdot xH_2O$.

Anhydrous chromium (III) oxide, Cr_2O_3, is prepared by calcining sodium dichromate with sulfur, or other reducing agents such as carbon, or ammonium chloride. For example: $Na_2CrO_7 + 1/8\,S_8 \rightarrow Cr_2O_3 + Na_2SO_4$. Sodium sulfate is removed by washing with water.

Cr_2O_3 can also be synthesized by thermal decomposition of ammonium dichromate (ADC). This reaction is often used as the "volcano demonstration".

$$(NH_4)_2\,Cr_2O_{7\,s} \xrightarrow{\text{(thermal decomposition)}} Cr_2O_{3\,s} + 4\,H_2O_g + 1\,N_{2\,g}$$

The thermal decomposition of ADC to anhydrous chromium (III) oxide was investigated [33]. The decomposition was monitored by digital thermal-gravimetry [6]. In this study, a sample of ADC was heated for discrete time periods, volatile products were allowed to escape, and the mass retained was measured. At each step, the solid residue was subjected to X-ray analysis in order to determine the composition. The sequence of compounds detected in this decomposition was:

$$(NH_4^+)_2\,Cr_2O_7 \rightarrow CrO_3 \rightarrow CrO_2 \rightarrow Cr_2O_3$$

ON	+6	+6	+4	+3

The oxidation number of chromium decreases from +6 to +3 as chromium is reduced. The reducing agent was NH_4^+, in which nitrogen was oxidized to N_2:

$$NH_4^+ \rightarrow N_2$$

ON	−3	0

Chromium is in group 6B, and its valence electron configuration is $3d^5 4s^1$,

3d   4s

Therefore, chromium can make a maximum of six covalent bonds. A suggested mechanism is presented based on the reported decomposition sequence of ammonium dichromate. It comprises a combination of proton transfers (acid-base) and electron transfers (redox). The formal charge rule was applied throughout assuming that the chromium atom has six valence electrons. In the *reductive* leg, oxygens are removed from chromium either as neutral atoms or as oxide anions. Oxygen atoms are eventually reduced to oxide ions, and these unite with protons to form water. The chromium species involved are $Cr_2O_7^{2-}$, CrO_3, CrO_2, Cr^{4+}, Cr^{3+}, Cr^{2+}, and Cr_2O_3, all of which are stable entities.

In the *oxidative* leg, NH_4^+ is first converted to NH_3 by proton transfer. Subsequently, oxidation occurs by removal of either hydrogen atoms (protons and 1 e−), or removal of electrons to form hydrazine, which is further oxidized to N_2. If we count up the pieces, the net reaction of all of the mechanistic steps yields the overall balanced equation, see Schemes 2.11 and 2.12.

Hydrated Chromium (III) Oxide, viridian, $Cr_2O_3 \cdot (xH_2O)$ is produced by a different process compared to the anhydrous material. Hydrated chromium (III) oxide, viridian, Guinet's green, has the formula $Cr_2O_3 \cdot (xH_2O)$. In the two-step synthesis patented by Guinet in 1859 [34], the solid reactants potassium dichromate and boric acid are heated (calcined), then rinsed with water to remove soluble material and finally dried, see Figure 2.6 [35].

Green paint samples from paintings of Jawlensky and other artists, dating between 1885 and 1943, were analyzed by FTIR and found to contain variants of hydrated chromium (III) oxide. The bands of interest are: 1063 and 792 cm^{-1} (assigned to viridian) and a doublet 1288, 1252 cm^{-1} assigned to chromic borate, Cr_3BO_6 [35,36].

Variations in calcination temperature and time affect the yield of viridian. At a mole ratio of 1:2:: $K_2Cr_2O_7$:H_3BO_3, calcination time of 0.5 h, reaction temperature was varied from 550°C–750°C in 50° increments. The reaction product was water-rinsed, dried and analyzed by FTIR, Raman and XRD. FTIR spectra showed bands at 1063 and 792 cm^{-1} which increased over the range 550°C–650°C. These bands were assigned to viridian, $Cr_2O_3 \cdot (xH_2O)$, where x~2. For T = 700°C and 750°C, the viridian bands diminished while bands at 1288 and 1252 cm^{-1} increased in intensity. These bands were assigned to chromic borate, Cr_3BO_6, see Figure 2.7. The effect of calcination time was also investigated (t = 0.5, 1, 3 h) at the 1:2 molar ratio. At 600°C, 1 h was optimal for viridian formation. At 700°C, the spectrum was essentially constant over the time range.

In summary, at T~600°C the product was $Cr_2O_3 \cdot (xH_2O)$ particles with some *incorporated* water (x = 2) and some surface adsorbed water. While at 700°C, $Cr_2O_3 \cdot (xH_2O)$-Cr_3BO_6 particles with low water content were formed. The insoluble

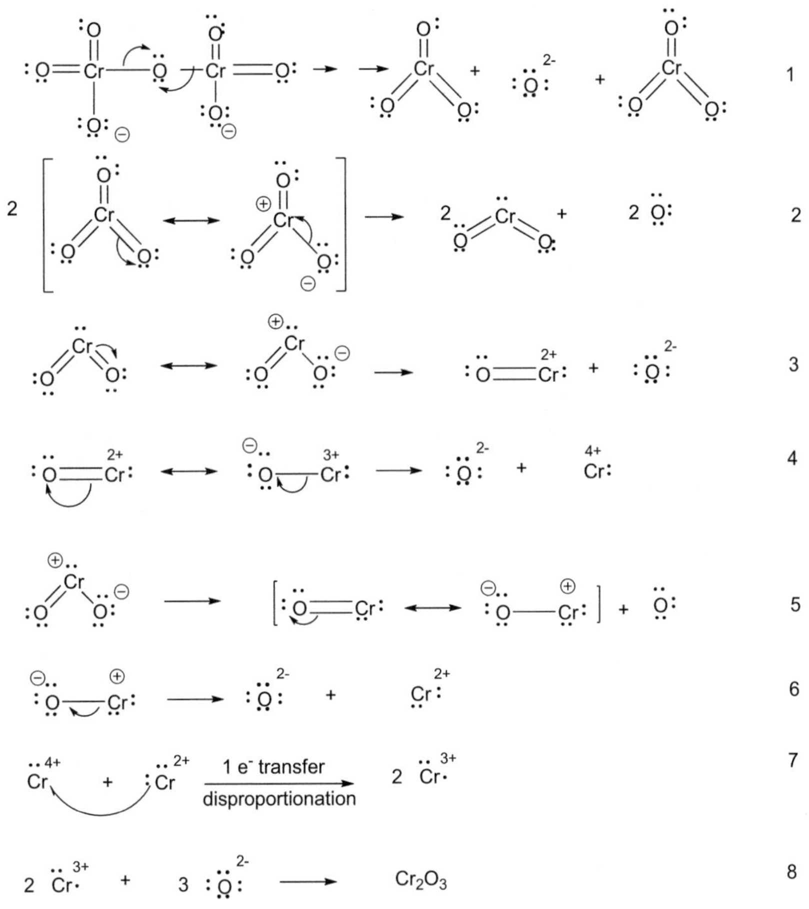

SCHEME 2.11 Reduction of dichromate to Cr^{3+} (III).

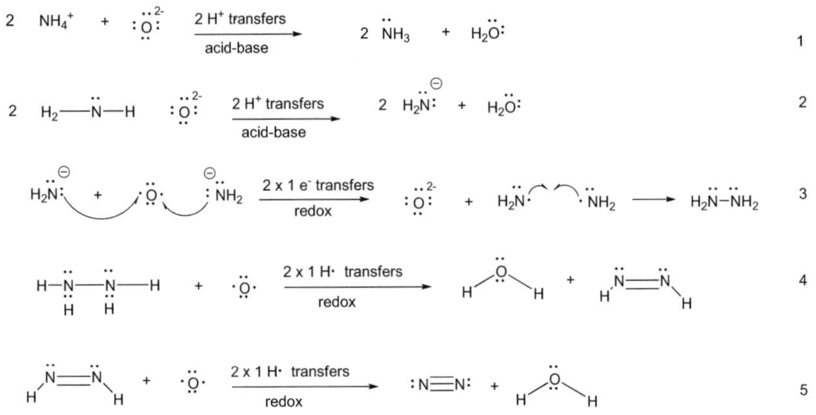

SCHEME 2.12 Oxidation of ammonium to dinitrogen.

FIGURE 2.6 Guinet green synthesis: calcination of the ground orange powder of reactants results in a vesiculate dark green glass. This glass transforms into a green pigment upon rinsing with water. (Reprinted with permission of S. Zumbuehl, A. Berger, N.C. Scherrer, U. Eggenberger (2009) *Stud Conserv* 54: 149–159. Copyright 2009, Taylor and Francis.)

Cr_3BO_6 coating minimized incorporation of water. The incorporated water (xH_2O) originates from the dimerization of boric acid at 150°C–250°C.

$$2 H_3BO_3 \rightarrow B_2O_3 + 3 H_2O$$

Stoichiometric equations relating to the two-step synthesis have been proposed for the formation of the *monohydrate*, $x = 1$, [37a] and also for the *dihydrate* $x = 2$, of Cr_2O_3 [37b]. For the dihydrate:

$$2 K_2Cr_2O_7 + 4 H_2B_2O_4 = 2 Cr_2B_2O_6 + 2 K_2B_2O_4 + 3 O_2 + 4 H_2O \quad \text{step 1}$$

$$Cr_2B_2O_6 + 3 H_2O = Cr_2O_3 \cdot 2 H_2O + H_2B_2O_4 \quad \text{step 2}$$

Malachite, see Section 2.2.

Verdigris, see Section 2.2.

Paris green, emerald green, Schweinfurt green, copper acetoarsenite, Pigment Green 21, $3 Cu(AsO_2)\cdot Cu(CH_3CO_2)_2$, is not a naturally occurring mineral. It was synthesized in Schweinfurt, Germany in 1814 in an attempt to improve the properties of another synthetic green compound (Scheele's green, $CuAsO_2 \cdot OH$, 1778). In the synthesis, verdigris, $Cu(CH_3CO_2)_2$, arsenic trioxide, As_2O_3 and sodium carbonate are

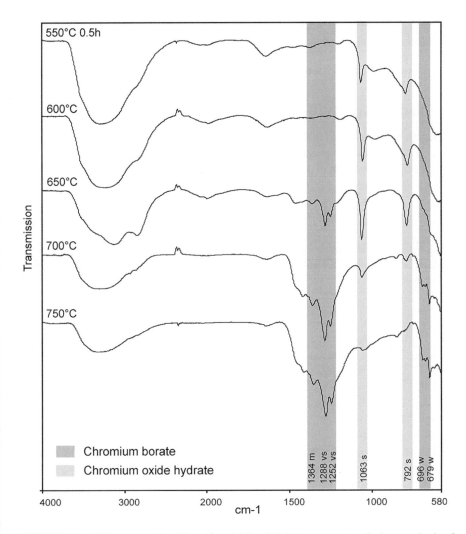

FIGURE 2.7 FTIR spectra for effect of variable calcining temperature during synthesis of Guinet's green. With increasing temperature of calcination, borate bands (1288, 1252 cm⁻¹) clearly decrease, while chromium (III) oxide hydrate bands (1063, 792 cm⁻¹) increase. These compounds exhibit an inverse relationship. (Reprinted with permission of S. Zumbuehl, A. Berger, N.C. Scherrer, U. Eggenberger (2009) *Stud Conserv* 54: 149–159. Copyright 2009, Taylor and Francis.)

combined in aqueous solution [2,3]. As_2O_3 dissolves in water to form the presumed intermediate, arsenous acid, $As(OH)_3$ which dehydrates to give meta-arsenite anion, $As(O_2)^-$. The product, $3\ Cu(AsO_2)\cdot Cu(CH_3CO_2)_2$, precipitates from solution and is washed and dried.

Paris green has a brilliant color which was attractive to artists, but was toxic to workers involved with its manufacture. Wallpaper impregnated with Paris green yielded toxic dust and when damp emitted the toxic gas arsine, AsH_3. IARC has classified Paris green as a known human carcinogen, Group 1 [38]. This compound was used as a pigment until the 1980s [39]. Paris green also had a long history of use as an agricultural pesticide, and was used until the 1990s [40].

2.5 RED PIGMENTS

α-Cinnabar, vermilion, HgS, mercury (II) sulfide. Cinnabar refers to the naturally occurring mineral and vermilion is the name of the synthetic compound. This red compound is the only ore of mercury. It is mined principally as a starting material for production of elemental mercury.

$$HgS_s + O_{2\,g} \xrightarrow{\text{(heat)}} Hg^o_1 + SO_{2\,g}$$

Vermilion is synthesized by several methods including precipitation from aqueous solution. In this reaction, HgS is insoluble and hence easily separated from the soluble product, NaCl.

$$HgCl_{2\,(aq)} + Na_2S_{(aq)} \rightarrow HgS_{(s)} + 2\,NaCl_{(aq)}$$

Solubility[a] 7.4   15.4 1×10^{-6} 37.5

[a] grams of solute per 100 mL of water at 25°C.

HgS can also be synthesized by reaction of elemental mercury and sulfur, see Scheme 2.13. The sulfur atom represents 1/8 of one cyclic S_8 molecule. HgS is considered to be *a network solid,* in which the atoms are connected by covalent bonds. In this case, $(HgS)_n$ units form chains so that the compound is essentially a macromolecule [41]. The difference in electronegativity between Hg and S is 0.6, which is consistent with covalent bonding that has a small component of ionic character.

In this synthesis, both reactants are in their elemental form. Mercury is combined with a 1.2-fold molar excess of molten sulfur, which results in the formation of the black form of HgS (β-HgS, meta-cinnabar). The intermediate is sublimed and re-condensed to yield the red polymorph [8]. Residual sulfur is removed by treatment with aqueous base. Elemental sulfur occurs principally as an eight-membered puckered ring, cyclo S_8. Hydroxide ion attacks the one of the sulfur atoms in the ring which

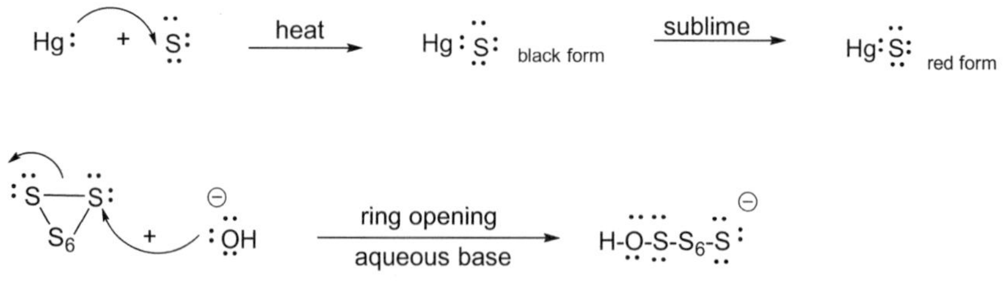

SCHEME 2.13   Synthesis of vermilion [41].

causes the ring to open, forming a negatively charged, water-soluble product, which can be easily separated from the insoluble HgS.

Red Lead, Pb_3O_4, lead tetroxide, lead (II, IV) oxide. Red lead is a distinct compound containing both Pb^{2+} and Pb^{4+} ions, see Figure 2.8. In the structure, Pb^{4+} ions are octahedral geometry and Pb^{2+} ions have pyramidal-trigonal geometry [42]. Red lead is a spinel. Spinels have the general formula AB_2O_4. It may be regarded as $2\ PbO \cdot PbO_2$, and can be prepared by several methods. A synthesis starting with litharge (m.p. 888°C), the red crystalline form of PbO, is presents in Scheme 2.14 [11]. Litharge is partially oxidized to yield Pb_3O_4, which contains both Pb^{2+} and Pb^{4+}.

Elemental lead has four valence electrons ([Xe] $6s^2\ 6p^2$); hence, lead (II) is represented as: Pb^{2+} and lead (IV) as Pb^{4+}. Mechanistically, a pair of electrons is transferred from [:PbO] to one oxygen atom to produce lead (IV) oxide, PbO_2. One unit of PbO_2 combines with two units of unreacted PbO to form the new compound, Pb_3O_4.

Very pure Pb_3O_4 can be obtained by extracting the reaction product with dilute aqueous acetic acid in order to remove PbO. The presence of residual PbO influences the stability of red lead (see Chapter 4, Section 4.1). It is also used in the manufacture

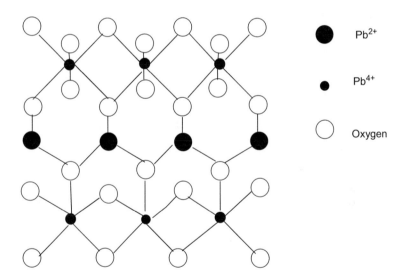

FIGURE 2.8 Red Lead. (Reprinted with permission of S. Fantacci, A. Amat, A. Sgamellotti (2010) *Acc. Chem. Res.* 43: 802–813. Copyright 2010, American Chemical Society.)

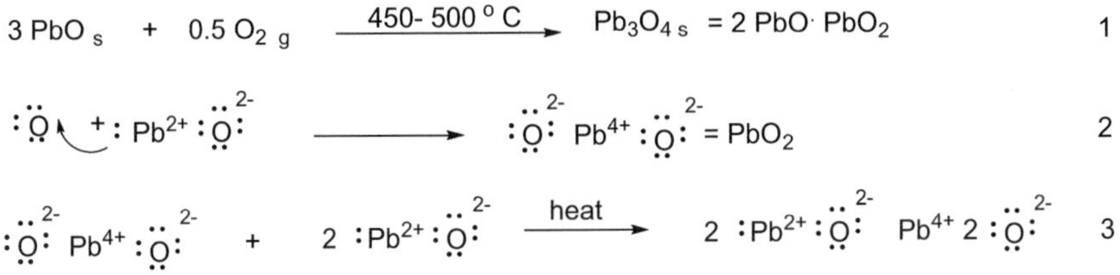

$$3\ PbO_s\ +\ 0.5\ O_{2\,g}\ \xrightarrow{450\text{-}500\,^\circ C}\ Pb_3O_{4\,s}\ =\ 2\ PbO \cdot PbO_2 \qquad 1$$

$$:\!\ddot{O}\!: \ +\ :Pb^{2+}:\!\overset{2-}{\ddot{O}}\!: \ \longrightarrow\ :\!\overset{2-}{\ddot{O}}\!:\ Pb^{4+}:\!\overset{2-}{\ddot{O}}\!:\ =\ PbO_2 \qquad 2$$

$$:\!\overset{2-}{\ddot{O}}\!:\ Pb^{4+}:\!\overset{2-}{\ddot{O}}\!:\ +\ 2\ :Pb^{2+}:\!\overset{2-}{\ddot{O}}\!: \ \xrightarrow{heat}\ 2\ :Pb^{2+}:\!\overset{2-}{\ddot{O}}\!:\ Pb^{4+}\ 2:\!\overset{2-}{\ddot{O}}\!: \qquad 3$$

SCHEME 2.14 Synthesis of red lead [11].

of lead crystal glass. The historical name of this pigment is minium, from which "miniature" literally means a painting colored with minium.

2.5.1 RED IRON (III) OXIDE PIGMENTS

Iron comprises ~7% of the Earth's crust. It is too reactive to occur naturally as the metal. The primary ore is iron (III) oxide. Iron ore can be converted to the metallic form by chemical reduction. Iron (III) oxides can be produced in different colors depending on reaction conditions. The well-known iron (III) oxide pigments are presented in Table 2.2.

Iron (III) oxides represent ~40% of the colored inorganic pigment production worldwide. Collectively, the group is the second-most widely used inorganic pigment after TiO_2. Iron (III) oxide pigments exhibit these advantages: excellent light-fastness (photo-stability), non-toxic, non-bleeding, inexpensive, and unreactive with either weak acids or weak bases. Generally, iron pigments exhibit low *chroma* (i.e., low color intensity per mass of pigment). Naturally occurring iron (III) oxide pigments are used to color construction and building materials such as cement, ceramics, roofing granules, rubber plastics and paints. There are several processes for the manufacture of these pigments [1].

Iron (III) red pigments, Copperas reds, are synthesized by four processes, including (a) the two-stage calcination of $FeSO_4 \cdot 7H_2O$, (b) precipitation from aqueous solution, (c) thermal degradation of α-FeO(OH), and (d) oxidation of Fe_3O_4 [43]. Calcination is a process of heating an ore in order to drive off a volatile byproduct. The *two-stage calcination process* begins with heating $FeSO_4 \cdot 7H_2O$ [iron (II) sulfate heptahydrate or green vitriol] under controlled conditions to volatilize six of the seven water molecules of hydration.

$$FeSO_4 \cdot 7H_2O_{solid} \quad heat \rightarrow \quad FeSO_4 \cdot 1\ H_2O_{solid} \ + 6\ H_2O_{gas} \qquad (2.1)$$

The second step (Copperas Process) is redox:

$$6\ FeSO_4 \cdot 1\ H_2O_{solid} + 3/2\ O_{2\ gas} \quad \rightarrow \quad 3\ Fe_2O_{3\ solid} + 6\ SO_{3\ gas} + 6\ H_2O_{gas}$$

ON   2 6 −2   0   3 −2   6 −2   1 −2

TABLE 2.2
Iron (III) Oxide Pigments

Name	Color	Chemical Formula
Goethite	Yellow	α-FeO(OH)
Lepidocrocite	Orange	γ-FeO(OH)
Hematite	Red	α-Fe$_2$O$_3$
Maghemite	Brown	γ- Fe$_2$O$_3$
Magnetite	Black	FeO$\cdot$Fe$_2$O$_3$=Fe$_3$O$_4$

2.6 VIOLET PIGMENTS

Pigment Violet 14, Co$_3$(PO$_4$)$_2$, Cobalt Violet, PV 14 is synthesized by calcination of cobalt (II) oxide and phosphorous (V) oxide [44]. P$_4$O$_{10}$ has a tricyclic covalent structure in which every phosphorous atom is bonded to three oxygen atoms by single bonds and to one oxygen atom by a double bond. A plausible mechanism for this reaction involves the attack of the P$_4$O$_{10}$ ring system by oxide anions which eventually generates four ortho-phosphate anions $\left(\text{PO}_4^{3-}\right)$, see Scheme 2.15. This reaction occurs by repeated nucleophilic attack by oxide anion on bonded phosphorous atoms. Redox is not involved.

2.7 WHITE PIGMENTS

Antimony White, antimony trioxide, Sb$_2$O$_3$, is synthesized by reaction of hydrolysis of antimony (III) chloride.

$$2\ SbCl_{3\,(aq)}\quad +\quad 3\ H_2O_{(l)}\quad \rightarrow\quad Sb_2O_{3\,(s)}\quad +\quad 6\ HCl_{(aq)}$$

sol'y in water[a] 910   0.00180

[a] grams of solute per 100 mL of water at 20°C.

Hydrolysis of SbCl$_3$ yields a mixture of orthorhombic Sb$_2$O$_3$ and the cubic Sb$_4$O$_6$. Pure Sb$_4$O$_6$ is obtained by calcining at 500°C, while pure Sb$_2$O$_3$ is obtained at 600°C.

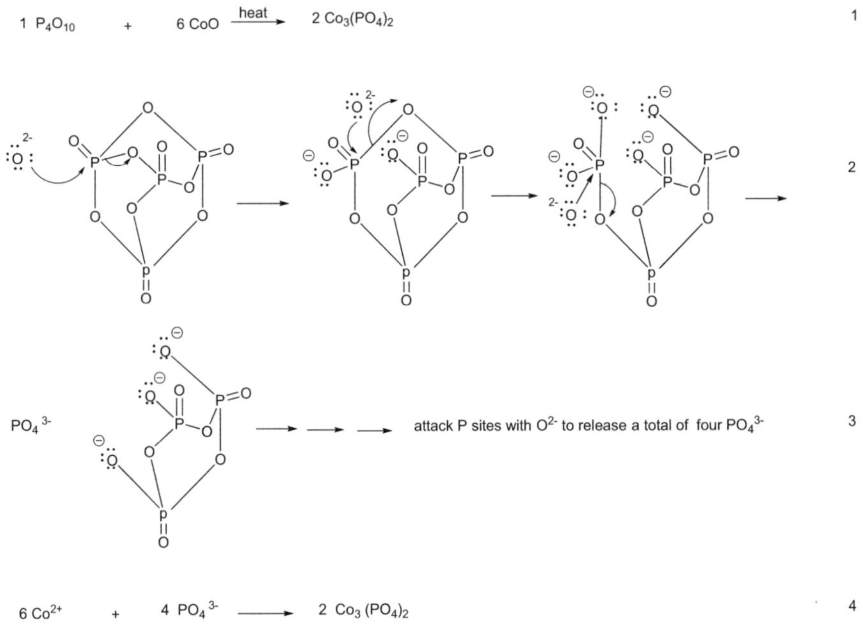

SCHEME 2.15 Synthesis of cobalt violet [44].

Sb_2O_3 forms chains consisting of (Sb_2O_3) units [45,46]. The material is mainly used in flame retardants. As a pigment, it is used to opacify glasses, ceramics and enamels.

Barium White, barium sulfate, occurs naturally and can be synthesized by reaction of aqueous solutions of barium chloride sodium sulfate [1].

$$BaCl_{2\,(aq)} + Na_2SO_{4\,(aq)} \rightarrow BaSO_{4\,(s)} + 2\,NaCl_{\,(aq)}$$

Lithopone, also known as Griffith's Zinc White, is used in coating materials such as paints, primers, putties and fillers. Lithopone is a 1:1 molar co-precipitated mixture of ZnS and $BaSO_4$. Because zinc compounds have fungicidal and algicidal activity, inclusion of lithopone to various products helps to prevent the growth of fungi and algae. It is produced in a two-step process:

$$BaS_{aq} + ZnSO_{4\,aq}\,(50°C - 60°C) \rightarrow ZnS_s$$

$$+ BaSO_{4\,s}\,(calcine\ 600°C - 700°C) \rightarrow ZnS \cdot BaSO_{4\,s}$$

The first step involves the formation of two insoluble products. The solid mixture is calcined at high temperature to produce lithopone. Crystal growth is controlled by traces of Na^+, K^+ and Mg^{2+} salts. The product is cooled quickly by quenching in water to prevent oxidation of ZnS to ZnO. The product is filtered, washed until salt-free and then ground to optimum particle size of ~300 nm. Lithopone is not a solid solution, because ZnS and $BaSO_4$ have different crystal habits [1,46].

Titanium White, titanium dioxide, TiO_2. Titanium is the seventh most abundant element in the Earth's crust. TiO_2 occurs in several minerals and ores of which ilmenite in the most abundant. Naturally occurring TiO_2 is colored because of the presence of iron oxides. TiO_2 is the most widely used inorganic pigment. Main uses include paints, lacquers, plastics and paper. Other applications include semiconductors, printing inks, rubber, textiles, leather, synthetic fibers, ceramics, white cement, cosmetics and film projection screens. TiO_2 exists in three crystalline forms: rutile, anatase and brookite. Of these, only rutile and anatase are used as pigments. Anatase transforms to rutile above 700°C [1]. TiO_2 is also used as a food additive [47].

Naturally occurring TiO_2 minerals and ores contain several metallic and non-metallic oxides which are listed in Table 2.3. These oxide impurities are all high melting compounds consistent with Coulomb's Law of Attraction. In the Chloride Process, impure TiO_2 is first treated with dry chlorine gas and carbon (coke) which converts the oxides to the respective chlorides. In contrast to the oxides, the chlorides have lower melting points. The combination of differences in boiling points and melting points among the chlorides is the key to the utility of the Chloride Process as a means to purify TiO_2.

In the Chloride Process, impure TiO_2 is converted to *gaseous* $TiCl_4$. In addition, oxide impurities are converted to their respective chlorides.

$$TiO_{2\,(s)} + Cl_{2\,(g)} + C_{(s)} \rightarrow TiCl_{4\,(g)} + CO_{2\,(g)}$$

A hypothetical mechanism for this reaction involves the reduction Ti^{4+} by carbon to Ti^0 and the formation of CO_2. In the third step, the Cl-Cl bond breaks *homolytically*

TABLE 2.3

Oxide Contaminants Present in TiO$_2$ Ores

	Oxides mp, °C	bp, °C	Chlorides	mp, °C	bp, °C
Ti metal	1800	>3000			
TiO$_2$	1640d		TiCl$_4$	−30	136
FeO	1420		FeCl$_2$	670	Sublimes
Fe$_2$O$_3$	1565		FeCl$_3$	282	315
MgO	2800		MgCl$_2$	708	1412
CaO	2580	2850	CaCl$_2$	772	>1600
V$_2$O$_3$	1970		VCl$_2$	subl. 1027	
VO$_2$	1967		VCl$_3$	d425	
V$_2$O$_5$	690		VCl$_4$	−25.5	152
SiO$_2$	>1600		SiCl$_4$	−70	59
Al$_2$O$_3$	1640d		AlCl$_3$	190[a]	Sublimes 181

[a] At 2.5 atm.

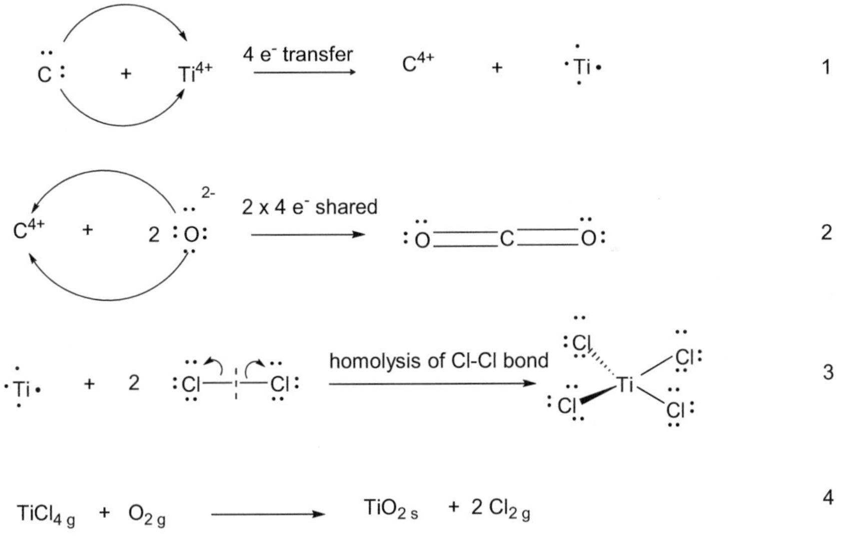

SCHEME 2.16 Purification of TiO$_2$ by conversion to TiCl$_4$ [1].

to produce two chlorine atoms which react with Ti° to form the intermediate TiCl$_4$, a covalent compound with symmetrical tetrahedral geometry, and hence non-polar character which underlies its low melting point and low boiling point. In the final step, TiCl$_4$ is re-oxidized to TiO$_2$, Scheme 2.16.

The reaction mixture is then cooled to <300°C which allows the chlorides of iron, calcium, magnesium and aluminum to solidify, and hence separate from the gaseous titanium tetrachloride. SiCl$_4$ is separated from TiCl$_4$ by fractional distillation based on the difference in boiling points. Vanadium chlorides are removed by reduction. Finally, titanium tetrachloride is re-oxidized to the oxide [1].

White Lead, $2PbCO_3 \cdot Pb(OH)_2$, occurs naturally as the mineral hydrocerussite. White lead is one of the earliest synthetic white pigments, and was described by Theophrastis (381–287 BC) and also by Pliny (23–79 BC). Synthetic processes, traditional as well as the modern, depend on the reaction of metallic lead with the vapors of acetic acid and water in the presence of carbon dioxide. This process is similar to the traditional process for production of verdigris.

The traditional process dates back to ancient Greece, and consists of placing strips of metallic lead in clay pots over a dilute solution of acetic acid (3%–5%). The pots were placed in tiers in a shed with spent tanning bark or manure separating and covering the pots. The fermentation (microbial anaerobic reactions) of this organic material releases heat, and the temperature rises to 55°C–60°C which is sufficient to vaporize both water and acetic acid. These vapors react with metallic lead. The process is quite slow, and the pigment was produced in about 3 months. The pigment was then scraped from the lead strips, washed, dried and ground [3]. These days, white lead is produced commercially by the Dutch process which is essentially the same as the traditional process.

What are the chemical steps which underlie this process? Metallic lead reacts with acetic acid, water and carbon dioxide to generate the double salt, $2PbCO_3 \cdot Pb(OH)_2$. The synthesis of white lead by the Stack Process was investigated [48], see Scheme 2.17. In this model study, metallic lead foils reacted with four gases: atmospheric O_2, water vapor, CO_2 generated by action of yeast on a sugar solution, and acetic acid vapor. Corrosion films formed on the surface of the lead foils, and were analyzed by XRD at various time intervals over a 10-day period. The results are summarized in Table 2.4.

In this sequence, the products were identified as a function of time: lead oxyacetate hydrate, plumbonacrite, hydrocerrusite ("HC", basic lead carbonate) and finally, cerrusite ("C", lead carbonate). In this sequence, lead acetate is an intermediate formed in the first step. Lead is oxidized by O_2. There was no evidence for the generation of H_2. In this study, the supply of CO_2 was excess, and this feature enabled the conversion of HC to C. The authors noted that in the actual Stack or Dutch processes, the supply of CO_2 would be limited and this resulted in a final product with HC and C *both* present in a mass ratio in the range of 6:4–8:2.

Due to the toxicity of lead, production of lead paints in the USA was stopped by the government in 1978. Artists successfully had the ban lifted so that white lead is available as an artist's pigment. Artists regard white lead as the best of the white pigments.

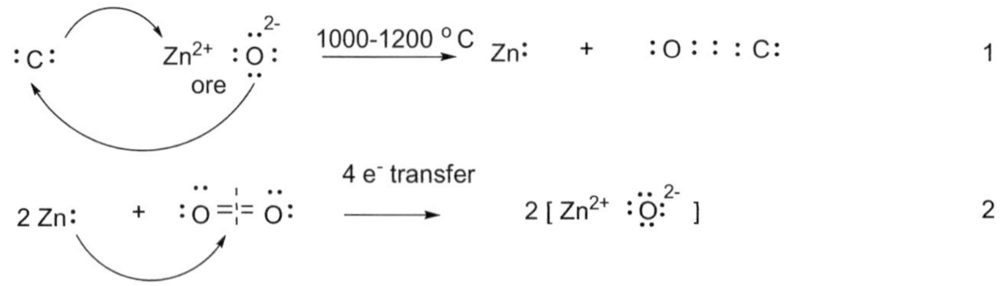

SCHEME 2.17   Zinc oxide ore refining [1].

TABLE 2.4

Products Identified by Corrosion of Lead by the Stack Process [46]

Time	Major Product	Minor Product
0.5 h	LOAH	
2 h	PN	HC
10 h	PN + HC	
2 days	HC	C
5 days	C	HC
10 days	C	

Abbreviations: LOAH, lead oxyacetate hydrate, $Pb_4O\ (CH_3CO_2)_6\cdot H_2O$; PN, plumbonacrite, $Pb_5O(CO_3)_3(OH)_2$; HC, hydrocerrusite, $2PbCO_3\cdot Pb(OH)_2$; C, cerrusite, $PbCO_3$.

Zinc White, Zinc Oxide, ZnO, is the second-most widely used white pigment on a volume basis. It is known as zinc white, Chinese white or flowers of zinc. ZnO production began in 1840, preceding TiO_2 by ~80 years. It is currently used in the production of rubber, plastic, ceramics, lubricants, pigments, paints, batteries and semiconductors. In the direct American Process, ZnO ores are reduced with coal at 1000°C–1200°C. Zinc metal boils at 907°C [1,46].

In the proposed mechanism for the refining of impure ZnO (ore), carbon transfers $2e^-$ to Zn^{2+} to form elemental zinc and carbon monoxide. The products of this step are both gases and are easily separated because of the large difference in boiling point. In the second step, pure zinc is air-oxidized to ZnO, Scheme 2.17. This process is analogous to the Chloride Process for TiO_2 because in both cases, the ore is reduced with carbon to form the metal, which after separation, is re-oxidized to the oxide.

Zinc Sulfide, ZnS, has the second highest refractive index (2.37) of all of the white pigments after TiO_2 (2.73). However, its chemical and thermal resistances are inferior to those of TiO_2. Its particles are spherical and softer than TiO_2. Thus for certain applications, ZnS is preferred to TiO_2, for example to reduce machinery damage during extrusion of plastics. Other uses include the preparation of special coatings, greases and lubricating oils, and in preparation the pigment lithopone. ZnS can be prepared by precipitation from aqueous solution. The synthesis depends on the solubility of the reactants and the insolubility of ZnS [1,46].

$$Na_2S_{aq}\ +\ ZnSO_{4\ aq}\ \rightarrow\ ZnS_s\ +\ Na_2SO_{4\ aq}$$

| 15.7 | 53.8 | 6.9×10^{-4} | 19.5 | g/100 g water at 20°C |

2.8 YELLOW PIGMENTS

Bismuth Vanadate, $BiVO_4$, has been developed to replace lead chromate as a non-toxic, yellow pigment with good hiding strength and light-fastness. It is synthesized either by chemical precipitation or high-temperature calcination. In the precipitation method, solutions of bismuth (II) nitrate and sodium metavanadate are combined, and the yellow product precipitates [49].

$$Bi(NO_3)_{3\,aq} + NaVO_{3\,aq} + 2\,NaOH_{aq} \rightarrow BiVO_{4\,s} + 3\,NaNO_{3\,aq} + H_2O_l$$

Cadmium Pigments. Cadmium pigments have been reliable as stable, bright pigments with a range of colors including yellow, red and maroon. However, these pigments are being replaced because of toxicity issues during manufacturing. Cadmium pigments are based on cadmium sulfide, CdS, which is synthesized by precipitation [11]. A range of colors can be made by calcining cadmium sulfide with the compounds in Table 2.5 [50].

$$CdSO_{4\,aq} \quad + H_2S_g \quad \rightarrow \quad CdS_s \quad + \quad H_2SO_{4\,aq}$$

Sol'y in water	75.5	0.71, 0°C,	0.00013	very soluble
grams/100 mL		1 atm		

Cobalt Yellow, $K_3[Co(NO_2)_6]$, 1.5 H_2O, potassium nitrocobaltate, aureolin, Fisher's yellow. This pigment was first synthesized by N.W. Fisher in 1831 by reaction of potassium nitrite with many metallic nitrites, including cobalt (III) nitrite to form what was then considered a double salt. Concentrated solutions of potassium nitrite reacting with cobalt (II) in the presence of acetic acid yield crystalline potassium cobaltinitrite [51].

The balanced equation for this reaction is:

$$Co^{2+}_{aq} + 7\,NO^{2-}_{aq} + 3\,K^{+}_{aq} + 2\,H^{+}_{aq} \rightarrow NO_g + H_2O_l + K_3\left[Co(NO_2)_6\right]_s$$

ON +2   +3 – 2   +1   +1   +2 – 2 +1 – 2   +1 +3 +3 – 2

This is a redox reaction in which Co^{2+} is oxidized to Co^{3+} and one of the nitrite ions is reduced to NO (nitric oxide). Further, the geometry around Co^{3+} in the pigment is octahedral with six ligated nitrites.

A concentrated solution of Co^{2+} is required, so that the very soluble salt, $CoCl_2$ (~3.5 M) is used. A large molar excess of KNO_2 is utilized, and this salt is also very soluble in water (~37 M). The synthesis is illustrated in Scheme 2.18.

TABLE 2.5
Cadmium Colors

Hue	Calcine CdS with
Red to maroon	CdSe
Orange	CdSe and BaSO$_4$
Orange	HgS
Reddish yellow	ZnS

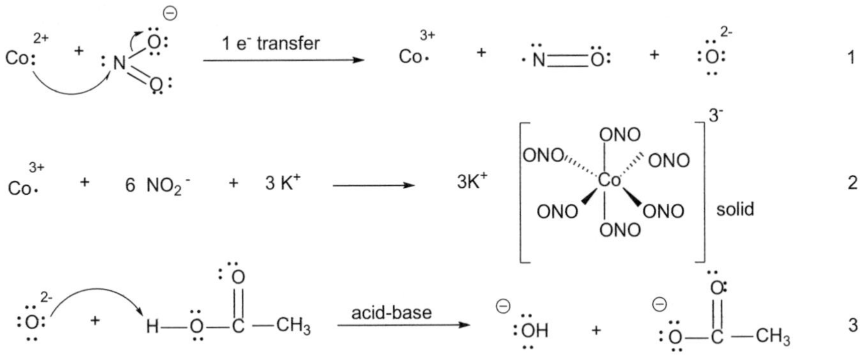

SCHEME 2.18 Synthesis of cobalt yellow [51].

Co^{2+} donates one electron to the nitrogen atom of nitrite ion yielding Co^{3+}. The N-O bond breaks to yield O^{2-} (oxide anion), and NO (nitric oxide). Co^{3+} forms an octahedral coordination complex with six nitrite ions (ligands). The other product is oxide anion which is a very strong base, and reacts with acetic acid in an acid-base reaction to form hydroxide and acetate anion. Cobalt yellow retains 1.5 water molecules of hydration in its crystal structure.

2.8.1 Yellow Iron (III) Oxide,_FeO(OH), Goethite

The Penniman-Zoph process is the most widely used process for the synthesis of yellow iron (III) oxide pigments [1], see Scheme 2.19. In the first stage of this process, crystal nuclei are formed by reaction of the slightly soluble iron (II) sulfate with sodium hydroxide solution. The products are the insoluble iron (II) hydroxide and

$$FeSO_{4\ aq} + 2\ NaOH_{aq} \xrightarrow{20 - 50\ ^\circ C} Fe(OH)_{2\ nuclei} + Na_2SO_{4\ aq} \qquad 1$$

$$Fe(OH)_{2\ nuclei} + 1/2\ O_{2\ gas} \longrightarrow Fe_2O_3 \cdot H_2O_{nuclei} + H_2O_{liq} \qquad 2$$

$$\underset{+2}{4\ FeSO_{4\ aq}} + 6\ H_2O_{liq} + \underset{0}{6\ O_{2\ gas}} \longrightarrow \underset{+3\ -2\ -2}{4\ FeO(OH)_{solid}} + 4\ H_2SO_{4\ aq} \qquad 3$$

$$4\ H_2SO_{4\ aq} + \underset{+2}{8\ FeSO_{4\ aq}} + \underset{0}{2\ O_{2\ gas}} \longrightarrow \underset{+3}{4\ Fe_2(SO_4)_{3\ aq}} + \underset{-2}{4\ H_2O_{liquid}} \qquad 4$$

$$4\ Fe_2(SO_4)_{3\ aq} + 4\ Fe^o_{solid} \longrightarrow 12\ FeSO_{4\ solid} \qquad 5$$

$$\underset{0}{4\ Fe^o_{solid}} + \underset{0}{3\ O_{2\ gas}} + 2\ H_2O_{liquid} \longrightarrow \underset{+3\ -2\ -2}{4\ FeO(OH)_{solid}} \qquad net$$

SCHEME 2.19 Synthesis of Fe(O)OH by the Penniman-Zoph process [1].

the very soluble sodium sulfate. Crystal nuclei are microscopic particles which grow into crystals by agglomeration. At this point, the reaction mixture is aerated which oxidizes Fe^{2+} to Fe^{3+}. $[Fe_2O_3H_2O]$ is formally equivalent to $2[FeO(OH)]$.

Depending on conditions, yellow, orange or red nuclei may be obtained. The next stage is to transfer the suspension of nuclei to a tank which contains scrap iron (Fe°), and additional water is added. Any residual $FeSO_4$ is oxidized by air blasts and the temperature is held in the range of 75°C–90°C. The next step in the sequence is oxidative hydrolysis of Fe_2O_3 to yield $FeO(OH)$. Water is a reactant, and it is split into H^+ and HO^-, hence "hydrolysis". Redox occurs as well. Sulfuric acid is formed and reacts with scrap iron to form $FeSO_4$ which is air-oxidized. The final stage of this process consists of a set of three interlocking reactions; the sum of lines 3–5 yields the net reaction.

The Penniman-Zoph process is an interesting set of overlapping reactions in which very little base is used and no salt by-products are formed; these factors are environmentally friendly. The reactants are scrap iron, atmospheric oxygen gas and water. The intermediates include sulfuric acid, iron (II) and iron (III) sulfates. The product is $FeO(OH)$.

Lead Chromate Pigments. Lead chromate, chrome yellow, $PbCrO_4$, occurs naturally as the orange mineral crocoite. It is prepared by mixing a solution of a soluble lead (II) salt with a solution of a soluble chromium (VI) salt. Among the former are lead nitrate, basic lead acetate, basic lead carbonate, respectively, $Pb(NO_3)_2$, $Pb_2(OH)(C_2H_3O_2)$ and $(PbCO_3)\cdot Pb(OH)_2$. Examples of soluble chromates are sodium chromate, Na_2CrO_4, and potassium dichromate, $K_2Cr_2O_7$. A typical synthesis involves hydrolysis of dichromate to chromate. A typical synthesis is:

$$2Pb(NO_3)_{2\,aq} + K_2Cr_2O_{7\,aq} + H_2O_l \rightarrow 2\,PbCrO_{4s} + 2\,KNO_{3\,aq} + 2\,HNO_{3\,aq}$$

| 56.5 | 180 | | 5.8 × 10⁻⁶ | 73 | 213[a] |

^{a} Solubility, g/100 mL water.

Lead chromate is far less soluble than the other compounds. Other chromate pigments which can be prepared by analogous precipitation methods include barium chromate (barium yellow), strontium chromate (strontium yellow) and zinc chromate (zinc yellow). In this class of pigments, the *chromophore* is a chromium atom in the 6+ oxidation state which is covalently to four oxygen atoms in the dichromate or chromate anion. The precipitated chromate salt forms quickly. The precipitate is filtered, washed with water to remove any soluble salts, dried and ground.

Lead chromate can be mixed with other lead compounds and calcined to form a family of pigments with a range of colors. These pigments are known as chrome yellows, chrome reds, and chrome oranges. Pigments which can be mixed with lead chromate include lead molybdate, $PbMoO_4$, lead (II) sulfate, $PbSO_4$, and lead (II) oxide, PbO [43].

These compounds form *solid solutions* with lead chromate. Solid solutions are one-phase systems; hence, phase separation does not occur. In order to form a solid solution, four criteria must be satisfied [52]:

i. two substances must have the same formula type, e.g., $PbCrO_4$ and $PbMoO_4$,
ii. two substances must have the same stereochemical form,
iii. the relative sizes of the structural units should be approximately equal,
iv. the ionic and covalent characteristics of the bonds should be similar.

Lead pigments have largely been replaced by cadmium pigments because of toxicity issues. However, cadmium pigments also have toxicity issues, and they are also being replaced.

Lead Tin Yellow Type I. The balanced equation for the solid-phase synthesis of lead tin yellow type I is:

$$2\ Pb_3O_{4\,s} + 3\ SnO_{2\,s}\ (900°C,\ air)\ \rightarrow\ 3\ Pb_2SnO_{4\,s} + O_{2\,g}$$

Red lead is calcined with cassiterite leading to the formation of the yellow pigment and expulsion of oxygen gas. In Scheme 2.20, red lead has been rewritten to show both oxidation states of ionic lead, and oxidation numbers are assigned. In this redox reaction, oxide anion is oxidized to di-oxygen gas and Pb^{4+} is reduced to Pb^{2+}. The other atoms in the system do not change oxidation state. Two oxide anions transfer $1e^-$ each to Pb^{4+} to form Pb^{2+} and $2\ O^{1-}$. The latter combine to yield peroxide anion, O_2^{2-}. Peroxide reduces a second Pb^{4+} to Pb^{2+} and O_2 gas is formed. The final step consists is calcination (high-temperature inter-diffusion of the two solids), to form $(Pb^{2+}O)_6·(SnO_2)_3$ (for accounting purposes), which is equivalent to $3\ Pb_2SnO_4$ [53,54].

Lead Tin Yellow Type II is represented as $PbSn_{1-x}\,Si_x\,O_3$ in which x varies. Consequently, tetravalent silicon replaces tetravalent tin. There are several synthetic routes. If $x=0$, SiO_2 is not a reactant, the balanced equation for the synthesis of this pigment is:

$$1\ Pb_3O_{4\,s} + 3\ SnO_{2\,s}\ (900°C - 1000°C) \rightarrow 3\ PbSnO_{3\,s} + 0.5\ O_{2\,g}$$

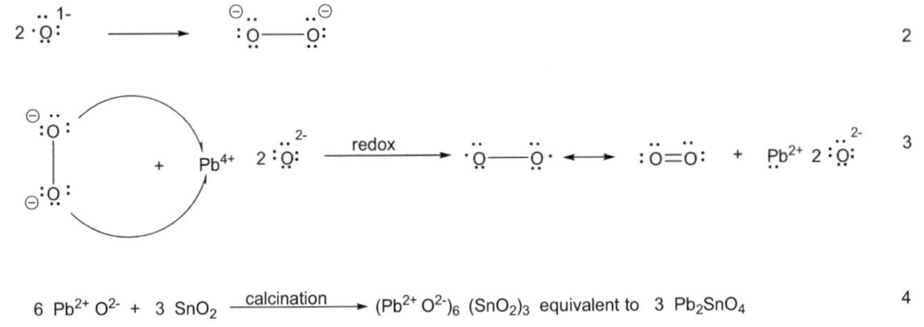

SCHEME 2.20   Synthesis of lead tin yellow type I [53,54].

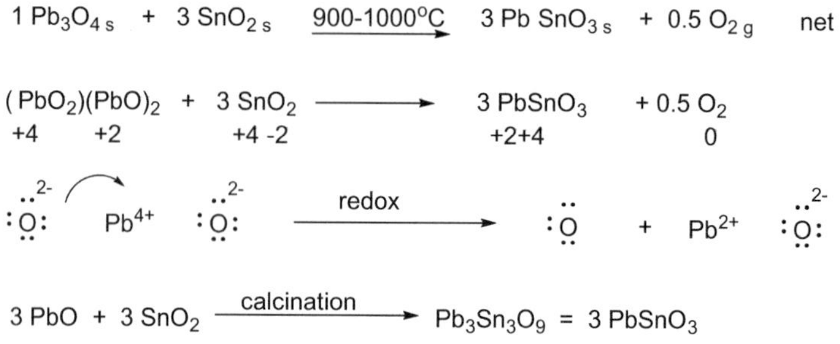

$$1 \text{ Pb}_3\text{O}_{4\,s} + 3 \text{ SnO}_{2\,s} \xrightarrow{900-1000°C} 3 \text{ Pb SnO}_{3\,s} + 0.5 \text{ O}_{2\,g} \quad \text{net}$$

$$\underset{\substack{+4 \quad +2}}{(\text{PbO}_2)(\text{PbO})_2} + \underset{+4\,-2}{3 \text{ SnO}_2} \longrightarrow \underset{+2+4}{3 \text{ PbSnO}_3} + \underset{0}{0.5 \text{ O}_2}$$

$$\overset{..}{\underset{..}{:}}\overset{2-}{\text{O}}: \quad \text{Pb}^{4+} \quad \overset{..}{\underset{..}{:}}\overset{2-}{\text{O}}: \quad \xrightarrow{\text{redox}} \quad :\overset{..}{\text{O}} \quad + \quad \text{Pb}^{2+} \quad \overset{..}{\underset{..}{:}}\overset{2-}{\text{O}}:$$

$$3 \text{ PbO} + 3 \text{ SnO}_2 \xrightarrow{\text{calcination}} \text{Pb}_3\text{Sn}_3\text{O}_9 = 3 \text{ PbSnO}_3$$

SCHEME 2.21   Synthesis of lead tin yellow type II [53,54].

In Scheme 2.21, red lead has been written to show both oxidation states of ionic lead, and assigning oxidation numbers and formal charges. The changes in oxidation numbers show that Pb^{4+} is reduced to: Pb^{2+} and that one oxide anion is oxidized to one oxygen atom. Two electrons are transferred from oxide to Pb^{4+} giving PbO and one oxygen atom which is formally the same as ½ O_2 molecule. Adding this newly formed PbO unit to the two unreacted PbO units yields three units of PbO. Finally, calcining with 3 units of SnO_2, the result is 1 unit of $\text{Pb}_3\text{Sn}_3\text{O}_9$ (for accounting purposes) equivalent to 3 PbSnO_3.

If the product is to contain silicon, the traditional preparation is to heat a 1:1 mixture of yellow type I and silica at 900°C for 5 h [54]:

$$\text{Pb}_2\text{SnO}_{4\,\text{solid}} + \text{SiO}_{2\,\text{solid}} \rightarrow \text{PbSn}_{1-x}\text{Si}_x\text{O}_{3\,\text{solid}}$$

An example of a single-step synthesis involves calcination of Pb, Sn and Si oxides in the molar ratio 6:3:2 at about 850°C. The reaction yields two phases and can be represented as follows:

$$6 \text{ PbO} + 3 \text{ SnO}_2 + 2 \text{ SiO}_2 \rightarrow [3\text{PbO} - 2\text{SiO}_2] + 3[\text{PbSn}_{1-x}\text{Si}_x\text{O}_3], \text{ where}$$

square brackets indicate approximate composition. $[3\text{PbO}-2\text{SiO}_2]$ is a glassy phase and $[\text{PbSn}_{1-x}\text{Si}_x\text{O}_3]$ is a rich yellow phase with variable composition.

Naples Yellow, Lead Tin Antimonate, $\text{Pb}_2\text{Sb}_2\text{O}_7$.

Naples Yellow is formed by calcination of red lead with stibnite (antimony (III) oxide), in the presence of 10–20 mass % of NaCl. In this synthesis, molten salt acts as a flux which allows the reaction temperature to be lower compared to a salt-free synthesis. This is advantageous because high temperatures often cause decomposition. The salt is removed by washing the product with water [54,55].

$$2 \text{ Pb}_3\text{O}_{4\,s} + 3 \text{ Sb}_2\text{O}_{3\,s} + 2 \text{ O}_{2\,g} \; (850°C - 900°C, \text{ molten NaCl}) \rightarrow 3 \text{ Pb}_2\text{Sb}_2\text{O}_{7\,s}$$

Rewritten to show the oxidation numbers:

$$2\left[\left(\text{Pb}^{2+}\text{O}^{2-} \right)_2 \cdot \text{Pb}^{4+}\text{O}_2 \right] + 3 \text{ Sb}_2\text{O}_3 + 2 \text{ O}_2 \rightarrow 3 \text{ Pb}_2\text{Sb}_2\text{O}_7$$

$$\text{O.N.} \quad +2 \; -2 \quad\quad +4 \; -2 \quad\quad +3 \; -2 \quad 0 \quad\quad\quad +4 \; +3 \; -2$$

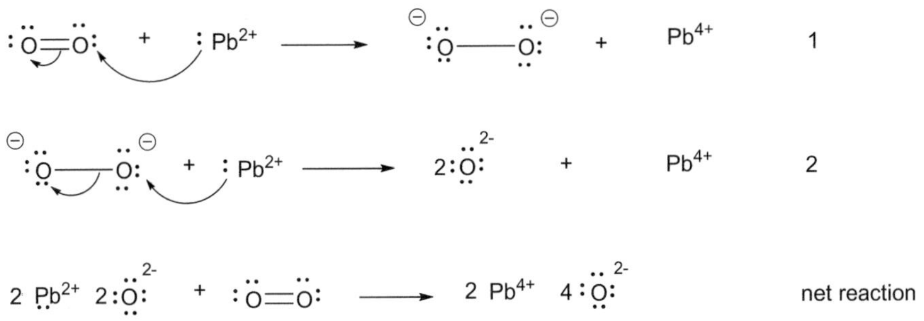

$$:\overset{..}{\underset{..}{O}}{=}\overset{..}{\underset{..}{O}}: \quad + \quad : Pb^{2+} \quad \longrightarrow \quad \overset{\ominus..}{:\underset{..}{O}}{-}\overset{..\ominus}{\underset{..}{O}}: \quad + \quad Pb^{4+} \qquad 1$$

$$\overset{\ominus..}{:\underset{..}{O}}{-}\overset{..\ominus}{\underset{..}{O}}: \quad + \quad : Pb^{2+} \quad \longrightarrow \quad 2:\overset{..}{\underset{..}{O}}:^{2-} \quad + \quad Pb^{4+} \qquad 2$$

$$2 \; \overset{.}{P}b^{2+} \; 2:\overset{..}{\underset{..}{O}}:^{2-} \quad + \quad :\overset{..}{O}{=}\overset{..}{\underset{..}{O}}: \quad \longrightarrow \quad 2 \; Pb^{4+} \; 4:\overset{..}{\underset{..}{O}}:^{2-} \qquad \text{net reaction}$$

SCHEME 2.22 Synthesis of Naples yellow, redox steps [53].

It's redox! Pb^{2+} is oxidized to Pb^{4+}, and di-oxygen is reduced to oxide. This mechanism is analogous to that used in lead tin yellow. It is useful to write out all of the reactive units for accounting purposes, see Scheme 2.22.

$$2 \left[Pb^{2+}O \; Pb^{2+}O \; Pb^{4+} \; O_2 \right] + 2 \, O_2 + 3 \, Sb_2O_3 \rightarrow 3 \, Pb_2Sb_2O_7$$

Next, focus on the species which participate in electron transfer. In step 1, Pb^{2+} transfers two electrons to di-oxygen. In step 2, Pb^{2+} transfers two electrons to peroxide anion to form Pb^{4+} and two oxide anions. If this two-step cycle is repeated once, a total of four equivalents of PbO_2 are produced. Add these to the two equivalents of PbO_2 originally present in red lead, and calcine with three equivalents of Sb_2O_3 to yield the final product.

Combining the pieces, we have:

$$6 \, Pb^{4+} + 6 \, Sb^{3+} + 21 \, O = 3 \, Pb_2Sb_2O_7$$

Lead Monoxide, PbO. Lead monoxide occurs in two crystalline forms (polymorphs). They are massicot (yellow) and litharge (orange-red). Massicot is used as an artists' pigment, while litharge is used as a drying agent for oil paints and varnishes [56]. At 300°C, white lead decomposes to form massicot, water and carbon dioxide:

$$2 \, PbCO_3 \cdot Pb(OH)_{2\,s} \xrightarrow{\text{(decomposition, 300°C)}} 3 \, PbO_s + 1 \, H_2O_g + 2 \, CO_{2\,g}$$

This reaction consists of two transformations, an acid-base/dehydration and a decarboxylation, Scheme 2.23. This process is reversible. Massicot reverts slowly to white lead when exposed to moist air.

Litharge forms when molten metallic lead is air-oxidized [3], see Scheme 2.24. In this synthesis, metallic lead donates electrons to di-oxygen. The electron configuration of metallic lead is [Xe] $4f^{14} \, 5d^{10} \, 6s^2 \, 6p^2$, with four valence electrons.

In this mechanism, elemental lead transfers a total of four valence electrons in two steps. The first transfer yields peroxide anion, and the second gives two equivalents of oxide anion. In the final step, divalent lead and oxide combine and crystalize as litharge.

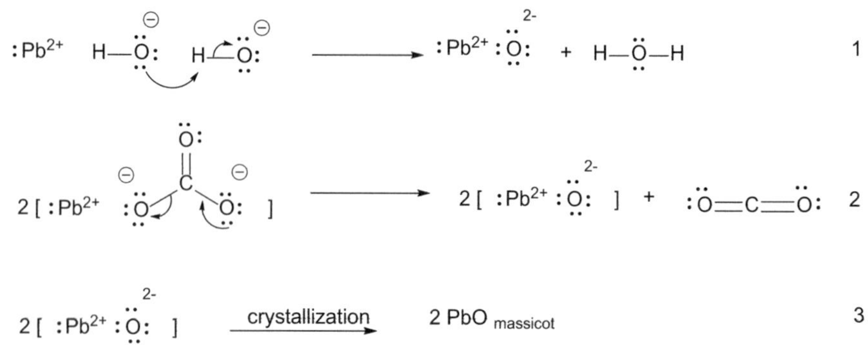

$$:Pb^{2+} \quad H-\overset{..}{\underset{..}{O}}:^{\ominus} \quad H-\overset{..}{\underset{..}{O}}:^{\ominus} \quad \longrightarrow \quad :Pb^{2+} :\overset{..}{\underset{..}{O}}:^{2-} \quad + \quad H-\overset{..}{O}-H \qquad 1$$

$$2\,[\; :Pb^{2+} \quad \overset{..}{\underset{..}{O}}:^{\ominus} \overset{\overset{\overset{..}{O}:}{\|}{C}}{} \overset{..}{\underset{..}{O}}:^{\ominus} \;] \quad \longrightarrow \quad 2\,[\; :Pb^{2+} :\overset{..}{\underset{..}{O}}:^{2-} \;] \quad + \quad :\overset{..}{O}=C=\overset{..}{O}: \quad 2$$

$$2\,[\; :Pb^{2+} :\overset{..}{\underset{..}{O}}:^{2-} \;] \quad \xrightarrow{\text{crystallization}} \quad 2\ PbO\ _{\text{massicot}} \qquad 3$$

SCHEME 2.23 Synthesis of massicot, PbO [56].

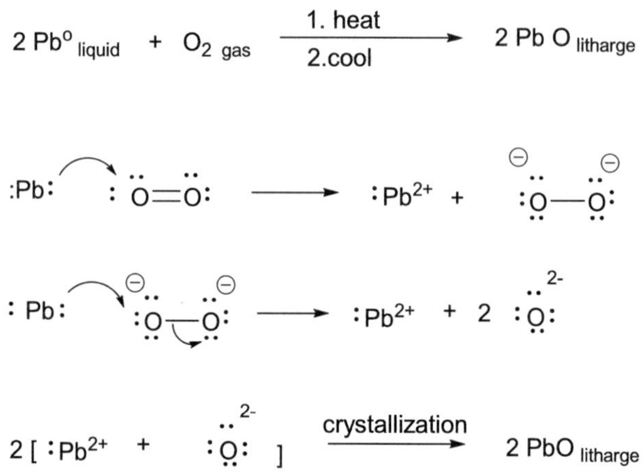

$$2\ Pb^{0}\ _{\text{liquid}} \quad + \quad O_2\ _{\text{gas}} \quad \xrightarrow[\text{2.cool}]{\text{1. heat}} \quad 2\ Pb\ O\ _{\text{litharge}}$$

$$:Pb:\quad :\overset{..}{O}=\overset{..}{O}: \quad \longrightarrow \quad :Pb^{2+} \quad + \quad :\overset{..}{O}-\overset{..}{O}:^{\ominus\ \ominus}$$

$$:Pb:\quad :\overset{..}{\underset{..}{O}}-\overset{..}{\underset{..}{O}}:^{\ominus\ \ominus} \quad \longrightarrow \quad :Pb^{2+} \quad + \quad 2\ :\overset{..}{\underset{..}{O}}:^{2-}$$

$$2\,[\; :Pb^{2+} \quad + \quad :\overset{..}{\underset{..}{O}}:^{2-} \;] \quad \xrightarrow{\text{crystallization}} \quad 2\ PbO\ _{\text{litharge}}$$

SCHEME 2.24 Synthesis of litharge, PbO [3].

Orpiment and α-Realgar. These pigments are naturally occurring minerals, and have been used since ancient times. The name, orpiment, a lemon-yellow pigment, is derived from a contraction of the Latin name, *auripigmentum* (golden pigment). Realgar (a red pigment) comes from Catalan and Spanish from Arabic, *rahj-alghar* (powder from the mine). Neither pigment is used these days because of toxicity. Elemental arsenic and sulfur react to form a series of arsenic sulfides, including As_4S_1, As_4S_4, As_2S_5 and As_4S_6. The specific product is controlled by the mole ratio of As/S. Only two of these sulfides have been used as artists' pigments; α-realgar, As_4S_4, and orpiment, As_2S_3 see Figure 2.9. Orpiment can be synthesized by the following reaction:

$$2[AsO_4]^{3-} + 6\,H^+ + 5\,H_2S \rightarrow As_2S_3 + 2S + 8\,H_2O$$

Realgar can be synthesized by fusing a mixture of arsenious oxide (As_2O_3) and sulfur [2].

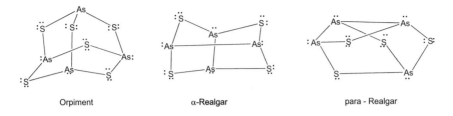

| Orpiment | α-Realgar | para - Realgar |

FIGURE 2.9 Structures of orpiment, α-realgar and para-realgar.

These inorganic pigments are unusual because of the absence of metal atoms and because the bonds between As and S are covalent.

Orpiment, As_4S_6, has the same structure as P_4S_6. The tricyclic structure consists of six-membered rings in which As and S alternate. The bonding is entirely covalent. Both pigments are often represented by empirical formulas; As or As_2S_2 for realgar and As_2S_3 for orpiment. Both compounds yield tricyclic molecular structures when vaporized; As_4S_4 for realgar and As_4S_6 for orpiment, see Figure 2.9. In the solid state, the photo-induced isomerization of realgar to pararealgar has been interpreted in terms of the molecular tricyclic structure, As_4S_4, see Chapter 4.4. In contrast solid orpiment has a polymeric chain structure, $-(S-As(S)-S-As(S)-S-)_n$, in which each S atom is bonded to two As atoms, while each As atom is bonded to three S atoms [57a]. Orpiment is stable to light and to dilute acids and bases. Orpiment and α-realgar are incompatible with pigments which contain ionic copper or lead and form black metallic sulfides [57b, 58].

Titanium Yellow is a relatively new pigment which was developed in the 1960s as a replacement for chrome yellow because of the latter pigment's toxicity and tendency to darken. It is made by calcination of titanium dioxide, nickel (II) oxide and antimony pentoxide which results in a solid solution [59,60]. The chemical formula of titanium yellow is given as: $(NiO)\cdot(Sb_2O_5)\cdot(TiO_2)_{20}$, with a typical analysis of 4, 14 and 80 mass percent, respectively.

REFERENCES

GENERAL

1. Swiler DR, (2007) Inorganic pigments. In: *Kirk Othmer Encyclopedia of Chemical Technology*, 5th ed, vol 19: 1–41, Wiley, New York.
2. Inorganic Coloring Matters. (1971) The Colour Index Society of Dyers and Colourists, 3rd ed, vol 4: 4651–4689, Bradford, West Yorkshire.
3. Gettens R, Stout G (1966) Painting Materials, A Short Encyclopedia: 91–181, Dover, New York.

ANTIMONY BLACK

4. Yang RX, Butler KT, Walsh A (2015) Assessment of hybrid organic-inorganic antimony sulfides for earth-abundant photovoltaic applications. *J Phys Chem Lett* 6:5009–5014.
5. Maiti N, Im SH, Lee YH, Seok SI (2012) Urchinlike nanostructure of single-crystalline nanorods of Sb_2S_3 formed at mild reaction condition. *ACS Appl Mater Interface* 4:4787–4791.

6. Smart LE, Moore EA (2012) *Solid State Chemistry An Introduction*, 4th ed: 23–25, 128–130. CRC Press, Taylor and Francis Group, Boca Raton, FL.

Carbon Black

7. Gardiner K, van Tongeren M, Harrington M (2001) Respiratory health effects from exposure to carbon black: results of the phase 2 and 3 cross sectional studies in the European carbon black manufacturing industry. *Occup Environ Med* 58:496–503.

Cobalt Black

8. Cotton FA, Wilkenson G (1962) Advanced Inorganic Chemistry: 484, 721, Interscience, John Wiley and Sons, New York.

Iron Oxide, Magnetite

9. Hayes PC, Grieveson P (1981) The effects of nucleation and growth on the reduction of Fe_2O_3 to Fe_3O_4. Metallur Mater Trans B 12:319–326.
10. Blaney L (2007) Magnetite (Fe_3O_4): properties, synthesis and applications. Lehigh Rev 15: paper 5. http://preserve.lehigh/.edu/cas-lehighreview-vol-15.

Manganese Black

11. Patnaik P (2003) Handbook of Inorganic Chemicals: 45–47, McGraw-Hill, New York.

Azurite

12. Tro N (2014) *Chemistry* A Molecular Approach, 3rd ed: 282, Pearson, Boston, MA.

Cerulean Blue

13. Jonynaite D, Senvaitiene J, Kiuberis J, Kareiva A, Jusneas R, Ramamauskas R (2009) XRD characterization of cobalt-based historical pigments and glazes. *Chemija* 20:10–18.
14. Shamirian A, Edrisi M, Naderi M (2013) Synthesis, characterization, and optimization of Co_2SnO_4 nanoparticles via co-precipitation method. *J Mat Eng Performance* 22:306–311.

Egyptian Blue

15. Berke H (2007) The invention of blue and purple pigments in ancient times. *Chem Soc Rev* 36:15–30.
16. Garcia-Fernandez P, Moreno M, Aramburu JA (2016) Origin of the anomalous color of Egyptian and Han blue historical pigments: going beyond the complex approximation in ligand field theory. *J Chem Ed* 93:111–117.
17. Belton DJ, Deschaume O, Perry CC (2012) An overview of the fundamentals of the chemistry of silica with relevance to biosilification and technological advances. *FEBS J* 279:1710–1720.

PRUSSIAN BLUE

18. Ware M (2008) Prussian blue: artists' pigment and chemists' sponge. *J Chem Ed* 85:612–621.
19. Samain L, Grandjean F, Long G, Martinetto P, Bordet P, Strivay D (2013) Relationship between the synthesis of Prussian blue pigments, their color, physical properties, and their behavior in paint layers. *J Phys Chem C* 117:9693–9712.

ULTRAMARINE

20. Ball E (2001) *Bright Earth*: 235–238, University of Chicago Press, Chicago.
21. Schmidt CM, Walton MS, Trentelman K (2009) Characterization of *lapis lazuli* pigmnts using a multitechnique analytical approach: implications for identification and geological provenancing. *Anal Chem* 81:8513–8518.
22a. Gobeltz N, Demortier A, Lelieur JP, Duhayon C (1998) Encapsulation of the blue chromophores into the sodalite structure during the synthesis of the blue ultramarine pigment. *J Chem Soc Faraday Trans* 94:2257–2260.
22b. Climent-Pascual E, Romero de Paz J, Rodriguez-Carvajal J, Suard E, Saéz-Puche R (2009) Synthesis and characterization of ultramarine-type analog. Na_{8-x} $[Si_6Al_6O_{24}]$. $(S_2, S_3, CO_3)_{1-2}$. *Inorg Chem*: 48:6526–6533.
23. Kowalak S, Jankowska A (2009) An inorganic sulfur pigment based on nanoporous materials. In: *Ordered Porous Solids, Recent Advances and Prospects*, Valtchev V, Mintova S, Tsapatsis M (eds): 511–620, Elsevier, Amsterdam, London.
24. Gobeltz-Hautecoeur N, Demortier A, Lede B, Lelieur JP, Duhayon C (2002) Occupancy of the sodalite cages in the blue ultramarine pigments. *Inorg Chem* 41:2848–2854.
25. Weller, MT (2000) Where zeolites and oxides merge: semi-condensed tetrahedral frameworks. *J Chem Soc Dalton Trans* 23:4227–4240.
26. Matsunaga Y (1959) Electron spin resonance absorption of ultramarine: effect of cations. *Can J Chem* 37:994–995.
27. Booth DG, Dann SE, Weller MT (2003) The effect of the cation composition on the synthesis and properties of ultramarine blue. *Dyes and Pigments* 58:73–82.
28. Reinen D, Lindner GG (1999) The nature of the chalcogen colour centers in ultramarine-type pigments. *Chem Soc Rev* 28:75–84.

VERDIGRIS

29. DeMeo S (1997) Does copper metal react with acetic acid? *J Chem Ed* 74:844–846.
30. Lopez-Delgado A, Cano E, Bastidas JM, Lopez FA (2001) A comparative study on copper corrosion originated by formic acid and acetic acid vapors. *J Mater Sci* 36:5203–5211.
31. Kuhn H, (1993) Verdigris and copper resinate. In: *Artists' Pigments, A Handbook of their History and Characteristics*, Roy A (ed) vol 2: 131–158, Oxford University Press, Oxford.
32. Salvadó N, Butí S, Cotte M, Cinque G, Pradell T (2013) Shades of green in 15th century paintings: combined microanalysis of the materials using synchrotron radiation XRD, FTIR and XRI, *Appl Phys A* 111:47–57.

CHROMIUM OXIDE

33. Park IH (1972) Thermal decomposition of ammonium salts of transition metal oxyacids. III. Thermogravimetric analysis of ammonium chromate. *Bull Chem Soc Japan* 45:2749–2752.

34. Newman R (1997) Chromium greens. Chromium oxide and hydrated chromium oxide. In: *Artists' Pigments, Handbook of their History and Characteristics*, Fitzhugh EW (ed) vol 3: 273–293, National Gallery of Art, London.

35. Zumbuehl S, Berger A, Scherrer N, Eggenberger U (2009) Early viridian pigment composition. Characterization of a (hydrated) chromium oxide borate pigment. *Stud Conserv* 54:149–159.

36. Rowsell JLC, Nazar LF (2001) Synthesis, structure and solid state electrochemical properties of Cr_3BO_6: a new chromium (III) borate with the norbergite structure. *J Mater Chem, RSC* 11:3228–3233.

37a. Skorova D, private communication (2011), equations representing the two steps for the synthesis of hydrated Cr (III) oxide:

$$6\ K_2Cr_2O_7 + 16\ H_3BO_3 = 12\ CrBO_3 + 4\ K_3BO_3 + 24\ H_2O + 9\ O_2 \qquad \text{step 1}$$

$$CrBO_3 + (3-x)\ H_2O = (CrO)_x (HO)_{(3-2x)} + H_3BO_3 \qquad \text{step 2}$$

Set x =1, multiply step 2 by 12, and add to step 1, yielding:

$$6\ K_2Cr_2O_7 + 4\ H_3BO_3 = 12\ CrO(OH) + 4\ K_3BO_3 + 9\ O_2 \qquad \text{sum, and}$$

$$12\ CrO(OH)\ \text{is formally equivalent to} 6\ Cr_2O_3 \cdot 1H_2O.$$

Therefore, the reaction is redox, $CrBO_3$ is an intermediate, and the product is the monohydrate of Cr_2O_3.

37b. Das Gupta SP, Bose HN (1948) A note on preparation of chromium oxide green. *Trans Indian Ceramic Soc* 7: 60–62.

38. Chromium and chromium compounds (2012) IARC Monograph 29 (Sup 7), 100C.

Paris Green, Emerald Green

39. Fiedler I, Bayard MA (1997) Emerald green and Scheele's green. In: *Artists' Pigments, Handbook of their History and Characteristics*, vol 3: 219–271, Fitzhugh EW (ed), Nat Gallery of Art, Washington, DC.

40. Davis E.R. (2017) Pesticides and the paradox of the Anthropocene: From natural to synthetic to synthesized nature. *Global Environ* 10:114–136, Doi: 10.3197/ge.2017.100105.

α-Cinnabar, Vermilion

41. Fahlman B, (2011) *Materials Chemistry*, 2nd ed: 40, Springer, Dordrecht, Heidelberg, London, New York.

Red Lead

42. Fantacci S, Amat A, Sgamellotti A (2010) Computational chemistry meets cultural heritage: challenges and perspectives. *Acc Chem Res* 43:802–813.

Iron (iii) Oxide Pigments: Red, Yellow, Brown

43. Böhland T, Brandt K, Brossaard H, etal, (2005) Colored pigments. In: *Industrial Inorganic Pigments*, 3rd ed, Buxbaum G, Pfaff G, (eds): 99–133, Wiley-VCH Verlag GmbH Wiley-VCH GmbH & KGaA, Weinheim FRG.

Cobalt Violet

44. Mayer R (1991) *The Artist's Handbook of Materials and Techniques*, 5th ed: 110, Penguin Books, New York (first published by Viking).

Antimony White

45. Wells AF (1975) *Structural Inorganic Chemistry*, 4th ed: 710–711, Oxford Univ Press, Oxford.

Titanium White

46. Auer G, Griebler WD, Jahn B (2005) White pigments. In: *Industrial Inorganic Pigments*, 3rd ed, Buxbaum G, Pfaff G, (eds): 51–94, Wiley-VCH GmbH & KGaA, Weinheim FRG.
47. Winkler HC, Notter T, Meyer U, Naegli H (2018) Critical review of the safety assessment of titanium dioxide additives in food. *J Nanobiotech* 16:51–70.

Lead White

48. Gonzalez V, Wallez G, Calligero T, Gourier D, Menu M (2019) Synthesizing lead white pigments by lead corrosion: New insights into the ancient manufacturing processes. *Corrosion Sci* 146:10–17.

Bismuth Vanadate

49. Wendusu T, Honda T, Masui T, Imanaka N (2013) Novel environmentally friendly (Bi, Ca, Zn, La) VO_4 inorganic yellow pigments. *RSC Adv* 3:24941–24945.

Cadmium Pigments

50. Dunning P (2002) Cadmium pigments. In: *High Performance Pigments*, Smith HM (ed): 13–25, Wiley-VCH Verlag GmbH & Co, KGaA, Weinheim, FRG.

Cobalt Yellow

51. Cornman M (1987) Cobalt yellow (aureolin). In: *Artists' pigments, Handbook of their History and Characteristics*, Feller, RL (ed), vol. 1: 37–46, National Gallery of Art, London.

Lead Chromate

52. Glasstone S, Lewis D (1960) *Elements of Physical Chemistry*: 219, Van Nostrand, New York.

LEAD TIN YELLOWS AND NAPLES YELLOW

53. Clark RHC, Cridland L, Kariuki B, Harris KDM, Withnall R (1995) Synthesis, structural characterization and Raman spectroscopy of the inorganic pigments lead tin yellow types I and II and lead antimonite yellow: their identification on medieval paintings and manuscripts. *J Chem Soc Dalton Trans* 16:2577–2582.
54. Hradil D, Grygar T, Hradilová T, et al. (2007) Microanalytical identification of Pb-Sb-Sn yellow pigment in historical European paintings and its differentiation from lead tin and naples yellow. *J Cult Herit* 8:377–386.
55. Wainsworth IN, Taylor JM, Harley RD (1985) Lead Antimonate Yellow. In: *Artists' Pigments, Handbook of their History and Characteristic*, Feller RL (ed), vol 1: 219-254, National Gallery of Art, Washington, DC.

LEAD MONOXIDE

56. Wiberg E, Wiberg N, Holleman AF (2001) *Inorganic Chemistry*: 915–916, Academic Press, San Diego, CA.

ORPIMENT AND REALGAR

57a. Fitzhugh EW (1997) Orpiment and Realgar. In: *Artists' Pigments, Handbook of their History and Characteristics*, Fitzhugh EW (ed), vol 3: 53, National Gallery of Art, Washington, DC.
57b. O'Day P (2006) Chemistry and mineralogy of arsenic. *Elements* 2:77–83.
58. Housecroft CE, Sharpe AG (2008) *Inorganic Chemistry*, 3rd ed: 435–485, Pearson Prentice Hall, Harlow.

TITANIUM YELLOW

59. Maloney J (2009) Titanate pigments. In: *High Performance Pigments*, Faulkner EB, Schwartz RJ (eds): 53–72, Wiley-VCH Verlag GmbH &Co., KGaA, Weinheim, FRG.

GENERAL

60. Eastaugh N, Walsh V, Chaplin T, Sisall R (2007), *Pigment Compendium: Dictionary of Historical Pigments*: 366, Routledge, Abingdon, England.

3 Silica, Silicates and Aluminosilicates

Silica, silicates and aluminosilicates are essential structural materials in glass and ceramics [1]. In addition, they are integral parts of the pigments Egyptian blue, Han blue and smalt [2,3].

3.1 SILICA

Silica, SiO_2, occurs naturally as pure sand. Silicon is a member of group 14 and is a cousin of carbon. Silicon and carbon both have four valence electrons, but carbon forms multiple bonds, and silicon does not. Carbon dioxide is a molecular compound, molar mass 44 g/mol, a gas at room temperature. In contrast, silicon dioxide is a solid at room temperature and has a boiling point greater than 2200°C. Further, it is not molecular, but instead, it is a network solid in which tetrahedral units of SiO_4 are linked together in polymeric chains and rings in a three-dimensional structure. In these structures, silicon maintains tetrahedral geometry; each silicon atom is covalently bonded to four oxygen atoms, and each oxygen atom is a corner atom shared by adjacent tetrahedra, see Figure 3.1. In this presentation, we are viewing the tetrahedra from the top, looking directly down the covalent bond which connects the top oxygen atom to the central silicon atom [4]. In each tetrahedral SiO_4 unit, only two oxygens "belong" to the central silicon atom, hence the formula, SiO_2. There are several crystalline forms (polymorphs) of SiO_2, as illustrated in Figure 3.2 [5].

3.2 SILICATES

Silica is acidic in the Lewis sense and can react with basic substances such as potash, K_2CO_3, when heated. Potash decomposes, releasing CO_2 leaving potassium oxide. K_2O reacts with silica in a solid-state reaction; the oxide anions attack the central

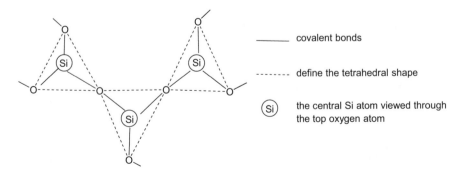

covalent bonds

-------- define the tetrahedral shape

(Si) the central Si atom viewed through the top oxygen atom

FIGURE 3.1 Silica, partial polymeric structure.

DOI: 10.1201/9781003053453-3

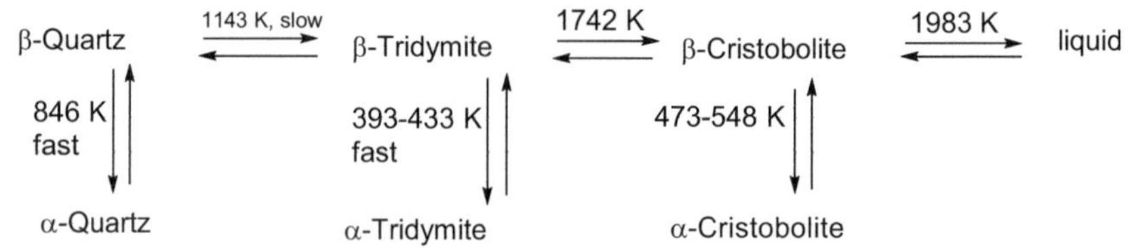

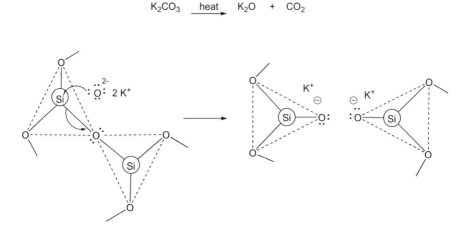

β-Quartz $\xrightleftharpoons{\text{1143 K, slow}}$ β-Tridymite $\xrightleftharpoons{\text{1742 K}}$ β-Cristobolite $\xrightleftharpoons{\text{1983 K}}$ liquid

846 K fast   393–433 K fast   473–548 K

α-Quartz   α-Tridymite   α-Cristobolite

FIGURE 3.2 Transition temperatures of silicon dioxide polymorphs. (Reprinted with permission of F.A. Cotton and G. Wilkenson, *Advanced Inorganic Chemistry*. Copyright 1962, Interscience, John Wiley and Sons.)

$$K_2CO_3 \xrightarrow{\text{heat}} K_2O + CO_2$$

FIGURE 3.3 Reaction of silica and potash to form potassium silicate.

silicon atoms and displace bridging oxygen atoms of a neighboring tetrahedron. Potassium silicate is formed and there are chain breaks wherever an oxide anion reacted with a silicon atom, see Figure 3.3. The attacker brings a negative charge with it, and K^+ is the counter-ion to maintain electrical neutrality.

There are many ways that tetrahedral units can form rings and chains, thereby creating a variety of silicate minerals. In Figure 3.4, the partial structure of $Si_4O_{10}^{4-}$ is shown. In this structure, the repeating unit is marked with a dashed line.

3.3 PIGMENT – SILICATE INTERACTIONS

In several pigment chromophores, oxygen atoms of the silicate structure are ligated to a heavy metal. Egyptian blue and Han blue share the general formula, $MCuSi_4O_{10}$; M is Ca^{2+} and Ba^{2+}, respectively. In these pigments, the chromophore is a square-planar complex, $[CuO_4]^{2-}$, in which Cu^{2+} is bonded to four terminal oxygen atoms from SiO_4 tetrahedra. The group 2 metal maintains electrical neutrality, see Figure 2.2. In smalt, the chromophore is $[CoO_4]^{2-}$ which has tetrahedral geometry. Based on the starting materials for a typical smalt formula (65–71 g of SiO_2, 16–21 g of K_2CO_3

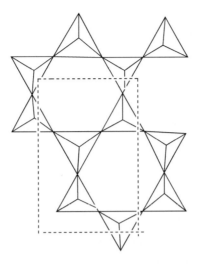

FIGURE 3.4 Repeating unit of $Si_4O_{10}^{4-}$.

and 6–7 g of CoO), the counter-ion for the chromophore would be K^+ [6]. In contrast, the chromophores in ultramarine, S_2 and S_3 radical anions, are not ligated to the aluminosilicate sodalite. These polysulfide ions are trapped inside β-cages of sodalite, with the counter-ion Na^+, see Figure 2.5.

3.4 CERAMIC GLAZE

Ceramic glaze is a thin glassy water-impervious layer which is applied to the surface of earthenware pottery, stoneware or porcelain. Glaze may or may not contain pigments. The function of glaze is to seal and optionally, to color a ceramic object. Glaze is produced by a synthetic process involving inorganic compounds. Organic compounds cannot be used because they would be destroyed during the high-temperature firing step, in which the glaze is fused to the ceramic surface. Unglazed pottery is porous and tends to "sweat" (allows water to seep through). Evaporation of the "sweat" is advantageous because this cools the liquid contained in the vessel. Pottery was first produced by fire (pyrotechnology) and evolved to become the modern science of ceramics. Other pyrotechnology "products" include metals, soap, lime and glass [7].

The technique for making pottery was discovered around 20,000 years ago, exact details are unknown. The possible discovery could been something like this: at first, people cooked over fires which were built on the ground. Later on, pit fires were

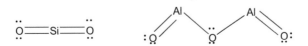

FIGURE 3.5 Silicon dioxide and aluminum oxide monomer structures. These structures do not occur in Nature.

found to produce hotter fire. If the pit happened to be lined with clay, the pit fire would convert clay to a hard material, brick. This led to clay mining for the production of earthenware vessels which were used for storage of solids (grains, etc.) and liquids (water, oil, etc.). Earthenware could be sealed with a thin layer of glass, known as glaze. Pure silica glass can be produced by melting sand (silicon dioxide). Silicon dioxide has a high melting point, and it was probably learned by accident that the presence of other minerals ("fluxes") would lower the melting point of glass. Hence, fluxes were practically useful in the production of glass because less thermal energy would be needed. Consequently, the development of glazed pottery is the result of pottery and glass pyrotechnology [8].

Clay is a family of materials known as hydrous aluminosilicates. Aluminum and silica are major components of the Earth's crust; hence, they are building blocks of the inorganic world. Silica (SiO_2) and alumina (Al_2O_3) are network solids. See Figure 3.5 for monomeric structures of SiO_2 and Al_2O_3. These structures, although appealing, do not exist in nature. The melting points of silica and alumina are 1713°C and 2015°C, respectively. They are both insoluble in water; think sand (silica) and ruby (alumina with traces of chromium, iron or titanium).

Glaze is composed of three types of oxides: silica, alumina and oxides of Groups 1 and 2 (Na_2O, K_2O and CaO). PbO is no longer used in glaze because lead is toxic. These building blocks are classified according to the Lux-Flood theory [4,7]. This theory is based on solvent-less reactions, in which oxides are grouped as acids or bases according to their location in the periodic table. Hence, the basic oxides are located in Groups 1 and 2 (Na_2O, K_2O, MgO and CaO). The acidic oxides are non-metallic oxides in the p-block (SiO_2). Amphoteric oxides behave as acids or bases depending on specific conditions (B_2O_3 and Al_2O_3). Colorants include CoO, CuO, Cr_2O_3 and Fe_2O_3. For example:

$$MgO\,(\text{base}) + CO_2\,(\text{acid}) \rightarrow MgCO_3 \text{ and}$$

$$CaO\,(\text{base}) + SiO_2\,(\text{acid}) \rightarrow CaSiO_3.$$

In these examples, the basic oxide acts as a Lewis base and donates a lone pair of electrons to the Lewis acid site: carbon and silicon, respectively.

3.5 ALUMINOSILICATES

In aluminosilicate minerals, tetrahedra with central Al atoms are part of the network of covalent bonds, see Figure 3.6. Aluminosilicates are formed by the introduction of Al-centered tetrahedra into the silica chains. Aluminum is in Group 13; hence, its three valence electrons are satisfied by making bonds with three atoms. Aluminum with a sextet of valence electrons can accept another pair of electrons and reaches a valence octet. In this state, Al is in the center of a tetrahedron, in which it is bonded to four oxygen atoms. Consequently, the formal charge on aluminum is −1, and this is counterbalanced by a cation, such as Na^+ or K^+, or Ca^{2+} [9].

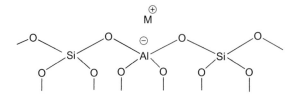

FIGURE 3.6 Partial structure for polymeric aluminosilicate.

Since Al and Si are next-door neighbors in the third row of the periodic table, their ionic radii are not too different. Consequently, Al-centered tetrahedra are about the same size as the Si-centered tetrahedra. Both types of tetrahedra link together to form chains and rings in aluminosilicate minerals. An example of a naturally occurring aluminosilicate minerals is anorthite, $Ca(AlO_2)_2(SiO_2)_2$, in which half of the tetrahedra are AlO_4 and the other half are SiO_4 [4].

REFERENCES

SILICA, SILICATES AND ALUMINOSILICATES

1. Carter CB, Norton MG (2007) *Ceramic Materials, Science and Engineering*: 15–29, 104–111, Springer, New York.
2. Berke H (2002) Chemistry in ancient times: the development of blue and purple pigments. *Angew Chem Int Ed* 41: 2483–2487.
3. Tercyznjska-Madej A, Cholewa-Kowalska K, Laczka M (2010) The effect of silicate network modifiers on colour and electron spectra of transition metal ions. *Opt Mater* 32: 1456–1462.
4. Rayner-Canham G, Overton T (2006) *Descriptive Inorganic Chemistry*, 4th ed: 332–336, W.H. Freeman, New York.
5. Cotton FA, Wilkenson G (1962) *Advanced Inorganic Chemistry*: 357, Interscience (Wiley), New York.
6. Gettens RJ, Stout GL (1966) *Painting Materials. A Short Encyclopedia*: 158, Dover Publications, New York.
7. Eppler RA, Obstler M (2005) *Understanding Glazes*: 1–15, American Ceramic Society, Westerville, OH.
8. Salzberg HW (1991) *From Caveman to Chemist*: 7–11, American Ceramic Society, Washington, DC.
9. Elias lecture, (2016) The chemistry of silicates and aluminosilicates. Web.iitd. in>~elias>links>Elias lecture silicates part 2 Sept 2016.

4 Discoloration Stories

The discoloration of paintings and other art objects is first observed visually and associated with "aging". The next stage consists of detailed analytical studies to establish the physical/chemical nature of the discoloration. This translates into determining the reactants and products of the color change. In such systems, the uniqueness of art objects prohibits the use of destructive methods, i.e., methods which require discrete physical mass. Instead, spectroscopic tools are utilized which have a very small impact on the integrity of the sample. Additional goals of art conservation are to propose a mechanism of degradation which would lead to stabilization of the art objects.

In the discoloration stories presented in this chapter, the goals are to present the observed signs of degradation, the chemical details and finally a mechanism. The number of chemical compounds and chemical reactions is enormous. However, fortunately, there are a relatively small number of general chemical mechanisms. Examples include acid–base, redox, free radical, substitution, addition, isomerization and others.

The first group of discoloration stories are those which involve a pigment that is also a semiconductor. The discovery of semiconductors is relatively recent, compared to the use of these pigments going back to ancient times. The pigments in this group are red lead, cadmium yellow, cinnabar/vermilion and realgar. Solid-state materials can be divided into three groups based on their electrical conductivity: conductors, semiconductors and insulators. Band theory provides the framework for the mechanism.

In discrete molecules, there are bonding molecular orbitals (MOs) and anti-bonding MOs. Electrons located in the bonding MOs absorb energy (heat or light) and can be promoted to an anti-bonding MO. In a solid-state crystalline structure, the number of MOs is very large and instead of discrete energy levels, there is a band of energy levels. According to band theory, electrons in the valence band (VB/ bonding MOs) acquire energy and jump from the highest energy bonding MO to the lowest energy anti-bonding orbital in the conduction band (CB). The energy difference between these orbitals is known as the band gap (E_g). In metals and other conductors, there is no band gap. In insulators, the band gap is too large for an electron to jump. However, in semiconductors (SCs), the band gap ranges from 10 to 240 kJ/mole (0.10–2.5 eV), see Figure 4.1. SCs are colored when $1.8 < E_g < 3.0$ eV. White SCs have band gaps >3.0 eV, and black SCs have band gaps <1.8 eV [1] (Table 4.1).

When a photo-SC absorbs light of energy $\geq E_g$, an electron is promoted from the VB to the CB. The loss of the negatively charged electron leaves a positively charged hole (h^+) in the VB. Consequently, electron flow from the CB may trigger chemical reduction if a reducible species is nearby. Similarly, the holes in the VB may cause chemical oxidation if a susceptible species is in the vicinity. The reactive species which can react with photo-activated SCs are the organic binder and water.

A rapid screening test for unstable photo-SC pigments was reported which is based on thermodynamic oxidation potentials of pigments and water. CdS, HgS,

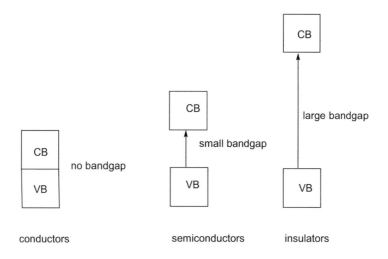

VB, valence band; CB, conduction band

FIGURE 4.1   Conductors, semiconductors and insulators.

TABLE 4.1
Physical Properties of Semiconductor Pigments

Compound	Color	λ_{max}, nm	Band Gap, eV	Band Gap, kJ/mole	E_{CB}, V	E_{VB}, V
TiO$_2$	White			290	−0.9	2.1
ZnO	White				−0.9	2.2
Cr$_2$O$_3$	Green		2.58		−0.8	−0.1
CdS	Yellow Orange	517	2.42	230	−0.75	0.2
α-Realgar	red		2.40			
Red Lead	Red	552	2.25	219	−0.08	2.17
α-HgS	Red		2.0	200	−0.4	0.7
CdSe	Red	540	1.7	160	−1.5	0.2
β-HgS	Black		1.6	160		
PbS	Black		0.4	40	−0.6	

E_{CB} and E_{VB}, respectively, are oxidation potentials versus Standard Hydrogen Electrode at pH 7, [2]. Band gap unit interconversion: 9705 eV/kJ/mol. Interconversion of band gap and wavelength: λ (nm) $\leq$ 1241/ E_g (eV), 1 eV = 1.6022 × 10^{-19}J.

CdSe, As$_2$S$_3$, PbS, SnS$_2$, ZnS and Cr$_2$O$_3$ were shown to be susceptible to oxidation when exposed to light and water. These results are consistent with known stability data [1–3].

When paints are created, pigments are ground with an oily binder so that the pigment grains are completely enveloped by the binder. As paintings age, the surface varnish coating and the binder degrade which exposes the pigments to minute amounts of condensed water. Water facilitates the movement of water-soluble species in the painting [4]. Photo-activated SC mechanisms have been advanced to explain the degradation of red lead, cadmium yellow, cinnabar/vermilion and realgar.

4.1 RED LEAD DISCOLORATION

Red lead, Pb_3O_4, has been in use as an artists' pigment since at least the second century C.E. It has a reputation for different types of discoloration. These include fading or lightening and also darkening-blackening [5], see Figure 4.2. Red lead is a mixed oxide which contains both Pb^{4+} and Pb^{2+} cations. The structure of red lead is shown in Figure 2.10. The chains of octahedral $[Pb^{4+} O_6]$ are connected by the trigonal–pyramidal units of $[Pb^{2+} O_3]$. The formula of red lead can be written as $Pb^{4+} O_2 \cdot 2Pb^{2+} O$. However, red lead is a distinct compound and not simply a 1:2 mixture of PbO_2 and PbO.

How can we account for the distinct types of discolorations? In paintings, when *darkening* occurs, the brown PbO_2 (plattnerite) and black PbS (galena) are formed. The transformation of red lead to PbO_2 is consistent with oxidation of $Pb^{2+} \rightarrow Pb^{4+}$. Another pathway to darkening is reduction of $Pb^{4+} \rightarrow Pb^{2+}$ followed by exposure to H_2S (atmospheric or microbial), which results in the formation of PbS. When red lead *lightens*, several white compounds are produced in the following sequence: $3PbCO_3 Pb(OH)_2 PbO$ (plumbonacrite), $2PbCO_3 Pb(OH)_2$ (white lead or hydrocerussite) and $PbCO_3$ (cerussite). $PbSO_4$, another white compound, is formed by the *sulfation* reaction of PbO with atmospheric H_2SO_4. Atmospheric SO_2 is oxidized to SO_3 and then hydrated to H_2SO_4.

For an example of red lead alteration, see Figure 4.3, which includes photographs of pustular particles from a discolored area in the van Gogh 1889 painting, *Wheat Stack under a Cloudy Sky*. The particles contained a red-orange core (red lead) and surrounding the core were several white lead carbonate compounds [5,6].

Red lead is an established photocatalytic SC with a band gap of 2.25 eV. When excited by visible light near 550 nm, an electron in the VB is promoted to the CB. The energized electron reduces $Pb^{4+} \rightarrow Pb^{2+}$. In parallel, a hole ($h^+$) is generated in

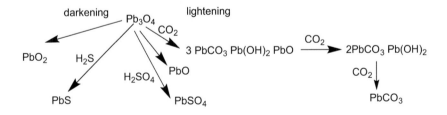

Pb_3O_4 (red)/reduction $\longrightarrow$ PbO (yellow)

PbO + H_2O/hydration $\longrightarrow$ $Pb(OH)_2$ (white)

PbO + CO_2/carbonation $\longrightarrow$ $PbCO_3$ (white)

FIGURE 4.2 Darkening and lightening of red lead [5].

FIGURE 4.3 Discoloration of red lead. (a) Photograph of *Wheat Stack Under a Cloudy Sky* by van Gogh (October 1889, oil on canvas, Collection Kröller-Müller Museum, Otterlo, the Netherlands). The sample area is indicated by the white circle. (b) Detail of the severed pustular mass on the painting surface. (c) Detail of the paint sample. (Reprinted with permission of F. Vanmeert, G. Van der Snickt, K. Janssens (2015) *Angew. Chem. Int. Ed.* 54: 3607–3610. Copyright 2015, Wiley-VCH Verlag GmbH & Co. KGaA, Weinheim.)

the VB which can oxidize the organics to CO_2. A mechanism was proposed for the photoreaction involving red lead [5], see Scheme 4.1.

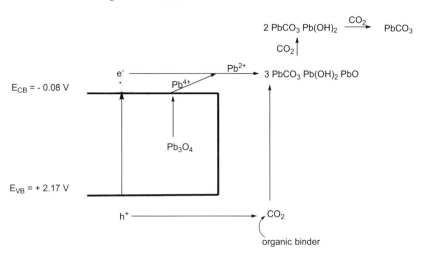

E_{CB} and E_{VB} are versus Standard Hydrogen Electrode at pH 7

SCHEME 4.1 Photo-induced redox of red lead. Proposed pathway for the photochemical degradation of Pb_3O_4 under light irradiation. Conductance and valence band potentials, E_{CB} and E_{VB}, respectively, are given relative to the normal hydrogen electrode. (Reprinted with permission of F.R. Vanmeert, G. van der Snickt, K. Janssens (2015) *Angew. Chem. Int. Ed.* 54: 3607–3610. Copyright 2015, Wiley-VCH Verlag GMBh & Co.)

$$3\ \alpha\text{-}PbO_{\text{litharge}}\ +\ ^1/_2\ O_{2\ gas}\ \xrightarrow{470\ ^\circ C}\ 1\ Pb_3O_{4\ red\ lead}\ \xrightarrow{512\ \text{-}\ 650\ ^\circ C}\ 3\ \beta\text{-}PbO_{\text{massicot}}\ +\ ^1/_2\ O_{2\ gas}$$

SCHEME 4.2 Thermal interconversion of lead oxides [6].

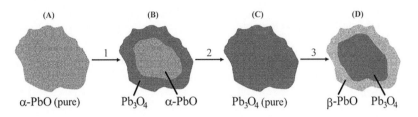

SCHEME 4.3 Shell-core model for lead monoxides and red lead thermal interconversions. (Reprinted with permission of S. Aze, J.M. Vallet, M. Pomey, A. Barronnet, O. Grauby (2015) *Euro. J. Mineral.*19: 883–890. Copyright 2007, Schweizerbart.)

There is more to the red lead story. Degraded red lead also yields PbO (yellow). The synthesis of red lead involves the oxidation α-PbO (litharge). Continued heating of the red lead product results in the formation of β-PbO (yellow). Consequently, the method of preparation can result in particles with different compositions, see thermal conversions of lead oxides in Scheme 4.2. The synthesis of red lead must be tightly controlled. Either under- or overheating will produce a mixture of red lead and lead monoxide. Further, the sequence produces pigment grains with cores of different compositions. Thus, underheating produces particles with a red shell and a yellow core, while overheating yields a yellow shell with a red core. The presence of PbO as an impurity decreases the band gap and thereby enhances the tendency for red lead photo-reduction [7]. The proposed core–shell model for red lead is presented in Scheme 4.3 [6].

4.1.1 Role of Photo-Semiconductor Pigments in Degradation of Organic Material

The role of photo-SC pigments in the oxido-reductive degradation of organic compounds has been documented. For example, red lead oxidized organic pollutants to CO_2 and water [8,9]. Titanium white, TiO_2, degraded linseed oil to a mixture of aldehydes, carboxylic acids and lactones [10].

4.1.2 Red Lead Degradation in Wall Paintings

Sulfuric acid encounters exterior wall paintings as acid rain. In this system, the PbO_2 component of red lead is a spectator. The reaction is an acid–base neutralization involving sulfuric acid and oxide anion to form water and sulfate. Pb^{2+} and sulfate combine to form the insoluble $PbSO_4$ [6], see Scheme 4.4. PbO_2 has been identified in sections of wall paintings which have darkened. $PbSO_4$ has been detected as white specs on aged wall paintings. (Also see Figure 7.3.)

$$PbO_2 \cdot 2\ PbO_{solid} + 2\ H_2SO_4\ _{aq} \rightarrow \beta\text{-}PbO_2\ _{solid} + 2\ PbSO_4\ _{solid} + 2\ H_2O\ _{liquid}$$

$$2\ O^{2-} + 2\ H_2SO_4 \rightarrow 2\ H_2O + 2\ SO_4^{2-}$$

$$2\ Pb^{2+} + 2\ SO_4^{2-} \rightarrow 2\ PbSO_4\ _{solid}$$

SCHEME 4.4 Sulfation of red lead [6].

The final piece to this puzzle is the observation of gypsum ($CaSO_4 \cdot 2H_2O$) in the surface of the wall painting. Calcite on the surface was converted to gypsum by the process of *sulfation* [6].

$$CaCO_3\ _{solid} + H_2SO_4\ _{aq} \rightarrow CaSO_4\ _{solid} + H_2O_{liquid} + CO_2\ _{gas}$$

$$CaSO_4\ _{solid} + 2\ H_2O_{liquid} \rightarrow CaSO_4 \cdot 2\ H_2O_{solid}$$

In summary, environmental factors influence the integrity of red lead in wall paintings. Incident radiation as well as atmospheric gases, CO_2, H_2O, SO_2, H_2SO_4 and H_2S each play a role in the discoloration of red lead.

4.2 DISCOLORATION OF CADMIUM YELLOW

Cadmium yellow, CdS, was first synthesized in 1819 but did not become commercially available until 1846. It was used by prominent artists in the 19th and 20th centuries including Claude Monet, Vincent van Gogh, Pablo Picasso, and Henri Matisse. It is more stable than chrome yellow, which was also developed in the 19th century. Cadmium yellow is used as an artists' pigment and also as a colorant for rubber, plastics and ceramics. Its popularity is based on its bright color, high tinting power and high covering power. This pigment was thought to be highly stable in oil paint and watercolor but was known to fade in the presence of moisture [11]. Analysis of cadmium yellow pigments manufactured between 1850 and 1950 revealed different crystal structures (hexagonal and cubic) and the presence of color-modulating additives such as $BaSO_4$ and $PbSO_4$. Also, solid solutions of CdS plus ZnS and CdSe, known as cadmiopone, were produced [12].

An unvarnished painting by the Belgian artist James Ensore, entitled *Still Life with Cabbage* (1921), was examined at the Kröller-Müller Museum in Otterlo, the Netherlands. Examination showed that the yellow areas which had been under the frame were vivid, while the yellow areas in the unprotected portion were dull. Also, whitish, transparent globules were observed by optical microscopy on the surface in the dull yellow areas. Tiny samples (<1 mm in diameter) were removed and analyzed by μ-XRF and μ-XRD at the European Synchrotron Radiation Facility in Grenoble, France, see Figure 4.4 [13].

The masking effect of the frame immediately suggested that the discoloration of cadmium yellow was, at least partially, caused by exposure to light. The use of CdS as a photo-catalyst and semiconductor led to an understanding of the discoloration problem [14].

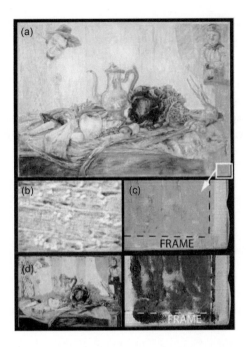

FIGURE 4.4 Degradation of Cadmium Yellow. (a) Optical photograph of the oil painting *Still Life with Cabbage* by James Ensor (1921, KM 105.303, Collection Kröller-Müller Museum, Otterlo, the Netherlands). (b) Detail of the exposed, yellow paint surface (×40) showing white globules. (c) Detail of the right-lower corner of the painting: the yellow paint covered by the frame displays a more vivid yellow color, whereas the paint in the exposed areas has become dull. (d) UV fluorescence photograph of the entire painting. (e) Detail of the same area as shown in panel C in UV fluorescence: the yellow paint under the frame fluoresces in brown. (Reprinted with permission of G. van der Snickt, J. Dik, M. Cotte, et al. (2009) *Anal. Chem.* 81: 2600–2610. Copyright 2009, American Chemical Society.)

μ-XRF revealed that the whitish globules on the surface of the painting contained the elements Cd and S, and XANES showed that S was not sulfide anion but sulfate. Further, μ-XRD data indicated that the globules were $CdSO_4 \cdot H_2O$. To account for this change, a mechanism is proposed based on the semiconducting property of CdS, see Scheme 4.5.

$$CdS + h\nu \rightarrow e^- + h^+$$

$$CdS + 2h^+ \rightarrow Cd^{2+} \; S^0$$

$$S^0 + O_2 \rightarrow SO_2$$

$$SO_2 + 2e^- \rightarrow SO_2^{2-}$$

$$SO_2^{2-} + O_2 \rightarrow SO_4^{2-}$$

SCHEME 4.5 Photo-oxidation of cadmium sulfide. (Modified and reprinted with permission of G. van der Snickt, J. Dik, M. Cotte, et al. (2009) *Anal. Chem.* 81: 2600–2610. Copyright 2009, American Chemical Society.

Radiant energy equivalent to the band gap of CdS (2.6 eV equivalent to 476 nm) is absorbed. A valence electron is energized to jump across the band gap from the VB to the CB. This process creates positively charged holes (h^+) in the VB. S^{2-} transfers two electrons to two holes resulting in the formation of S^o which is then oxidized to sulfur dioxide. SO_2 is reduced to SO_2^{2-} (hyposulfite) which in turn is oxidized to sulfate. Hydration yields the observed whitish globules, $CdSO_4 \cdot H_2O$.

The roles of atmospheric moisture, exposure to light and the presence of Zn^{2+} were investigated with regard to photo-lability of cadmium yellow. Three mockup paints were prepared by suspending CdS-hexagonal, CdS-cubic and a solid solution pigment, $Cd_{.76}Zn_{.27}S$ in linseed oil. The latter is a type of cadmiopone pigment. The IR spectra of these samples were monitored after exposure to three stress conditions and compared: (a) unstressed controls, (b) thermal dark/40°C/95%RH/90–100 days, (c) UVA/25°C–30°C/45%RH/18–27 days and (d) UVA/25°C–30°C/95%RH/18–27 days. The results are summarized in Table 4.2.

For all three samples, thermal/dark/95%RH exposure caused the loss of absorption ~1730 cm^{-1} (triglyceride ester carbonyl stretch) with the appearance of a band ~1705 cm^{-1} assigned to free carboxylic acids produced by hydrolysis of the linseed oil esters. Stress condition (UVA/45%RH) was associated with the appearance of a band ~1620 cm^{-1}, attributed to ionized carboxyl. The solid solution sample exposed to both conditions which included 95% RH produced bands assigned to Zn^{2+} soaps. Other bands were assigned to zinc oxalate anion produced by oxidation of the fatty acids. For all samples, exposure to UVA/95%RH was associated with the appearance of bands between 1150 and 1070 cm^{-1} and <650 cm^{-1}, consistent with the presence of SO_4^{2-}. Consequently, exposure to 95%RH, but not 45%RH, and UVA caused oxidation of sulfide to sulfate. In addition, atomic absorption spectroscopy (μ-XANES) detected S^{VI} (consistent with the presence of SO_4^{2-}) at and close to the surface of

---

TABLE 4.2

IR Spectral Changes in cm^{-1} for Cadmium Yellow Paints Associated with Various Storage Conditions [14]

Storage Condition	CdS-hex	CdS-cubic	Cd$_{.24}$Zn$_{.76}$S
Control[a]	1735	1735, 1710	1725, 1710, 1635
Thermal[b]	1705	1710	1710, 1620
UVA, 45%RH[c]	1705	1705	1710, 1620
UVA, 95%RH[d]	1700	1705	1710, 1640
All samples	1172, 1068, 991, 612	1172, 1068, 991, 612	1172, 1068, 991, 612

Assignment of IR bands (cm^{-1}): 1735, ester carbonyl; 1710–1700, unionized carboxyl, 1640–1620, Zn soaps; 1171, 1068, 991, 612, sulfate anion.

Storage Conditions:

[a] unstressed control;

[b] thermal, dark/40°C/ 95%RH/ 90-100 da;

[c] UVA/25°C/45%RH/18-27 da;

[d] UVA/25°C/95% RH/18-27 da.

the samples exposed to UVA/95%RH. It is noted that 45%–55%RH/20°C–21°C represents typical storage conditions for paintings in museums [15].

Therefore, based on the cited work, the mechanism of CdS photo-degradation consists exposure to light (≤ 436 nm) and excessively high moisture which promotes photo-oxidation of sulfide to sulfate with loss of color. Hydrolysis of triglyceride esters in the oily binder produced carboxylic acids. Zinc soaps were produced in the Cadmiopone samples.

4.3 BLACKENING OF CINNABAR IN WALL PAINTINGS

Naturally occurring mercury (II) sulfide is known as cinnabar and the synthetic compound from the reaction of elemental mercury and sulfur is vermilion. They are chemically and physically identical. HgS crystallizes in two forms (polymorphs); the red form is α-HgS (cinnabar, vermilion) and the black form is β-HgS (meta-cinnabar). Both polymorphs are semiconductors. The band gaps are 2.25 eV for vermilion and 1.6 eV for meta-cinnabar. The red form has been widely used in both easel and wall paintings. For the most part, the pigment is stable with the exception of darkening and lightening of (usually) small areas which have been exposed to light. For many years, it was assumed that the black degradation product was β-cinnabar. However, this has been difficult to prove experimentally.

For an example of photo-activated blackening of HgS, see Figure 4.5 [16], *The Adoration of the Magi*, (1609) by Peter Paul Rubens (1617–1618). Small samples were

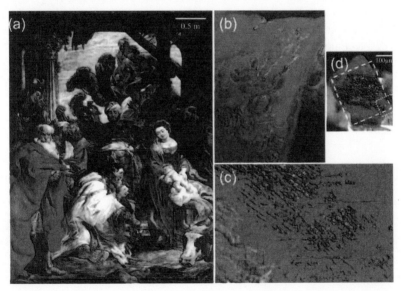

FIGURE 4.5 Degradation of HgS. (a) *The Adoration of the Magi* by Peter Paul Rubens, Royal Museum of Fine Arts, Antwerp, Belgium; copyright: Adri Verburg/Arcobaleno (b) optical photograph of a degraded area near the right sleeve of the figure on the left; (c) higher magnification photograph showing darkened areas and white precipitates on the top surface; (d) optical micrograph of one analyzed sample. (Reprinted with permission of M. Radepont, W. de Nolf, K. Janssens, et al. (2011) *J. Anal. At. Spectrom.* 26: 959–968. Copyright 2011, Royal Society of Chemistry.)

taken from the discolored areas of the red cloak of the figure on the left side of the painting. Magnified optical photographs reveal the presence of darkened areas and on top of these are white crystals.

Conditions required for photo-degradation of the pigment include light ($\lambda \leq 590$ nm), water vapor and a source of chlorine atoms. The following compounds were identified as degradation products: two polymorphs of $Hg_3S_2Cl_2$ (the alpha form, corderoite, is light-gray to black and the gamma form, kenhsuite, is white). Also detected were $HgCl_2$ (white) and Hg_2Cl_2 (white). In addition, another gray/black product has been observed; its identity has been suggested to be elemental mercury ($Hg°$). Photon energy is required for activation of the photo-semiconductor pigment. The role of moisture (water) has not been specified. A source of chlorine atoms is required to account for the presence of chlorinated mercury compounds. There are several possible sources of chlorine atoms: other pigments, protective wax coating, residual chlorine introduced from cleaning with chlorinated solvents (CCl_4) and ClO which is present in the air [17].

A scheme was proposed to account for the photo-degradation of α-HgS [17,18], see Figure 4.6. Light with $\lambda \leq 590$ nm corresponds to the semiconductor bandwidth of 2.25 eV. Water is probably required as a solvent to allow migration of ions and possibly as a source of oxygen atoms. Photo-activated α-HgS reacts with "chlorine" to form the alpha and gamma crystalline forms of $Hg_3S_2Cl_2$, hypothetically as:

$$2\ Cl^- + 3HgS \rightarrow \left[2HgS \cdot HgCl_2 = Hg_3S_2Cl_2 \right] + S^{2-}$$

Elemental mercury has been suggested as the gray/black degradation product but has not been identified in degraded paintings. Degradation products have been identified by XRD, a technique which detects crystalline phases. $Hg°$ is a liquid at room temperature and therefore is not detectable by XRD. A model electrochemistry study has shown that elemental mercury can be produced by photo-reduction of α-HgS in the presence of aqueous NaCl [19].

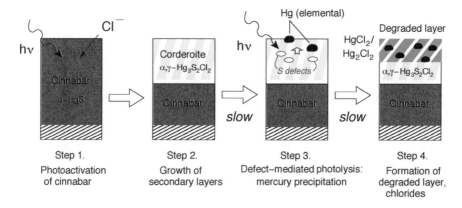

FIGURE 4.6 Discoloration of HgS, cinnabar/vermilion. (Reprinted with permission from C. Hogan and F. DaPieve (2015) *J. Anal. At. Spectrom.* 30:588–598. Copyright 2014, Royal Chemical Society.)

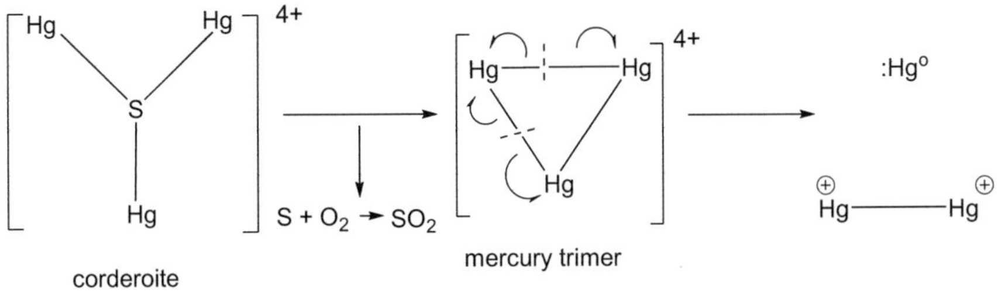

corderoite

mercury trimer

SCHEME 4.6 HgS, cinnabar/vermilion discoloration after [17]. Degradation mechanism for α-corderoite. (Modified and reprinted with permission of F. DaPieve, C. Hogan, D. Lamoen, et al. (2013) *Phys. Rev. Lett.* 111:208302-1–208302-5. Copyright 2013, American Physical Society.)

The proposed mechanism accounts for the presence of Hg_2Cl_2 and SO_2 as degradation products and predicts that elemental mercury would be another degradation product, see Scheme 4.6 [17]. The degradation mechanism begins with α-corderoite, $Hg_3S_2Cl_2$, represented by the triangular planar complex, $[Hg_3S]^{4+}$ This complex loses atomic sulfur to yield the triangular species $[Hg_3]^{4+}$. Sulfur is oxidized to SO_2, most likely by the atmosphere. $[Hg_3]^{4+}$ decomposes to Hg_2^{2+} and Hg°. A minor pathway was suggested which involves S→O substitution and the formation of $[Hg_3O]^{4+}$, which also forms degradation products.

Pump-probe microscopy was used to investigate the photo-activated conversion of α-HgS to β-HgS. For details of this technique, see references [20,21]. The method consists of the *pump* [a train of intensity-modulated laser femtosecond (fs) pulses, typically 720 nm] and the *probe* (a synchronized laser fs train of a different wavelength, typically 817 nm) which are spatially superimposed and are observed with a microscope.

In an experimental test system, this method distinguished α-HgS, β-HgS and elemental liquid mercury, Hg°. Exposure to UV (mercury lamp) drove the conversion of α-HgS to β-HgS, and this process was accelerated by temperature. The presence of small zones of β-HgS served as seeds for the transformation, and liquid mercury was formed. The method was then employed to examine a 14th century painting, *St. John the Evangelist Reproving the Philosopher Crato*, (1375) by Francescussio di Cecco Ghissi. In areas of degraded vermilion, β-HgS was detected, and, elemental mercury was not detected. This work indicates that the photo-activated degradation of vermilion can proceed by at least two different routes: Cl-assisted pathway and the β-HgS-assisted pathway.

4.4   LIGHT-INDUCED REARRANGEMENT OF REALGAR

Realgar (α-realgar, As_4S_4) is a naturally occurring pigment which was used by artists all over the world since ancient times. Realgar has an orange-red color and was often confused with red lead before the development of specific identification tests. In contrast to the yellow pigment orpiment (As_2S_3), realgar is *labile* to light in the visible range. The photo-transformation leads to a yellow product, which was thought

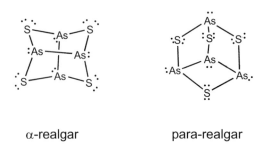

α-realgar   para-realgar

FIGURE 4.7   α-Realgar and para-realgar.

to be orpiment. This was shown not to be the case. This conversion is understood to be a rearrangement of α-realgar to para-realgar, an *isomer*, see Figure 4.7 [22]. The transformation of α-realgar to para-realgar is captured in Figure 4.8 which shows the UV–vis spectra of both compounds, the colors of the solids and a time course for the photo-conversion process monitored by Raman spectroscopy at 274 cm^{-1} [23a].

In α-realgar, there are a pair of As-As bonds. In para-realgar, there is a trimeric unit of three covalently bonded arsenic atoms. This story is about the rearrangement of a covalent structure. α-Realgar is one of the few inorganic pigments which does not have a metallic chromophore. In 1996, Trentelman et al. solved a pigment discoloration mystery [24]. During the cleaning of Tintoretto's painting, *The Dreams of Men* (1549), the team of conservation scientists removed a tiny fragment of paint for analysis. From SEM-EDS (scanning electron microscopy-energy dispersive X-ray

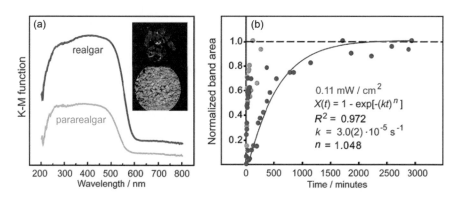

FIGURE 4.8   (a) UV–vis spectra of α-realgar and para-realgar (shown in the inset), powdered and diluted with NaCl (1%), recorded in the reflectance mode. (b) Temporal profiles and kinetic constants of the conversion of α-realgar to para-realgar induced by excitation at 1.96 eV and monitored by the reaction extent, expressed as the normalized integrated intensity of the 274 cm^{-1} Raman band of para-realgar (green, blue and red marks correspond to excitation at 1.81, 0.77 and 0.11 mW/cm^2, respectively). The red line in (b) represents the kinetic curve fitted to the excitation with the lowest power density (0.11 mW/cm^2) according to the JMAK model [23b]. (Reprinted with permission of P. Naumov, P. Makreski, G. Petrusevski, T. Runcevski, G. Jovanovski (2010) *J. Am. Chem. Soc.* 132: 11398–11401. Copyright 2010 American Chemical Society.)

$$5 \ As_4S_4 \ + \ 3 \ O_2 \quad \xrightarrow{\text{light}} \quad 4 \ As_4S_5 \text{, uzonite} \ + \ 2 \ As_2O_3 \qquad 1$$

$$As_4S_5 \text{, uzonite} \quad \xrightarrow{\text{light}} \quad As_4S_4 \text{, para-realgar} \ + \ S \qquad 2$$

$$\alpha\text{-realgar} \ + \ S \quad \xrightarrow{\text{dark}} \quad \text{uzonite} \qquad 3$$

$$\text{uzonite} \quad \xrightarrow{\text{dark}} \quad \text{para-realgar} \qquad 4$$

SCHEME 4.7 Photo-induced isomerization of α-realgar. (Reprinted with permission of P. Naumov, P. Makreski, G. Petrusevski, T. Runsebski, G. Javanovski (2010) *J. Am. Chem. Soc.* 132: 11398–11401. Copyright 2010, American Chemical Society.)

spectroscopy), they found that the yellow top layer of the paint fragment contained arsenic and sulfur and initially they speculated that the yellow material was orpiment. However, the use of Raman spectroscopy and X-ray diffraction led them to realize that the yellow material was para-realgar, a structural isomer of As_4S_4.

Since 1980, mineralogists had been aware that realgar changes to a yellow substance when irradiated by sunlight in the presence of air. The yellow substance was identified as para-realgar [22]. Compare the structures of orpiment, para-realgar and α-realgar. Despite sharing the same elemental composition, isomers generally have different chemical and physical properties, including color! The realgar isomers are covalent compounds. In crystalline solids, individual molecules attract each other by weak interactions such as dispersion forces and dipole-dipole forces. Based on the electronegativity difference of the As-S bond ($\Delta EN = 0.5$), these bonds would be classified as weakly polar covalent. The As-As bonds would be non-polar covalent. Based on the respective structures of the two realgar isomers, the question is: which bonds are broken, and which atoms rearrange their positions during the isomerization process?

The mechanism of this interconversion has been studied by several groups. Because arsenic sulfides and oxides are photo-sensitive, they are used in a variety of applications including lithography resists, optical memory devices, radiation modulators, optical computing and pn junctions in semiconductors. The band gap of α-realgar is 2.40 eV. Therefore, the investigation of the photo-isomerization of α-realgar was of wide interest. While the pathway has not been completely defined, the main features are these. First, there is a light-induced step in which atmospheric oxygen gas reacts with α-realgar to form uzonite, As_4S_5 and As_2O_3, see Scheme 4.7. After this, one sulfur atom is ejected from uzonite to yield the isomeric para-realgar. This is followed by insertion of sulfur into the α-realgar structure to form uzonite. Finally, uzonite ejects one sulfur atom giving para-realgar [23]. All of these changes occur in the crystalline solid phase where molecules are locked into a lattice structure.

A suggested mechanism for insertion and ejection of sulfur atoms in the isomerization process is presented in Scheme 4.8. The atoms have been numbered for convenience. In α-realgar there are two As-As bonds, and all of the sulfur atoms bridge between two arsenic atoms. Sulfur forms two bonds which is consistent with Group 16. Similarly, arsenic atoms each form three covalent bonds, and each has a lone pair of non-bonding electrons; consistent with Group 15.

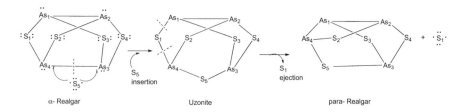

α- Realgar   Uzonite   para- Realgar

SCHEME 4.8 Mechanism for α-realgar isomerization to para-realgar. (Reprinted with permission of P. Naumov, P. Makreski, G. Petrusevski, T. Runsebski, G. Javanovski (2010) *J. Am. Chem. Soc.* 132: 11398–11401. Copyright 2010, American Chemical Society.)

A sulfur atom reacts with α-realgar as the $As_4 - As_3$ bond breaks homolytically. The "new" sulfur atom is given the number 5 in the intermediate uzonite structure. To form para-realgar, it is clear that a sulfur atom different from S_5 must leave. In this scheme, S_1 leaves as two covalent bonds break ($As_1 - S_1$ and $S_1 - As_4$). S_1 leaves, attacks another molecule of α-realgar and a new bond is formed: $As_4 - As_1$. This yields the characteristic triplet of three arsenic atoms bonded to each other, $As_4 - As_1 - As_2$.

4.4.1 RAMAN SPECTRA OF α-REALGAR AND PARA-REALGAR

Tiny pieces of the painting, *The Dreams of Men*, containing as many as 15 paint layers, were removed for analysis. Samples were analyzed by μ-XRD and micro-Raman spectroscopy. The Raman spectrometer was equipped with a microscope. These layers included ground, different pigments, binder and varnish. The microscope was focused on the layer containing the yellow pigment, and the spectrum was scanned. Comparison of the structures of α-realgar and para-realgar shows that the former is more symmetrical. Raman spectroscopy is based on vibration of covalently bonded atoms. In Raman, *the more symmetrical the bond, the weaker the vibration*. Hence, the less symmetrical isomer, para-realgar, should have stronger absorptions in its Raman spectrum; compare the spectra in Figure 4.9 [24]. The Raman spectral peaks

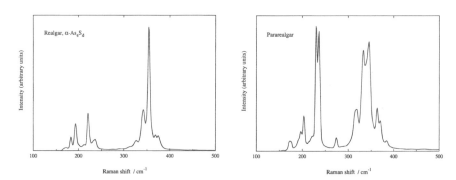

FIGURE 4.9 Raman spectra of α- and para-realgar. (Reprinted with permission of K. Trentelman and L. Stodulski, M. Pavloski (1996) *Anal. Chem* 68:1755–1761. Copyright 1996, American Chemical Society.)

in Figure 4.9, matched within $\pm 2\,cm^{-1}$ compared to the spectra of realgar and para-realgar found in the Raman spectral library of natural and synthetic pigments [25].

4.5 BROWNING OF CHROME YELLOW

Vincent van Gogh and other late 19th century painters used chrome yellow (CY). This pigment has long had a reputation for discoloration. Recently, several groups have investigated the cause of browning of chrome yellow, focusing on the paintings of van Gogh [26,27]. In his private letters, van Gogh referred to different types of this pigment (types 1, 2 and 3), which corresponded to CY with lemon, yellow and orange hues. CY was and is produced as pure lead (II) chromate, $PbCrO_4$, or as a co-precipitate with lead (II) sulfate, $PbSO_4$. Chromate and sulfate anions are *isoelectronic* and are close in size (240 and 230 pm, respectively). For these reasons, they are able to co-crystallize, see Figure 4.10. The mixed crystalline formula is represented as $Pb\,Cr_{(1-x)}\,S_xO_4$ which is equivalent to $(PbCrO_4)_{1-x} \cdot (PbSO_4)_x$. In this notation, x is the mole fraction of sulfur or lead sulfate, and $1-x$ is the mole fraction of chromium or lead chromate.

The tendency of CY to decolorize is related to the sulfate content in the pigment. To test photosensitivity, synthetic mixtures of CY with the sulfate mole fraction varying from 0 to 0.8 were irradiated with a xenon lamp (290–800 nm) for various time intervals (up to 800 h) at a storage temperature of 50°C–60°C. It was found that a brown surface layer (thickness ~2–3 µm) developed when the mole fraction of sulfur was ≥ 0.5. Figure 4.11 shows optical photographs in which model paint containing $PbCrO_4$ in the monoclinic crystal form barely changed color after light stress. In contrast, model paint and historic 19th-century paint which contained $PbCr_{(1-x)}\,S_xO_4$ in the orthorhombic crystal form turned distinctly brown. (Monoclinic and orthorhombic are two types of crystal habits which differ with respect to minimum symmetry and unit cell dimensions [26b]). Also shown are the XANES spectra of chromium. In the samples which contained $PbCr_{(1-x)}S_xO_4$, the Cr^{6+} content decreased by 60% with the formation of Cr^{3+}. The sample of pure $PbCrO_4$ lost ~20% of the original Cr^{6+} with essentially no change in the Cr spectrum. XANES spectra of the sulfur region (not shown in the figure) revealed no change in any of the samples. Therefore, the browning of CY paint was shown to be due to the presence of ≥ 50 mole % sulfate which caused reduction of Cr^{6+} to Cr^{3+}.

Wavelengths of radiant energy including UVA–vis, UV and blue light all caused CY to turn brown. Wavelength (λ) is *inversely proportional* to energy (E) associated with electro-magnetic radiation:

$$E = hc/\lambda, \text{ where h = Planck's constant and c = the speed of light.}$$

FIGURE 4.10   Chromate and sulfate are isoelectronic.

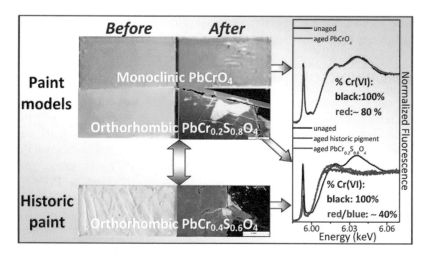

FIGURE 4.11 Degradation of chrome yellow oil paint. Effect of light exposure on chrome yellow paint samples. Optical photographs show that the pure $PbCrO_4$ (monoclinic form) changed color very little. $PbCr_{(1-x)} S_x O_4$, where $x \geq 0.5$ (orthorhombic form) turned brown. Changes in the XANES chromium spectra correspond to the transformation of Cr^{6+} to Cr^{3+}. (Reprinted with permission of L. Monico, K. Janssens, C. Miliani, et al. (2013) *Anal. Chem.* 85: 860–867. Copyright 2013, American Chemical Society.)

The authors suggested that the painting should not be exposed to light below 525 nm.

Tan et al. [28] investigated 100-year-old linseed oil-based paint sample which contained CY. Three types of paint particles were identified: $PbCr_{(1-x)} S_x O_4$, where $x < 0.5$, for convenience these particles were considered to be $PbCrO_4$. The other types of particles were $PbCr_{(1-x)} S_x O_4$, where $x > 0.5$ and $PbSO_4$. With respect to this composition, lead (II) chromate was the intended product of a synthesis with lead (II) nitrate and potassium dichromate. Lead (II) sulfate was frequently added to control the color of the pigment. Calcination of the reaction mixture yielded the three particle types. Samples of this paint were analyzed by scanning transmission electron microscopy and electron loss spectroscopy before and after exposure to UVA for 40 days at RT. The results are summarized in Figure 4.12. The composition of these particles in their original state is depicted in the first line. The middle line presents the status at age ~100 years and pre-stressing with UVA radiation. The bottom line represents composition after UV stress.

Based on the types of particles observed before and after UVA stress, a mechanism was proposed to explain the photo-induced browning of CY paint. Particles of $PbCrO_4$ (Cr^{6+}) were transformed into Cr_2O_3 (Cr^{3+}) consistent with assumed redox coupling with the binder. The lattice of $PbCr_{(1-x)} S_x O_4$ particles was progressively destabilized with increasing sulfur content. These particles released CrO_4^{2-} into minute amounts of water located between the particles and the binder. CrO_4^{2-} and organic binder reacted to yield Cr_2O_3, an extremely insoluble product, which deposited on the surface of particles. $PbSO_4$ particles were found to be coated with Cr_2O_3. No attempt was made to identify presumed reaction products of the binder. The interaction of pigments and oil binder is discussed in Chapter 6.

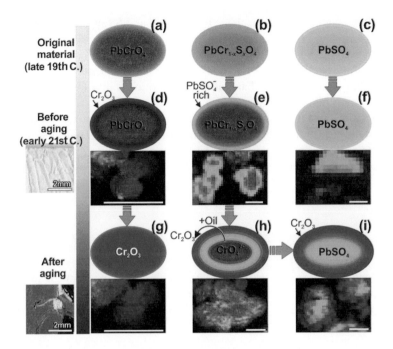

FIGURE 4.12 Proposed model of the degradation process of chromium yellow pigments. The original pigments in late 19th century consisted of three types of particles: (a) $PbCrO_4$, (b) $PbCr_{1-x}S_xO_4$ (high sulfate content) and (c) $PbSO_4$. When the paint was taken out of the tube for investigation/middle frame, the particles had gradually evolved to: (d) $PbCrO_4$ – Cr_2O_3 core–shell; (e) $PbCrO_4$ – $PbSO_4$ core–shell; and remaining (f) $PbSO_4$ particles, respectively. The subsequent artificial aging process speeds up the evolution and will lead them to (g) Cr_2O_3; (h) $PbCrO_4$–$PbSO_4$ – Cr_2O_3 core–shell; or (i) $PbSO_4$–Cr_2O_3 core–shell structures. $PbSO_4$ particles will remain as a catalyst. The intermediate or final states were observed by electron microscopy in the experiment as shown in the bottom row. Scale bar: 100 nm. (Reprinted with permission of H. Tan, H. Tian, J. Verbeeck, L. Monico, K. Janssens, G. Van Tendeloo (2013) *Angew. Chem. Int. Ed.* 52: 11360–11363. Copyright 2013, Wiley-VCH Verlag GmbH & Co. KGa, Weinheim.)

4.6 BLACKENING OF HEMATITE IN WALL PAINTING OF POMPEIAN HOUSE

Pompei is an ancient Roman city which was buried by the eruption of the Mount Vesuvius volcano in 79 AD. About 150 years ago, many Pompeian buildings were excavated and thereby exposed red pigmented walls and wall paintings of these buildings which then blackened. The Romans used two red pigments in these buildings, cinnabar (HgS) and hematite (Fe_2O_3). The cause of blackening of the walls of the Marcus Lucretius house was investigated [29].

Elemental composition (qualitative and quantitative) of sections of blackened wall was determined with XRF. The major elements were: Ca, Fe and S. The presence of sulfur was a surprise because this element is not part of the original composition of the walls. Raman spectroscopy established the linkage between elemental analysis and associated compounds: Ca (calcite, $CaCO_3$); Ca and S (gypsum, $CaSO_4 \cdot 2H_2O$); Fe (Fe_2O_3, hematite and magnetite, Fe_3O_4); and coquimbite [$Fe_2(SO_4)_3 \cdot 9H_2O$]. An optical microscopic image of a cross section of blackened wall and accompanying Raman spectra from the Marcus Lucretius house is shown in Figure 4.13. The blackened layer has a strong Raman band at $660\,cm^{-1}$ which is diagnostic for magnetite along with bands for calcite and gypsum.

The preparation of fresco wall paintings is described in Chapter 7. The causative agent hematite blackening was proposed to be sulfur dioxide, SO_2, an environmental pollutant released during the past 150 years by various human activities, mainly the burning of coal. Consider the redox reaction between sulfur dioxide and hematite:

$$3\,Fe_2O_{3\,(s)} + 1\,SO_{2\,(g)} \rightarrow 2\,Fe_3O_{4\,(s)} + 1\,SO_{3\,(g)}$$

$$2\,Fe_3O_4 = 2\,\left(Fe_2O_3 \cdot FeO\right)$$

Hematite and sulfur dioxide yield the crystalline, black iron-oxide, magnetite, Fe_3O_4. For the purpose of teaching, magnetite can be re-written as ($Fe_2O_3 \cdot FeO$), which shows that it is formally a 1:1 combination of Fe(II) and Fe(III) oxides. A mechanism for this reaction follows, see Scheme 4.9.

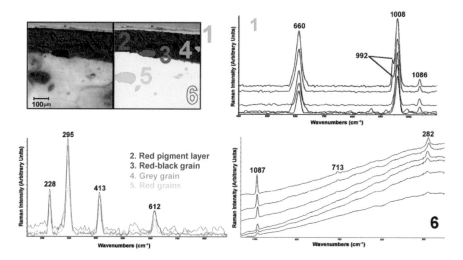

FIGURE 4.13 Blackening of hematite. Optical microscope image (100 X) of cross-section entrance to Marcus Lucretius house (Pompei), different areas mapped with Raman spectroscopy. Raman excitation: 785 nm with laser power at 1 mW. In the black layer (1), calcite ($1086\,cm^{-1}$), gypsum ($1008\,cm^{-1}$), and in some measurements, mirabilite (Na_2SO_4 $10H_2O$) and thenardite (Na_2SO_4, $992\,cm^{-1}$) as part of the mortar and magnetite ($660\,cm^{-1}$) are observed. Areas from 2 to 5 show typical Raman features of hematite whereas all the measurements done on area 6, show the characteristic Raman spectra of calcite. (Reprinted with permission of M. Maguregui, U. Knuutinen, I. Martinez-Arkarazo, K. Castro, J.M. Madariaga (2011) *Anal. Chem.* 83: 3319–3326. Copyright 2011, American Chemical Society.)

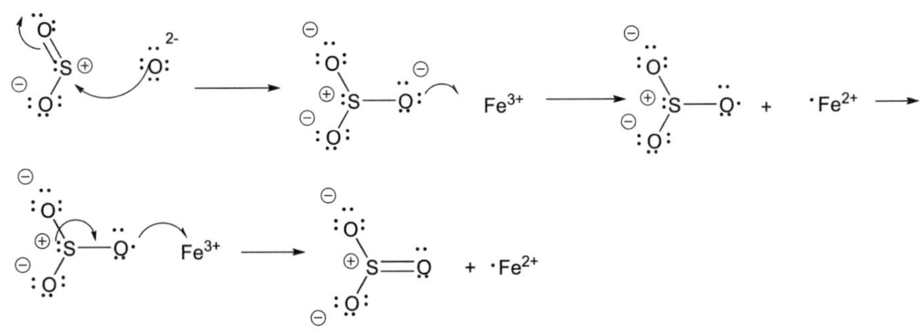

SCHEME 4.9   Blackening of hematite. Redox coupling of SO_2 and Fe^{3+} [28].

In this redox process, oxide anion attacks the electron-deficient sulfur atom in SO_2 to form an intermediate which then reductively donates two electrons to two Fe^{3+} cations, each of which receives one electron to form two Fe^{2+} cations. The loss of 2 e$^-$ from intermediate (I) leaves the neutral SO_3 molecules. In this scheme, single- and double-headed arrows denote transfer of 1e$^-$ and 2e$^-$, respectively.

If we account for all of the atomic "pieces" of reactants, there are 6 Fe's, 11 O's and 1 S on both sides of the balanced equation. We have accounted for the formation of magnetite, the agent which blackened the walls of the Pompeian house.

What remains is to account for the formation of gypsum ($CaSO_4 \cdot 2H_2O$) and coquimbite ($Fe_2(SO_4)_3 \cdot 9H_2O$). Sulfur trioxide and water combine to form sulfuric acid. Sulfuric acid is deposited on surfaces as acid rain. In this instance, the contact of calcite ($CaCO_3$) and sulfuric acid produces calcium sulfate which hydrates to form gypsum ($CaSO_4 \cdot 2H_2O$). These reactions are acid–base with no redox involved.

$$H_2SO_{4\,(aq)} + CaCO_{3\,(s)} \rightarrow CaSO_{4\,(s)} + H_2O_{(g)} + CO_{2\,(g)}$$

$$CaSO_{4\,(s)} + 2\,H_2O_{(l)} \rightarrow CaSO_4 \cdot 2\,H_2O_{(s)}$$

This set of reactions represents the process of *sulfation* in which limestone is chemically converted to gypsum. It may seem surprising that the double hydrate of calcium sulfate is physically *harder* than the anhydrous form, while also having a larger water content. This is because the water content of gypsum is bound into the unit cell of gypsum and does not appear as liquid water. Further, solubility of gypsum is ~*100-fold* greater than that of calcite, and this leads to erosion of the surface by rain water.

The last piece of this puzzle is the formation of coquimbite. This material results from the combined action of dissolved carbonic acid (from carbon dioxide) and sulfuric acid on hematite.

$$Fe_2O_{3(s)} + 3\,H^+_{(aq)} + 3\,HCO_3^-_{(aq)} + 3\,SO_3^{2-}_{(aq)} + 3\,Ca^{2+}_{(aq)}$$

$$+\,6\,H_2O_{(l)} \rightarrow Fe_2(SO_4)_3 \cdot 9H_2O_{(s)} + 3\,CaCO_{3(s)}$$

4.7 GENERAL BLACKENING OF PIGMENTS BY H₂S

Hydrogen sulfide, H_2S, is a minor component of the atmosphere (0.11–0.33 ppb). It is produced mainly by the action of anaerobic bacteria on sulfur-containing molecules (proteins, etc.). It is also produced by industrial activity such as: viscose rayon plants, pulp paper mills, iron smelters, tanneries and manure processing. It is more toxic than hydrogen cyanide and has the odor of rotten eggs with a low olfactory level of detection. When inhaled, it is toxic because sulfide anion, S^{2-}, binds tightly to the iron in hemoglobin forming a species known as sulf-hemoglobin, which stops oxygen transport.

Because hydrogen sulfide is a naturally occurring component of air, it was present long before the Industrial Revolution and has a reputation for reacting with certain pigments [30]. Smith and Clark conducted controlled exposure tests with about 20 mg of various pigments in glass vials which were flushed with 100% H_2S gas and then sealed for 5 days. The pigments tested included: lead pigments (white lead, red lead, massicot and litharge) and copper pigments (malachite, basic verdigris and azurite). This was a *model study,* in which powdered pigments were exposed to an excess (overkill) of H_2S for 5 days. The authors stated that *atmospheric H_2S does not react with many pigments in actual paintings.* This may be because the pigments may have been protected by a layer of varnish or other material, and the level of atmospheric H_2S was too low to react with pigments in paintings. This study showed that prolonged exposure of most copper and lead pigments to gaseous hydrogen sulfide leads to the formation of the corresponding black metal sulfide, PbS or CuS.

Visual inspection of the test samples showed that all of the pigments reacted to yield a gray or black product. Raman spectroscopy revealed that the blackened lead pigments contained galena (lead (II) sulfide). In these cases, sulfide is a soft Lewis base and Pb^{2+} and Cu^{2+} are both soft Lewis acids. An example is the reaction of PbO with hydrogen sulfide:

$$PbO_{(s)} + H_2S_{(g)} \rightarrow PbS_{(s)} + H_2O_{(g)}.$$

The copper pigments were converted to CuS (covelite). An example of this type of reaction is:

$$2\,H_2S_{(g)} + CuCO_3 \cdot Cu(OH)_{2\,(s)} \rightarrow 2\,CuS_{(s)} + CO_{2(g)} + 3\,H_2O_{(g)}$$

4.8 SMALT DISCOLORATION

Smalt is a blue cobalt glass which has been crushed to small pieces and then suspended in oily binder. It has a tendency to discolor and become brown or gray, see Figure 4.14 [31]. Discoloration of smalt was mentioned in 17th-century books about painting. In the 19th century, experiments showed that even a short immersion of smalt in water led to discoloration as the water became alkaline. At that time, most people believed that discoloration was associated with loss of Co^{2+} from the glass. However, this was rejected when it was found that Co^{2+} was retained in discolored smalt.

FIGURE 4.14 Smalt: blue reference (left) and discolored gray material (right) from the painting, *St. Cecile*, 16th century (sampling Institut royale du Patrimoine artistique, Brussels). (Reprinted with permission of R. Giovanoli and B. Muhlethaler (1970) *Stud. Conserv.* 15: 37–44. Copyright 1970, Taylor and Francis.)

Tiny samples were removed from five paintings dating between the 16th and 18th centuries and were analyzed by X-ray spectroscopy [32,33]. From the X-ray spectra of these painting samples, it was concluded that the coordination of Co^{2+} was tetrahedral in blue areas but in discolored areas, the coordination number had increased above four, the central cation was still Co^{2+}, and the ligands were oxygen atoms of the silicate network. Elemental composition for Si, Al, K, Ca, Mg, Fe, Co, As, Ni, Pb and Bi as the respective oxides were obtained by SEM-EDX. In discolored areas, the K^+ composition was decreased from 23% to 89%. None of the other elements showed such a large relative change, see Figure 4.15 [32].

A mechanism was suggested based on ion-exchange [33]. Entry of water (neutral molecule) into glass causes leaching of K^+. In order to balance electrically, hydroxyl ions also leave the glass. The net ion-exchange is then: H^+_{in} and K^+_{out}. This is consistent with the observed pH increase of the water in which smalt is immersed. The leached KOH can then hydrolyze glyceride esters or react with fatty acid molecules in the oil binder to form potassium salts, see Scheme 4.10.

How does loss of K^+ relate to change of coordination number of Co^{2+} and loss of blue color? Robinet etal. (2011) proposed that the Co^{2+} coordination number in decolorized smalt increased to 6 (octahedral). The argument is based on the role of potassium ions in the glass. Cobalt requires additional positive charges in the tetrahedral coordination to compensate the charge of the four surrounding oxygen ligands contributed by the silicate network. In glass, charge compensation is generally provided by Group 1 cations. The loss of K^+ results in decrease in the number of charge-compensating cations available in the structure, which creates a charge deficiency around the cobalt ion. This causes a shift to octahedral coordination with loss of blue color [34].

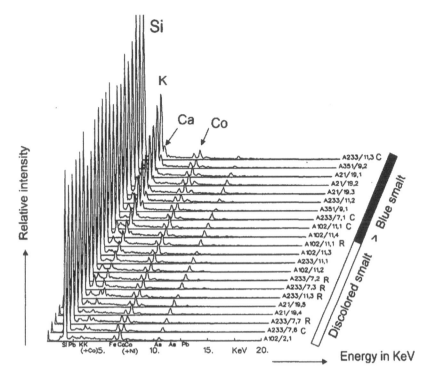

FIGURE 4.15 SEM-EDX data for smalt cross-sections in order of increasing relative amount of potassium. The blue to gray color transition corresponds to a Co:K ratio of approximately 1:1. (Reprinted with permission of J.J. Boon, K. Keune, J. van der Weerd, M. Geldof, J.R.J. van Asperen (2001) *Chimia* 55: 952–960. Copyright 2001, Swiss Chemical Society.)

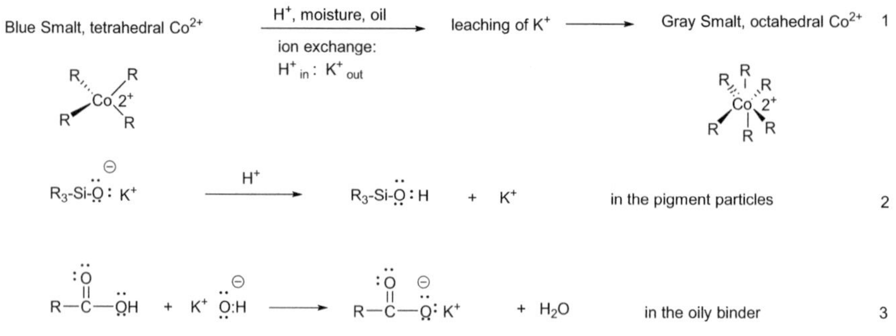

SCHEME 4.10 Smalt discoloration mechanism [32].

4.9   ULTRAMARINE DISEASE

"UM Disease" or "UM Sickness" describes the gray appearance of aged UM paint, often accompanied by cracks in the surface. At this time, the cause of this degradation has not been firmly established. The two suggested causes for UM Disease are chemical change in the pigment and chemical change in the oil binder [35,36].

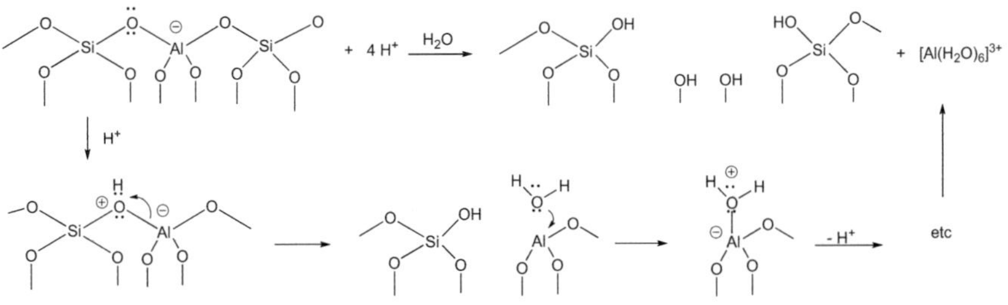

SCHEME 4.11   Ultramarine framework destruction in aqueous acid.

4.9.1   CHEMICAL CHANGE IN THE PIGMENT

The color of UM can be altered by reacting the pigment with salts of mono- and divalent cations. Matsunaga [37] and Booth et al. [38] demonstrated that color change was due to cation-exchange in which the "new" cation would replace Na^+ inside the β-cages of sodalite. The sulfur anion radicals are too large to leave the cages. For example, Li^+ UM is gray. However, there is no data to support cation-exchange as a cause of UM Disease.

See Figure 2.5 for the structure of UM. The chromophores, $S_2^{1-\cdot}$ and $S_3^{1-\cdot}$ are radical anions which are known to be stable provided that they are protected by the aluminosilicate β-cages of the mineral sodalite. The rapid reaction of blue UM with dilute aqueous HCl constitutes a *qualitative identification test* for UM. Within minutes of exposure, the color changes to gray or yellowish-gray and gaseous H_2S is evolved [39]. See Scheme 4.11 for mechanism of framework hydrolysis in aqueous acid.

4.9.2   CHROMOPHORE DESTRUCTION

Acidic destruction of the aluminosilicate framework of sodalite opens the cages and releases the chromophores into solution. The chromophores of UM are polysulfide radical anions. The proposed mechanism is a series of reactions which are based on general principles and experimental data. The radical anions will be protonated in acidic solution. Two radical anions react to form a polysulfane (HS_nH, where $n \geq 3$). Polysulfanes are known to decompose to yield H_2S and elemental sulfur [40]. Decomposition of the sulfane is accomplished by homolysis of one of the H-S bonds to yield H_2S, see Scheme 4.12.

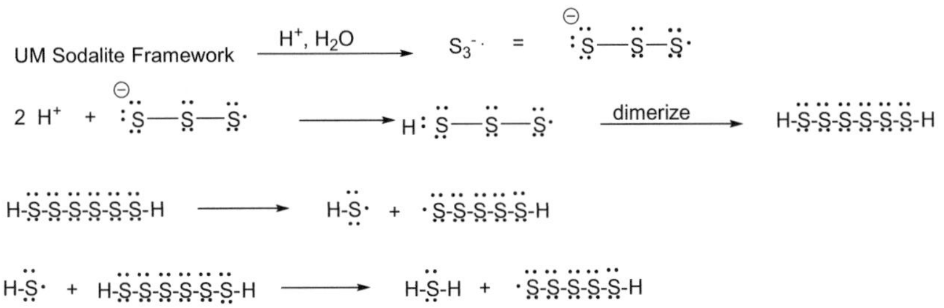

SCHEME 4.12   Ultramarine chromophore destruction in aqueous acid.

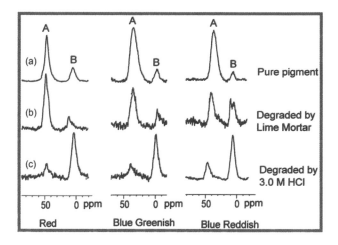

FIGURE 4.16 Ultramarine degradation. Comparison between the ^{27}Al magic angle spinning NMR spectra for the (a) red, blue-greenish and blue-reddish ultramarine pigments. (b) The corresponding pigments faded by lime mortar (fresco), and (c) corresponding pigments faded by the action of acid. (Reprinted with permission from E. Del Federico, W. Shofberger, J. Shelvis, et al. (2006) *Inorg. Chem.* 45:1270–1276. Copyright 2006, American Chemical Society.)

Del Federico et al. subjected blue UM pigment to 3M HCl and also to alkaline stress conditions [41]. The acid-stressed samples yielded the gray color and H_2S. In addition, the ^{27}Al NMR spectrum was perturbed; the A/B peak height ratio was inverted, see Figure 4.16. This is consistent with *framework destruction* due to acid hydrolysis. Sodalite and zeolites, in general, exhibit two NMR peaks which reflect two environments for aluminum. The "A" peak (48–57 ppm) was assigned to tetrahedral sites of the aluminosilicate framework. The "B" peak (~0 ppm) did not respond to chromophore loading was assigned to octahedral sites (non-framework).

Alkaline conditions (UM on lime mortar/85% RH/2 weeks) which simulated UM in wall paintings, also resulted in loss of color but not H_2S emission.^{27}Al NMR spectra were altered consistent with *framework destruction*, see Figure 4.16. UM is usually stable in wall paintings. The instability observed with the model study was possibly caused by the high RH which prevented evaporation of water, thereby facilitating basic hydrolysis, see Scheme 4.13. When a wall painting is created, evaporation of water is not impeded which allows the pigment to be trapped in the solid-state matrix.

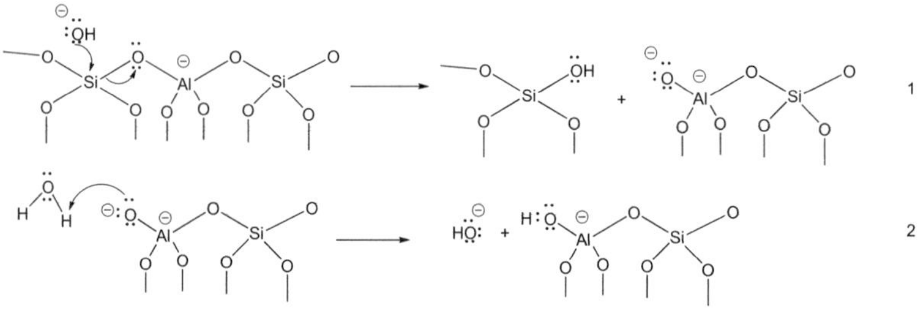

SCHEME 4.13 Ultramarine framework destruction in aqueous base.

4.9.3 ZEOLITES

The aluminosilicate matrix of UM is known as sodalite, which is type of zeolite. Zeolites are aluminosilicate compounds with porous structures which are naturally occurring and also prepared by synthesis. They have many industrial uses, including refining of hydrocarbons, purification of industrial gases and dehydration of alcohols [42]. The catalytic activity of zeolites can be manipulated by *dealumination*, which is triggered by acids [43]. Further, zeolites are utilized as catalysts in free radical reactions [44].

4.9.4 DEGRADATION OF THE OILY BINDER

De la Rie et al. [35] investigated the effect of photo-stress on a model system comprising UM/linseed oil paint or UM/urea-aldehyde resin. Samples of UM pigment were pelletized in a hydraulic press and then subjected to photo-stress. UM paint samples with and without a free radical inhibitor were applied to glass slides at a thickness of 60 μm and stressed. Results are summarized in Table 4.3. Paint samples (± radical inhibitor) had a very weak reflectance spectrum before stress; which was greatly enhanced after stress. The stressed samples showed no change in Raman spectrum which indicates that there was no structural change in the pigment, see Figure 4.17. The Raman spectra essentially match the spectrum with band assignments reported earlier [45], see Table 4.4. The lack of reflectance in the pre-stress samples was explained by the near matching of refractive indices of UM and linseed oil (both near 1.5) [46]. After stress, the reflectance spectrum was markedly enhanced because the surface of the paint was not smooth as it was initially, see Figure 4.18 which shows the SEM image. Microcracks in the paint caused light scattering and enhanced reflectance. Degradation of the reflectance spectrum was entirely prevented by addition of a radical scavenger. The ^{27}Al NMR spectrum did not change as a result of stress for a paint sample prepared with UM/urea-aldehyde resin, which indicated that stress had no effect on the aluminosilicate structure. Finally, stress had a very small effect on

---

TABLE 4.3
Ultramarine Paint Model Stress Study [35]

Sample	Before Stress	After Stress
UM/LO	Reflectance spectrum was ~nil	Reflectance spectrum was enhanced
		Raman spectrum was not changed
		FEG-SEM microscopic image was significantly changed
UM/LO/RS	Reflectance spectrum was ~nil	Reflectance spectrum was not changed
UM alone	Reflectance spectrum was ~nil	Reflectance spectrum was not changed
		Raman spectrum was not changed

Stress: exposure to xenon lamp (320–800 nm) for 1500 h at 50% relative humidity, 34°C. Xenon lamp radiation was cut off below 320 nm.

FEG-SEM, field emission gun scanning electron microscopy, UM/LO paint (60% UM:40% linseed oil by mass); RS, radical scavenger, 1,2,2,6,6-pentamethyl-4-piperidyl sebacate.

TABLE 4.4

Raman Spectra of Ultramarine [45]

Raman Shift, cm⁻¹	Intensity	Band Assignment
255	w	ν_2, bending mode for S_3^{1-}
547	s	ν_1, symmetrical stretching mode for S_3^{1-}
590	sh	S_2^{1-}
804	w	$\nu_1 + \nu_2$, combination band (255 + 547 = 802)
1096	m	$2 \times \nu_1$, overtone band ($2 \times 547 = 1094$)

Synthetic ultramarine blue was obtained from Kremer, PIG085; excitation, 632.8 nm HeNe laser.
m, medium; s, strong; sh, shoulder; S_2^{1-}, yellow chromophore; S_3^{1-}, blue chromophore; w, weak.

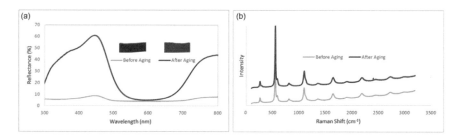

FIGURE 4.17 Diffuse reflectance-ultraviolet-visible spectra (a) and Raman spectra (b) of ultramarine blue in linseed oil before aging and after aging for ca. 1500 h in a xenon arc chamber. Photographs of the paints before and after aging have been inserted. (Reprinted with permission of E.R. de la Rie, A. Michelin, M. Ngako, E. Del Federico, C. Del Grosso (2017) *Polym. Degrad. Stability* 144: 43–52. Copyright 2017, Elsevier.)

FIGURE 4.18 FEG-SEM, field emission gun scanning electron microscopy images of ultramarine blue in linseed oil, before aging (a) and after aging for ca. 1500 h in a xenon arc chamber (b). (Reprinted with permission of E.R. de la Rie, A. Michelin, M. Ngako, E. Del Federico, C. Del Grosso (2017) *Polym. Degrad. Stability* 144: 43–52. Copyright 2017, Elsevier.)

the reflectance spectrum of the *pigment alone*. This decolorization story is consistent with this cautionary line: "Changes in surface must be accounted for before real changes in pigmentation can be accurately determined" [47].

Based on the model studies cited, the conclusions are:

Photo-stress of UM/LO paint initiated free radical reactions which degraded the LO binder. In turn, this led to erosion of the surface and caused light scattering. Photo-stress did not degrade the chromophore.

The loss of UM pigment color caused by acid or alkali was due to degradation of the aluminosilicate framework. Exposure to acid degrades the chromophore by a plausible mechanism.

Exposure to lime mortar/85% RH/2 weeks caused framework degradation and loss of color. A mechanism has not been proposed to explain how the chromophore was affected.

4.10   AZURITE AND MALACHITE

Azurite, $Cu_3(CO_3)_2(OH)_2$, and malachite, $Cu_2CO_3(OH)_2$, are, respectively, blue and green minerals which usually occur naturally in close proximity. They have both been used as artists' pigments. They are chemically related by the following equilibrium expression:

$$2\left[Cu_3(CO_3)_2(OH)_2\right] + H_2O \rightleftarrows 3\left[Cu_2(CO_3)(OH)_2\right] + CO_2$$

azurite   malachite

In the presence of water, azurite converts to malachite with the release of CO_2 gas. For this reason, azurite cannot be used in an aqueous environment. Azurite gradually converts to malachite in frescoes, particularly in outdoor structures. In mineral collections, azurite should be stored in a dry place. Both minerals may be thermally decomposed (> 300°C) in a helium atmosphere to the black copper (II) oxide, tenorite, see Scheme 4.14 [48]. The change of azurite to tenorite has also been attributed to alkaline conditions released from altered plaster [49].

Degradation of blue azurite to green shades was investigated on a gypsum shield on top of a door in the Monastery of Santes Creus (Catalonia, Spain) [50], see Figure 4.19. This study was based on the use of optical microscopy, SR XRD and SR FTIR. The compounds identified include the green isomorphs, atacamite and

Azurite: $2\,[\,2\,Cu_3(CO_3)_2(OH)_2\,] \xrightarrow{\;300\text{-}400°C\;} Cu_2CO_3(OH)_2 + 4\,CuO + CO_2 + H_2O$

$Cu_2CO_3(OH)_2 \rightarrow 2\,CuO + CO_2 + H_2O$

Malachite: $CuCO_3 \cdot Cu(OH)_2 \xrightarrow{\;300\text{-}400°C\;} 2\,CuO + H_2O + CO_2$

SCHEME 4.14   Thermal decomposition of azurite and malachite [47,48].

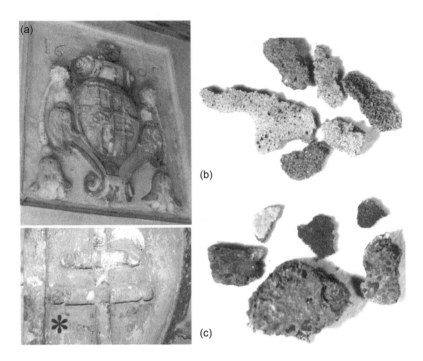

FIGURE 4.19 Degradation of azurite. Ornamental shield (a and b), Monastery of Santes Creus (Catalonia, Spain). *Red asterisk* marks the sampling point in the *blue area*; several fragments of the sample of different characteristics: *blue* and *green shades*; fragments showing the *brown layer* (c). (Reprinted with permission of A. Lluveras, S. Boularand, A. Andreotti, M. Vendrell-Saz (2010) *Appl. Phys. A* 99: 363–375. Copyright 2010, Springer.)

paratacamite, $Cu_2Cl(OH)_3$; the calcium oxalate hydrates, weddelite, $CaC_2O_4 \cdot 2H_2O$ and wewhellite, $CaC_2O_4 \cdot H_2O$; the copper (II) oxalates, $CuC_2O_4 \cdot nH_2O$; as well as the starting materials, azurite and gypsum, $CaSO_4 \cdot 2H_2O$. Consequently, the copper (II) chlorides were identified as the green degradation products. Since chlorine is not part of the chemical formula of azurite, it must have come from an external source which has not been identified.

What can be said about the presence of the various oxalate salts? Oxalate was most likely produced by microbes. There is a substantial literature which describes the microbial colonization of surfaces, including stone, ceramics and paintings. Microbes produce various inorganic and organic acids which can contribute protons (acidity) which leads to corrosion. Certain acids, such as oxalic acid, also act as chelating agents for polyvalent metal cations [51]. This would account for the presence of calcium oxalate and copper (II) oxalate. For example, the reaction of lead white with oxalic acid (2:3 mole ratio) would generate lead oxalate, water and carbon dioxide.

$$2\, PbCO_3 \cdot Pb(OH)_2 + 3\, HO_2C - CO_2H \rightarrow 3\left[{}^-O_2C - CO_2^- Pb^{2+}\right] + 4\, H_2O + 2\, CO_2$$

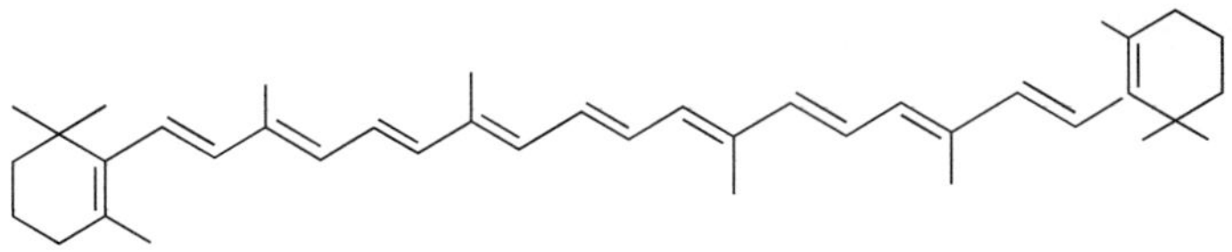

FIGURE 4.20 All trans-β-carotene.

It has been suggested that the chelation of polyvalent cations in the artwork (Pb^{2+}, Cu^{2+}, Hg^{2+}, Cd^{2+}, etc.) by oxalate dianion will *deactivate* the cation and thereby protect the microbe against its toxic effects. Deactivation in a chemical sense means that the valence orbitals of the cation have been filled by *ligands*. Metal oxalates form from the acid–base reaction of oxalic acid and basic pigments. Basic pigments which formed metal oxalates included: lead white, malachite, azurite, calcite, cadmium yellow (CdS) and zinc yellow (zinc chromate) [52]. Oxalic acid is toxic/fatal to humans because it chelates Ca^{2+} in the tissues and forms insoluble calcium oxalate [53]. Raw rhubarb contains oxalic acid, and the stalks must be cooked so that the acid is decomposed.

Maguregui et al. (2012) reported on the production of brown patinas are associated with a deteriorated Pompeian wall painting [54]. These patinas were caused by the deposition of (principally) microbial all trans-β-carotene, a poly-conjugated red compound, Figure 4.20, along with calcium oxalate. The biodegradation of artwork caused by microorganisms is a serious problem, the scope of which is magnified by the very large number of microbes and the equally large number of different environments in which the artworks are displayed [55].

4.10.1 MALACHITE TO MOOLOOITE

Green malachite biodegrades to blue-white moolooite [copper (II) oxalate] [56]. This work concluded that microbial action led to oxalic acid production, which reacted with calcite, $CaCO_3$; gypsum, $CaSO_4 \cdot 2H_2O$; and malachite to form various products, including carbon dioxide, water, calcium oxalate dihydrate, posnjackite, antlerite and copper (II) oxalate (moolooite), see Scheme 4.15.

$(HO\text{-}CO)\text{-}_2$ (A) $+ CaCO_3 + H_2O \longrightarrow CaC_2O_4 + CO_2$

$(HO\text{-}CO)\text{-}_2 + CaSO_4\,2H_2O + 2\,Cu_2CO_3(OH)_2 \rightarrow Cu_4SO_4(OH)_6$ (B) $+ CaC_2O_4\,2H_2O + CO_2$

$(HO\text{-}CO)\text{-}_2 + CaSO_4\,2H_2O + 3\,Cu_3SO_4(OH)_4 \rightarrow 4\,Cu_3SO_4(OH)_4$ (C) $+ CaC_2O_4\,2H_2O + 2\,H_2O$

$(HO\text{-}CO)\text{-}_2 + Cu_3SO_4(OH)_4 \rightarrow 3\,CuC_2O_4$ (D) $+ HSO_4^- + 4\,H_2O$

SCHEME 4.15 Reactions of oxalic acid with calcium and copper minerals [55]. (A) Oxalic acid; (B) Posnjackite; (C) Antlerite; (D) Moolooite.

4.11   PRUSSIAN BLUE FADING

Blue pigments presented a problem for artists until about 1750 when Prussian blue became commercially available. Indigo and azurite were cheap but were known to fade, and lazurite (from which lapis lazuli was obtained) was light-stable but very expensive. Therefore, PB was welcomed by artists! However, PB has two limitations. First, it is incompatible with base, and cannot be applied over CaO-based wall paintings. Second, in paintings or in dyed textiles, PB has a variable property of fading because of exposure to light when stored under air or anoxic conditions. The color of the faded colorant is restored in darkness when O_2 is present and is not restored when O_2 is absent. Pure PB is stable to these conditions. Therefore, the substrate (textiles; paper, cotton, silk, etc.) plays a role when the pigment fades [57]. (When used as a *pigment*, an insoluble *colorant* is suspended in a binder to form paint. In contrast, when used as a *dye,* a colorant is dissolved in a solvent, producing a solution into which a textile is placed such that the dye binds to the textile material.)

PB in paint layers prepared with linseed oil binder and white pigments and exposed to light in air yields a white product (fading) and also a green product [58,59]. The white product is Berlin white, formed by reduction,

$$KFe^{3+}\left[Fe^{2+}(CN)_6\right] \times H_2O \qquad light/[R] \rightarrow Fe_2^{2+}\left[Fe^{2+}(CN)_6\right].$$

The blue color of the pigment is due to absorption of light at ~640 nm which causes the transfer of one electron from Fe^{II} to Fe^{III}. The process is known as *intervalence charge transfer*:

$$\left[Fe^{3+} - C \equiv N - Fe^{2+}\right], \text{ light absorption} \leftrightarrow \left[Fe^{2+} - C \equiv N - Fe^{3+}\right]^*, \text{ excited state}$$

Therefore, reduction of Fe^{III} to Fe^{II} prevents the charge-transfer process, and the blue color is lost [60].

The green product is Berlin green, formed by partial oxidation, where x = 0.6–0.8.

$$2\,KFe^{3+}\left[Fe^{2+}(CN)_6\right] light/[O] \rightarrow \left\{KFe^{3+}\left[Fe^{2+}(CN)_6\right]\right\}_x\left\{Fe^{3+}\left[Fe^{3+}(CN)_6\right]\right\}_{1-x}$$

White pigments (ZnO, TiO_2 and lead white) were added to PB as diluents, in order to diminish the intensity of blue color. A redox mechanism was proposed based on the known photo-semiconductor properties of ZnO and TiO_2. Activated by light, hole-electron ($h^+ e^-$) pairs form, the electron migrates to the surface and reduction of PB occurs with consequent fading. The hole remains in the bulk paint and causes partial oxidation with formation of Berlin green. Lead white is not strongly photoactive. The suggested role of lead white in PB degradation is to furnish hydroxide ions which promote hydrolysis of the fatty ester linkages in the oil binder with the formation of metal soaps [58].

Museum objects which contain organic matter are subject to air oxidation and attack by insects and fungi. Anoxic storage under argon or nitrogen gas protects

SCHEME 4.16 Light-induced fading of Prussian-blue-dyed textiles in (a) air and (b) anoxia. In air and anoxia, PB reduction/fading is influenced by light and substrate. In air, re-oxidation and color recovery requires the darkness and oxygen. Re-oxidation of faded PB does not occur in anoxia/darkness. (Reprinted with permission of C. Gervais, M.A. Languille, S. Regeur, C. Garnier, M. Gillet (2014) *Herit. Sci.* 2: 26–34. Copyright 2014, Springer.)

both dyes and textiles in vulnerable objects from oxidation and pests. The effect of anoxia on fading of *PB-dyed textiles* has been investigated [61,62]. In these systems, there is complex interaction of several factors including PB pigment, textile substrate, mordant, gaseous atmospheric composition and exposure to light, see Scheme 4.16. [Mordants are compounds which assist in the dyeing of textiles; for example, alum, $KAl(SO_4)_2 \cdot 12\, H_2O$. Most mordants contain a polyvalent metal ion which forms bonds to the dye and also to the fabric.] The overall message is that fading of PB-dyed textiles is driven by light and occurs in both air and anoxia. Recovery of the blue color requires darkness and the presence of O_2.

4.12 BROWNING OF SILVERPOINT DRAWINGS

Metalpoint drawings are produced by drawing a metal stylus over a specially prepared surface. Silver, gold or copper have been used as the metal tip. The surface consists of a ground layer of bone white (calcium phosphate obtained from burned bone) which has been deposited on cellulose-based paper. The technique was popular during the Renaissance but was displaced by oil painting. A newly drawn Silverpoint is gray-blue in color due to the trail of metallic nanoparticles deposited on the surface. With time, the color darkens to brown, which is the characteristic appearance of these drawings [63].

Silverpoint drawings of Albrecht Dürer (1471–1528), Jan van Eyck (~1390–1441) and Hans Baldung Grien (1484–1545) have been analyzed by Synchrotron Radiation X-Ray Fluorescence (SRXRF). These studies concluded that the major components of the drawn metallic lines in these drawings were: Ag (85%–96%WT), Cu (6%–15%WT) and Zn (0.2%–2%WT). In addition, a lesser amount of mercury was detected in all of the drawn strokes. According to art historians, mercury was not (commonly) used in silver styli during the Renaissance. The conclusion therefore was that mercury came from an external source. Most likely, atmospheric mercury vapor reacted with metallic silver to yield an alloy with the composition Ag_2Hg_3.

In a test experiment with silver strokes on paper, exposure to a mercury-enriched atmosphere quickly led to the formation of this alloy.

$$2\, Ag_{(s)} + 3\, Hg_{(g)} \rightarrow Ag_2Hg_{3\,(s)}$$

In this equation, $Ag_2Hg_{3(s)}$ represents an *alloy* which is composed of metal atoms, not ions. An alloy is a metallic compound composed of two or more metals. In order to form an alloy, constituent metals must be close in size. In addition, their crystalline unit cells must be similar so that the different metals can co-crystallize. In this case, the respective atomic radii for silver and mercury are 144.4 and 160 pm, and their respective unit cell types are face-centered cubic and hexagonal-close-packed. This pair of unit cells will co-crystallize.

What about the possible reactions of metallic silver with atmospheric O_2 and H_2S? These reactions are well established and lead to surface coatings of Ag_2O and Ag_2S, the latter is the conventional *tarnishing* of silver. The authors did consider these reactions, but their levels were too small to detect. They assumed that both products form, and the formation of Ag_2S is probably the reason that the color changes from gray-blue to brown [64].

4.13   TARNISHING OF SILVER

Silver has a long history as an art material, in which the elemental form dominates; the ionic form is not used. Silver was formerly an integral part of silver halide/gelatin photography, a major 20th technology which is no longer used [65]. Metallic silver objects tarnish because of the reaction of silver atoms with hydrogen sulfide in the atmosphere. In this redox process, silver atoms are oxidized to Ag^+ ions (Ag_2S) and H_2 gas is produced.

Tarnish (Ag_2S) can be removed by various reducing agents. For example, aluminum foil (Al^o), baking soda ($NaHCO_3$), and warm water will remove tarnish according to the following reaction sequence. This process releases sulfide ions into solution, and these are captured by Al^{3+} to form aluminum sulfide, which decomposes to release hydrogen sulfide gas (back) into the atmosphere, see Scheme 4.17. In the last step, Al^{3+} captures four hydroxide ions to form a soluble tetrahedral complex ion. This method of cleaning silver is superior to silver polish because the re-oxidized silver remains on the surface of the object. With silver polish, the outer skin of Ag_2S is removed from the object [66].

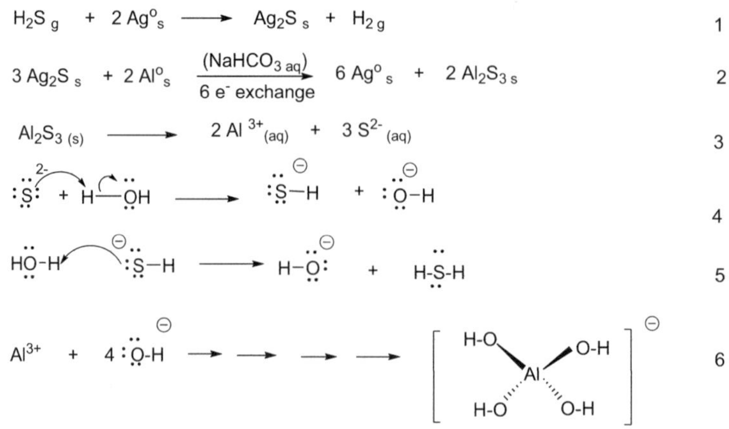

SCHEME 4.17   Removing silver tarnish [66].

4.14 ENVIRONMENTAL FACTORS AND PIGMENT STABILITY

The stability of inorganic artist pigments can be viewed as the result of the interaction of the pigments with environmental factors. The latter includes: exposure to light, atmospheric gases (SO_2, NO_x, H_2S, H_2O and O_3) and microbial activity [67–70].

REFERENCES

SEMICONDUCTOR PIGMENTS

1. Anaf W, Schalm O, Janssens K, DeWael K (2015) Understanding the (in)stability of semiconductor pigments by a thermodynamic approach. *Dyes Pigments* 113:409–415.
2. Janssens K, Van der Snickt G, Vanmeert F, Legrand S, Nuyts G, Alfeld M, Monico M, Anaf W, De Nolf W, Vermeulen M, Verbeeck J, De Wael K (2016) Noninvasive and non-destructive examination of artistic pigments, paints, by means of X-ray methods. *Top Curr Chem (Z)* 374:81, Doi: 10.1007/41061-016-0079-2.
3. Chen S, Wang L-W (2012) Thermodynamic oxidation and reduction of photocatalytic semiconductors in aqueous solution. *Chem Mater* 24:3659–3666.
4. Bonaduce I, Duce C, Lluveras-Tenorio A, et al. (2019) *Acc Chem Res* 52:3397–3406.

RED LEAD

5. Vanmeert F, van der Snickt G, Janssens K (2015) Plumbonacrite identified by x-ray powder diffraction tomography as a missing link during degradation of red lead in a Van Gogh painting. *Angew Chem Int Ed* 54:3607–3610.
6. Aze S, Vallet J-M, Pomey M, Baronnet A, Grauby O (2007) Red lead darkening in wall paintings: Natural ageing of experimental wall paintings versus artificial ageing tests. *Eur J Miner* 19:883–890.
7. Ayelew E, Janssens K, DeWael K (2016) Unraveling the reactivity of minium toward bicarbonate and the role of lead oxides therein. *Anal Chem* 88(3):1564–1569.
8. Zhou Y, Long J, Gu Q, Lin H, Wang X (2012) Photoinduced reactions between Pb_3O_4 and organic dyes in aqueous solution under visible light. *Inorg Chem* 51(23):12594–12596.
9. Zhou Y, Lin H, Gu Q, Lin J, Wang X (2012) Visible light-induced highly efficient organic pollutant degradation and concomitant CO_2 fixation using red lead. *RSC Adv* 2:12624.
10. Morsch S, van Driel BA, van den Berg KJ, Dik J (2017) Investigating the photocatalytic degradation of oil paint using ATR-IR and AFM-IR. *ACS Appl. Mater. Interfaces* 9:10169–10179.

CADMIUM YELLOW

11. Mayer R (1991) *Artists' Handbook of Materials and Techniques*, 5th ed: 118, Penguin, New York.
12. Ghiradello M, Mosca S, Marti-Rujas J, Nardo L, Burnstock A, Nevin A, Bondani M, Toniolo L, Valentini G, Comelli D (2018) Time-resolved photoluminescence microscopy combined with X-ray analyses and Raman spectroscopy sheds light on the imperfect synthesis of cadmium pigments. *Anal Chem* 90:10771–10779.
13. van der Snickt G, Dik J, Cotte M, et al. (2009) Characterization of degraded cadmium yellow (CdS) pigment in an oil painting by means of synchrotron radiation based on x-ray techniques. *Anal Chem* 81:2600–2610.

14. Monico L, Chieli A, DeMeyer S, et al. (2018) Role of the relative humidity and the Cd/Zn stoichiometry in the photooxidation process of cadmium yellows ($CdS/Cd_{1-x} Zn_xS$) in oil paintings. *Chem Eur* 24:11584–11593.

15. Shelley M (1987) *The care and handling of art objects. Practices in the Metropolitan Museum of Art, 15*, Metropolitan Museum of Art, New York.

CINNABAR

16. Radepont M, de Nouf W, Janssens K, van der Snickt G, Coquinot Y, Klaassen L, Cotte M (2011) The use of microscopic x-ray diffraction for the study of HgS and its degradation products corderoite (α-$Hg_3S_2Cl_2$), kenhsuite (γ-$Hg_3S_2Cl_2$) and calomel (Hg_2Cl_2). *J Anal At Spectrom* 26:959–968.

17. Hogan C, DaPieve F (2015) Colour degradation of artworks: an *ab initio* approach to X-ray, electronic and optical spectroscopy analyses of vermilion photodarkening. *J Anal At Spectrom* 30:588–598.

18. DaPieve F, Hogan C, Lamoen D, et al. (2013) Casting Light on the darkening of colors in historical paintings. *Phys. Rev Lett* 111:208302-1–208302-5.

19. Anaf W, Jannsens K, DeWael K (2013) Formation of metallic mercury during photodegradation /photodarkening of α-HgS: electrochemical evidence. *Angew Chem Int Ed* 52:12568–12571.

20. Fischer MC, Wilson JW, Robles FE, Warren WS (2016) Invited review article: pump-probe microscopy. *Rev Sci Instrum* 87:031101.

21. Yu J, Warren WS, Fischer MC (2019) Visualization of vermilion degradation using pump-probe microscopy. *Sci Adv* 5: eaaw3136.

REALGAR

22. Roberts A, Ansell H, Bonardi M (1980) Pararealgar, a new polymorph of AsS from British Columbia. *Canad Mineralog* 18:525–527.

23a. Naumov P, Makreski P, Petrusevski G, Runcebski T, Jovanovski G (2010) Visualization of a discrete solid-state process with steady-state x-ray diffraction: Observation of hopping of sulfur atoms in single crystals of realgar. *J Am Chem Soc* 132:11398–11401.

23b. Ballirano P, Maras A (2006) In-situ X-ray transmission powder diffraction study of the kinetics of the light induced alteration of realgar (-$As_4 S_4$). *Euro J Mineral* 18: 589-599.

24. Trentelman K, Stodulski L, Pavloski M (1996) Characterization of pararealgar and other light-induced transformation products from realgar by Raman microspectroscopy. *Anal Chem* 68(10):1755–1761.

25. Bell IM, Clark RJH, Gibbs PJ (1997) Raman spectroscopic library of natural and synthetic pigments (pre-~1850). *Spectrochim Acta A* 53:2159–2179.

CHROME YELLOW

26a. Monico L, Janssens K, Miliani C, et al. (2013) Degradation process of lead chromate in paintings by Vincent van Gogh studied by means of spectroscopic methods. 4. Artificial ageing of model samples of co-precipitates of lead chromate and lead sulfate. *Anal Chem* 85:860–867.

26b. Wells AF (1975) *Structural Inorganic Chemistry*, 4th ed. : 39,45 , Clarendon Press-Oxford, London.

27. Munoz-Garcia AB, Massaro A, Pavone M (2016) Ab initio study of $PbCr_{(1-x)}S_xO_4$ solid solution: an inside look at Van Gogh Yellow degradation. *Chem Sci* 7:4197–4203.
28. Tan H, Tian H, Verbeeck J, Monico L, Janssens K, Van Tendeloo G (2013) Nanoscale investigation of chrome yellow paint by quantitative electron loss spectroscopy mapping of chromium species. *Angew Chem Int Ed* 52:11360–11363.

Hematite

29. Maguregui M, Knuutinen U, Martinez-Arkarazo I, Castro K, Madariaga J (2011) Thermodynamic and spectroscopic speciation to explain the blackening process of hematite formed by atmospheric SO_2 impact: the case of Marcus Lucretius house (Pompeii). *Anal Chem* 83:3319–3326.

Blackening by H₂S

30. Smith G, Clark RJH (2002) The role of H_2S in pigment blackening. *J Cult Herit* 3:101–105.

Smalt

31. Giovanoli, R, Muhlethaler, B (1970) Investigation of discoloured smalt. *Stud Conserv* 15:37–44.
32. Boon JJ, Keune K, Van der Weerd J, Geldof M, Van Asperen de Boer JRJ (2001) Imaging microspectroscopic, secondary mass spectroscopic and electron microscopic studies on partially discolored smalt in cross-sections of 16th century paintings. *Chimia* 55: 952–960.
33. Robinet L, Spring M, Pages-Camagna S, Vantelon D, Trcera T (2011) Investigation of the discoloration of smalt pigment by micro-x-ray absorption spectroscopy at the Co K edge. *Anal Chem* 83:5145–5152.
34. Tercyznjska-Madej A, Cholewa-Kowalska K, Laczka M (2010) The effect of silicate network modifiers on colour and electron spectra of transition metal ions. *Opt Mater* 32:1456–1462.

Ultramarine

35. de la Rie RE, Michelin A, Ngako M, Del Federico E, Del Grosso C (2017) Photocatalytic degradation of binding media of ultramarine blue containing paint layers: A new perspective on the phenomenon of "ultramarine disease" in paintings. *Polym Degrad Stab* 144:43–52.
36. Schnetz K, Gambardella AA, van Elsas R, et al. (2020) Evidence for the catalytic properties of ultramarine pigment. *J Cult Herit* 45:25–32.
37. Matsunaga Y (1959) Electron spin resonance absorption of ultramarine: effect of cations. *Can J Chem* 37:994–995.
38. Booth DG, Dann SE, Weller MT (2003) The effect of cation composition on the synthesis and properties of ultramarine blue. *Dyes and Pigments* 58:73–82.
39. Gettens R, Stout, G (1966) *Painting Materials, A Short Encyclopedia*: 163–167, Dover Publications, New York.
40. Cotton, FA, Wilkenson G (1962) *Advanced Inorganic Chemistry*: 412, Interscience (Wiley), New York.

41. Del Federico E, Shöfberger W, Schelvis J, Kapetanaki S, Tyne L, Jerschow A (2006) Insight into framework destruction in ultramarine pigments. *Inorg Chem* 45:1270–1276.

42. Smart LE, Moore EA (2012) *Solid State Chemistry*, 4th ed: 271–295, CRC Press, Taylor and Francis, Boca Raton, FL.

43. Apelian MR, Fung AS, Kennedy GJ, Degnan TF (1996) Dealumination of zeolite β via dicarboxylic acid treatment. *J Phys Chem* 100:16577–16583.

44. Turro N (2000) From boiling stones to smart crystals: Supramolecular and magnetic isotope control of radical-radical reactions in zeolites. *Acc Chem Res* 33:637–646.

45. Aguayo T, Clavijo E, Villagran A, Espinosa F, Sagües FE, Campos-Vallette M (2010) Raman vibrational study of pigments with patrimonial interest for the Chilean cultural heritage. *J Chil Chem Soc* 55:347–351.

46. Plesters J (1993) *Ultramarine Blue, Natural and Synthetic, in: Artists' Pigments: A Handbook of their History and Characteristics* 2: 37–65, ed. A. Roy, National Gallery of Art, London.

47. Johnston Feller R (2001) *Color Science in the Examination of Museum Objects: Nondestructive Procedures.* Tools for conservation: 205. Getty Conservation Institute, Los Angeles, CA. http://hdl.handle.net/10020/gci_pubs/color_science.

AZURITE AND MALACHITE

48. Brown IWM, MacKenzie KJD and Gainsford G (1984) Thermal decomposition of the basic copper carbonates malachite and azurite. *Thermochim Acta* 74:23–32.

49. Mattei E, de Vivo G, DeSantis A, Gaetano C, Pelosi C, Santamaria U ((2008). Raman spectroscopic analysis of azurite blackening. *J Raman Spect* 39:302–306.

50. Lluveras A, Boularand S, Andreotti A (2010) Degradation of azurite in mural paintings: distribution of copper carbonate, chlorides and oxalates by SRFTIR. *Appl Phys A*, 99:363–375.

51. Gadd GM, Metals, minerals and microbes: geomicrobiology and bioremediation. *Microbiol* (2010) 156:609–643.

52. Monico L, Rosi F, Miliani C, Daveri A, Brunetti BG (2013) Non-invasive identification of metal-oxalate complexes on polychrome artwork surfaces by reflection mid-infrared spectroscopy. *Spectrochim Acta Part A: Molecular and Biomolec Spectros* 116:270–280.

53. Toxnet (2005) *Oxalic Acid.* National Library of Medicine, NIH. https://toxnet.nlm.nih. gov.

54. Maguregui M, Knuutinen U, Trebolazabala J, et al. (2012) Use of in-situ and confocal Raman spectroscopy to study the nature and distribution of carotenoids in brown patinas from a deteriorated wall painting in Marcus Lucretius house (Pompeii). *Anal Bioanal Chem* 402:1529–1539.

55. Cieffre O (1999) Microbial degradation of paintings. *Appl Environ Microbiol* 65:879–885.

56. Castro K, Sarmiento A, Martinez-Arkarazo I, Madariaga JM, Fernandez LA (2008) Green copper pigments biodegradation in cultural heritage: from malachite to moolooite, thermodynamic modeling, X-ray fluorescence and Raman evidence. *Anal Chem* 80:4103–4110.

PRUSSIAN BLUE

57. Ware M (2008) Prussian blue: artists' pigment and chemists' sponge. *J Chem Ed* 85:612–620.

58. Samain L, Gilbert B, Grandjean F, Long GJ, Strivay D (2013) Redox reactions in Prussian blue containing paint layers as a result of light exposure. *J Anal At Spectrom* 28:524–535.
59. Samain L, Grandjean F, Long GJ, Martinetto P, Bordet P, Stivray D (2013) Relationship between the synthesis of Prussian blue pigments, their color, physical properties, and their behavior in paint layers. *J Phys Chem C* 117:9693–9712.
60. Gervais C, Languille M-A, Reguer S, et al. (2013) Why does Prussian blue fade? Understanding the role(s) of the substrate. *J Anal At Spectrom* 28:1600–1609.
61. Gervais C, Languille MA, Regeur S, Garnier C, Gillet M (2014) Light and anoxia fading of Prussian blue dyed textiles. *Herit Sci* 2:26–34.
62. Koestler D, Ballard MW, Charola AE, Koestler RJ (2018) Does argon anoxia cause a color change in Prussian blue? *J Amer Inst Conserv* 57:47–61.

SILVERPOINT

63. Smith R (2003) *The Artists' Handbook*, Revised Edition: 97–98, Dorling Kindersley Limited, London.
64. Reiche I, Berger A, Duval A, et al. (2007) SY-XRF study of Hans Baldung Grier silverpoint drawings and the silver stylus from the *'Karlsruhe sketchbook'*. *X-Ray Spectrom* 36:173–177.

SILVER TARNISH

65. Rösch ES, Helmerdig S (2017) Understanding photography as applied chemistry: using Talbot's Calotype Process to introduce chemistry to design students. *J Chem Ed* 94:916–921.
66. Moore J, Stanitski C, Jurs P (2008) *Chemistry, The Molecular Science*, 3rd ed: 940, Thomson Brooks/Cole, Pacific Grove, CA.

STABILITY OF INORGANIC ARTISTS' PIGMENTS

67. Coccato A, Moens L, Vandenabeele P (2017) On the stability of mediaeval inorganic pigments: a literature review of the effect of climate, material selection, biological activity. Analysis and conservation methods. *Heritage Sci* 5:12. Doi: 10.1186/s40494-017-0125-6.
68. Eastaugh N, Waalsh V, Chaplin T, Sidall R (2007), *Pigment Compendium: Dictionary of Historical Pigments*. Routledge, Abingdon.
69. Janssens K, Stivray D, Sanyova J (2017) *Long-Term Role and Stability of Metal Sulfides in Painted Works of Art*. Final report, Research Program for Sustainable Development, Belgian Science Policy, Brussels.
70. *Artists' Pigments, a Handbook of Their History and Characteristics*. (1986) vol 1 Feller RL ed; (1993) vol 2 Roy A ed; (1997) vol 3 Fitzhugh EW ed; (2007) vol 4 Berrie BH ed, National Gallery of Art.

5 Toxicology of Art Materials

Around 1740, for the first time, pigments were crushed by stone rollers in horse-powered "paint mills" [1]. Prior to this time, artists ground their own pigments and came into contact with volatile organics and pigments to a much greater extent than today. Some artists licked their brushes to form a pointed tip. Anecdotes about famous artists and their medical problems are provocative. For example, Rubens, Renoir and Dufy used "bright" heavy metal-containing pigments, and these masters all suffered from debilitating rheumatic disease. Their "controls" (artists who lived in the same time-frame and used Earth colors based on iron; Rembrandt and Vermeer van Delft for Rubens and Monet for Renoir) did not suffer from rheumatism. The naïve conclusion is that the metals in bright colors were responsible for the development of rheumatic disease. The authors of this paper admit that there is no known linkage between heavy metals and rheumatic disease. In general, such anecdotes are conjectural, and there is no "hard" data to substantiate cause and effect in the various situations [2].

In this section, information is presented concerning the toxicology (branch of science concerned with the nature, effects and detection of poisons) of specific art materials. Inspection of online catalogs of art supply companies shows that toxic (poisonous) art materials are commercially available. Many art materials are toxic, including pigments which contain heavy metal ions, e.g., Hg^{2+}, Pb^{2+}, Cd^{2+}, Cr^{6+} and As^{5+}. In addition, silica, a non-metallic compound causes silicosis and mineral dusts are generally toxic. All organic solvents are toxic and should be used with adequate ventilation. Most college art departments teach safety rules, which resemble analogous rules followed by chemistry departments. Hobbyists continue to suffer from exposure to toxic art materials. See McCann [3] and Rossel [4] for books written for artists and art teachers, regarding hazardous materials used in the production of art. An association between bladder cancer and professional artistic and non-artistic painters, respectively, was shown [5,6]. Hazardous materials and toxic injuries to specific organ systems for different types of artists have been reviewed [7]. The cancer risk for many compounds used in artists' materials, assessed by IARC, is summarized in Table 5.1 [8].

In this chapter, there is no attempt to present an encyclopedic treatment of every toxic art material. It is instructive to look at these examples to illustrate how specific materials used in production of art are chemically transformed in mammalian systems. The examples were selected to illustrate how the body transforms the compound of interest to generate a metabolite which reacts with target molecules (small molecules, proteins and DNA) and causes the observed toxicity. The examples are all toxic to humans with the exception of silver. Most of the mechanistic work is based on the use of animal models. This section brings us into to "biosphere", in which we will combine inorganic, organic and biochemical thinking. This integration makes the chemistry compelling and also complex.

DOI: 10.1201/9781003053453-5

TABLE 5.1

IARC Classification of Selected Substances

Substance	IARC Group	IARC Monograph/	Year
Asbestos, all forms	1	14, Sup 7, 100C	2012
Arsenic, inorganic forms	1	100C	2012
Benzene	1	29, Sup 7, 100f, 120	in prep
2-Butoxyethanol	3	88	2006
Cadmium and compounds	1	58, 100C	2012
Carbon Black	2B	Sup 7, 65, 93	2010
Carbon Tetrachloride	2B	20, Sup 7, 71	1999
Chloroform	2B	Sup 7, 73	1999
Chromium metal	3	Sup 7, 49	1990
Cr (III) compounds	3	49	1990
Cr (VI) compounds	1	Sup 7, 49, 100C	2012
Cobalt and compounds	2B	52	1991
Methylene Chloride	2A	Sup 7, 71, 110	2017
Hematite	3	1, Sup 7	1987
Lead metal	2B	23, Sup 7	1987
Pb compounds, inorganic	2A	Sup 7, 87	2006
Pb compounds, organic	3	23, Sup 7, 87	2006
d-Limonene	3	56, 73	1999
Mercury and inorg forms	3	58	1993
Methylmercury	2B	58	1993
Nickel compounds	1	Sup 7, 49, 100C	2012
Petroleum solvents	3	47	1989
Silica	1	68	1997
Styrene	2A	60, 82, 121	in prep
Toluene	3	47, 71	1999
Toluene diisocyanate	2B	39, Sup 7	1999
Xylenes	3	47, 71	1999

Source: Agents classified by IARC Monographs 1-123 (2019). Reprinted with
permission of IARC/WHO, Lyon, France. Copyright 2018, IARC/WHO.
Group 1, carcinogenic to humans; Group 2A, probably carcinogenic to humans; Group
2B, possibly carcinogenic to humans; Group 3, not classifiable as to its carcinogenicity to
humans; Group 4, probably not carcinogenic to humans.

5.1 ORGANIC COMPOUNDS

5.1.1 Methylene Chloride

The first example is the solvent, methylene chloride, CH_2Cl_2 (dichloromethane); IARC Group 2A [8]. Organic solvents are used by artists and art restorers primarily to dilute ("thin") paint in order to control viscosity and also for the cleaning of paintings. This solvent was banned by the US EPA (US Environmental Protection Agency) from use in paint remover products after September 2019 [9]. Methylene chloride is

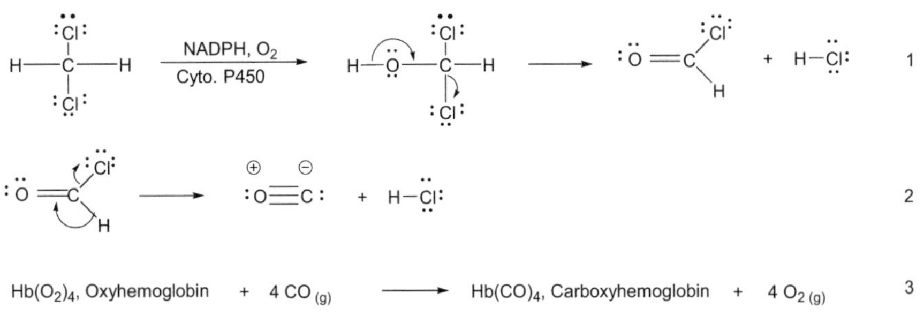

SCHEME 5.1 Metabolism of methylene chloride. (Modified and reprinted with permission of M.L. Gargas, H.J. Clewell, M.E. Andersen (1986) *Toxicol. Appl. Pharmacol.* 82:211–223. Copyright 1986, Elsevier. V.L. Kubic, M.W. Anders (1978) *Biochem. Pharmacol* 27:2349–2355. Copyright 1978, Elsevier.)

a chlorinated hydrocarbon which is used to remove paint and varnish from wood and furniture (non-flammable paint stripper), in silicone resins, and as a solvent in cementing plastics. The metabolism of methylene chloride is shown in Scheme 5.1. CH_2Cl_2 is volatile and enters the body through the lungs. It is oxidized by NADPH in a reaction which is catalyzed by an enzyme in the cytochrome P450 family (CYP450). This family of enzymes evolved to oxygenate *xenobiotic* compounds such as hydrocarbons and chlorinated hydrocarbons. Introduction of oxygen atoms into the chemical structure increases the polarity of the molecule, and hence, its solubility in water, so that the metabolites can be eliminated from the body. (On the other hand, if a compound evades oxygenation, it will tend to accumulate in fatty tissue, which is non-polar.)

If sufficient methylene chloride enters the body, there is the possibility of death caused by carbon monoxide poisoning. In the metabolic pathway, formyl chloride decomposes into carbon monoxide and hydrochloric acid. HCl can be absorbed by the buffering systems in the body (including CO_2/HCO_3^- and $H_2PO_4^- / HPO_4^{2-}$), which will cause the pH of the blood to decrease (acidosis). Carbon monoxide, CO, has a very strong affinity for the Fe^{2+} centers in the oxygen-carrying hemes of the protein, hemoglobin. Consequently, CO displaces O_2, and carboxyhemoglobin is formed. This type of hemoglobin cannot carry oxygen, and depending on the percentage of poisoned hemoglobin, death can result. Carbon monoxide poisoning can be reversed by inhalation of pure O_2 [10,11].

5.1.2 CARBON TETRACHLORIDE AND CHLOROFORM

Carbon tetrachloride, CCl_4, is a chlorinated hydrocarbon and belongs to the family of chlorinated methanes, which includes methyl chloride, CH_3Cl; methylene chloride, CH_2Cl_2; and chloroform, $CHCl_3$. Except for methyl chloride, these compounds are liquids at room temperature, with boiling points increasing with the number of chlorine atoms, and all are used as "de-greasing/defatting" solvents. Carbon tetrachloride is used as a non-flammable fire extinguisher and as a solvent for oils, fats, waxes, lacquers, varnishes, rubber waxes and resins. It is used by artists to dissolve wax. Carbon tetrachloride is classified by IARC as a Group 2B carcinogen [8] and targets the liver and kidneys. Carbon tetrachloride was banned by the EPA for use in all

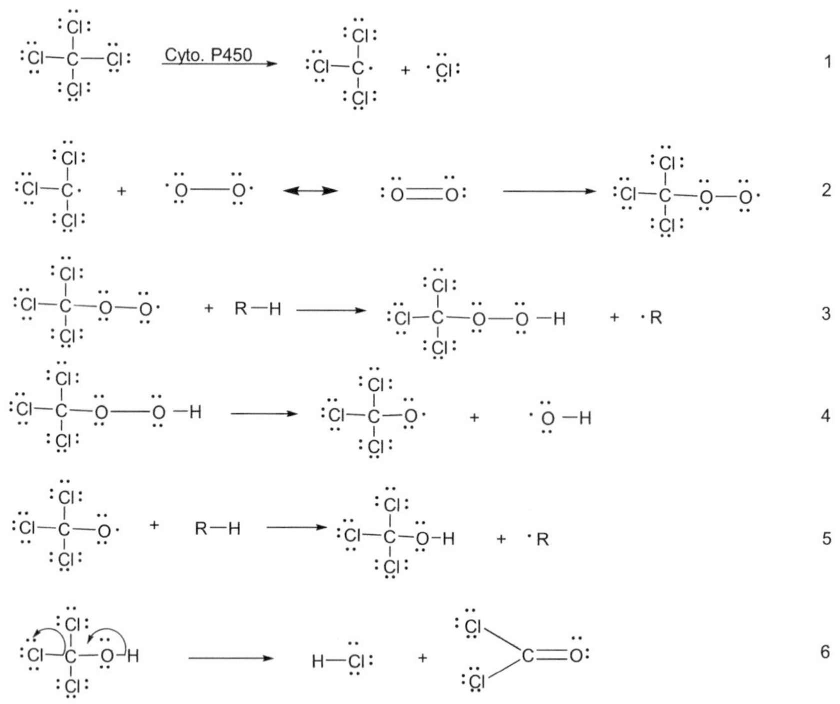

SCHEME 5.2 Metabolism of carbon tetrachloride. (Reprinted with permission of L.W. D. Weber, M. Boll, A.Q. Stampl (2003) *Crit. Rev. Toxicol.* 33:105–136. Copyright 2003, Taylor and Francis.)

commercial products in 1970 [12]. The metabolism of carbon tetrachloride is shown in Scheme 5.2. The solvent is converted to phosgene, ($Cl_2C=O$), a very reactive and toxic compound which was used as a nerve gas in World War I [13].

In this series of transformations, carbon tetrachloride loses a chlorine atom in a free-radical reaction catalyzed by CYP450. The resulting radical then reacts with dioxygen to form a peroxide radical which scavenges a hydrogen atom from a hydrocarbon donor (RH) to yield an alkoxy radical. The alkoxy radical takes a hydrogen atom from RH, and trichloromethanol falls apart to form phosgene and HCl. Phosgene is very reactive toward nucleophiles, e.g., the sulfhydryl group of cysteine (CySH) or glutathione (GSH), water and also amino groups of proteins (RNH_2), Scheme 5.3.

The metabolism of chloroform is similar to that of carbon tetrachloride. It is oxidized via a pathway catalyzed by CYP450 resulting in phosgene which reacts with water to yield carbon dioxide and HCl, and with glutathione to give carbon monoxide and GSSG [14].

5.1.3 TRICHLOROETHYLENE

Trichloroethylene, TCE, "Tri", $Cl_2C=CHCl$ is another chlorinated hydrocarbon which has been used as a solvent for waxes, resins, oils, rubber, paints, and varnishes, cleaning metal surfaces, and for dry cleaning of clothes. This compound has been classified as an IARC Group 1 carcinogen [8] and also as a neurotoxin [15].

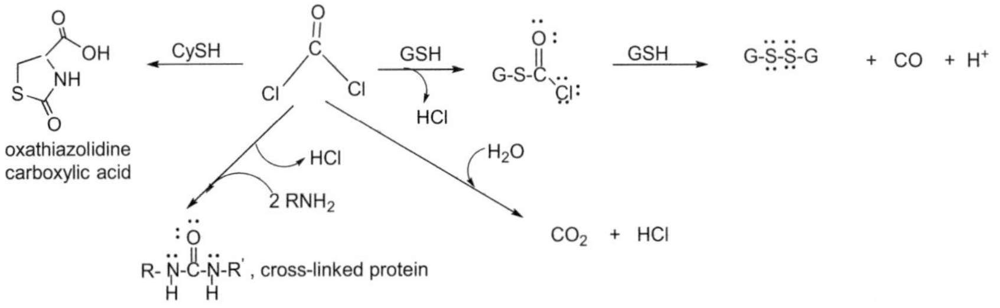

SCHEME 5.3 Reactions of phosgene with bio-nucleophiles. (Reprinted with permission of S. Gemma, L. Vittozzi, E. Testai (2003) *Drug Metab. Disp.* 31:266–274. Copyright 2003, ASPET.)

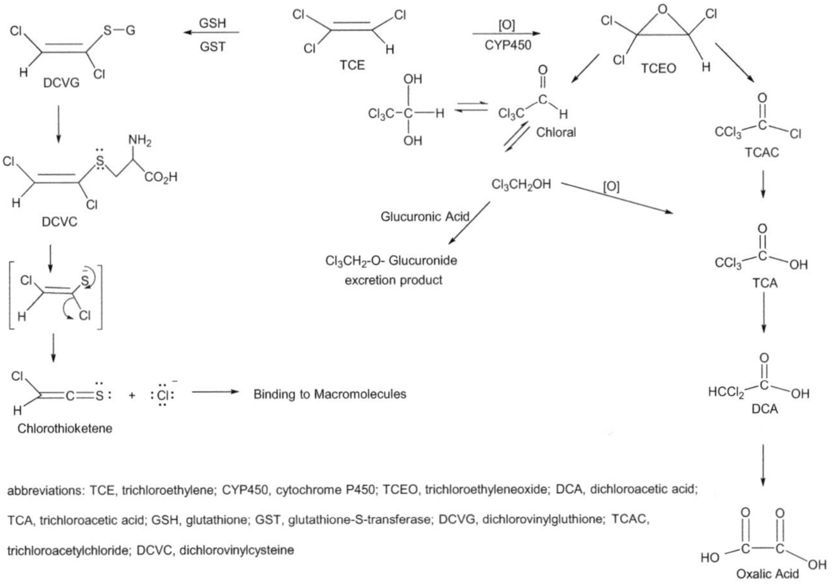

abbreviations: TCE, trichloroethylene; CYP450, cytochrome P450; TCEO, trichloroethyleneoxide; DCA, dichloroacetic acid; TCA, trichloroacetic acid; GSH, glutathione; GST, glutathione-S-transferase; DCVG, dichlorovinylgluthione; TCAC, trichloroacetylchloride; DCVC, dichlorovinylcysteine

SCHEME 5.4 Trichloroethylene metabolism. (Modified and reprinted with permission of L.H. Lash, J.W. Fisher, J.C. Lipscomb, et al. (2000) *Env. Health Perspectives* 108 (Supp. 2):177–200. Copyright 2000, National Institute of Environmental Sciences (USA).)

TCE is metabolized by two main routes: the oxidative pathway catalyzed by CYP450 and the conjugative pathway catalyzed by glutathione-S-transferase (GST). The oxidative pathway consists of trichloroethylene oxide (TCEO), an epoxide, which ring-opens to give either chloral or trichloroacetylchloride (TCAC). Chloral is oxidized to trichloroethanol which forms a glucuronide excretion product. TCAC is converted to oxalic acid. In the conjugative pathway, TCE is converted to dichlorovinylglutathione (DCVG) and then to dichlorovinylcysteine (DCVC) which yields chlorothioketene. The latter is either hydrolyzed to give dichloroacetic acid (DCA) or reacts with protein nucleophilic groups and thereby modifies the structure and function of proteins [16–18] (Scheme 5.4).

5.1.4 N-HEXANE

n-Hexane, n-C_6H_{14}, is a saturated hydrocarbon. Surprisingly, the "normal" or straight-chain isomer is much more toxic than branched-chain isomeric hexanes or the adjacent normal homologs, n-pentane, (n-C_5H_{12}) or n-heptane, (n-C_7H_{16}). The discovery of the pathology associated with n-hexane was discovered because of its use in the American shoe manufacturing industry during the 1960s and 1970s. Other uses include a component in petroleum ether (ligroin) and in some spray fixatives used to treat pastel drawings and in some rubber cements and contact adhesives. It is highly toxic by inhalation, causing damage to the nerves of the arms and legs [3]. IARC has not classified n-hexane as carcinogenic. This compound does not appear in the master table of the investigated substances [8].

A breakthrough in the understanding of the toxicity mechanism of n-hexane came from the observation that methyl-n-butyl ketone (MBK) caused the same neuropathology as n-hexane in factory workers following substitution of MBK for methyl isobutyl ketone. It was then discovered that n-hexane and MBK were both metabolized to hexane-2,5-dione, a γ-diketone [19], see Scheme 5.5.

Further research revealed that hexane-2,5-dione undergoes reaction with protein amino groups to form a Schiff base, then dehydrates to an imine which isomerizes to

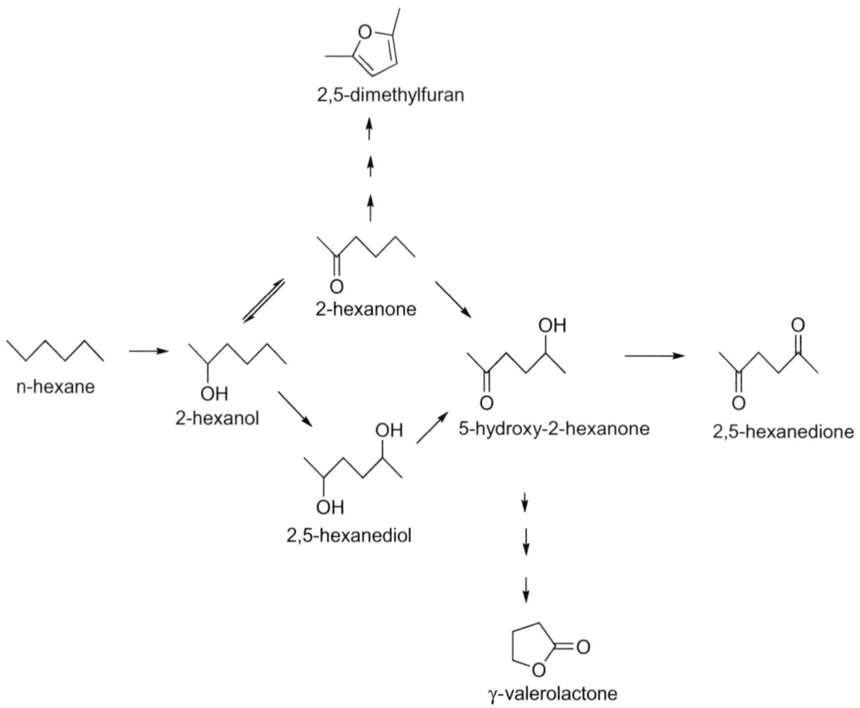

SCHEME 5.5 Metabolites of n-hexane in human urine. (Modified and reprinted with permission of L. Perbellini, P. Brugnone, G. Faggionato (1981) *Brit. J. Indust. Med.* 38:20–26. Copyright 1981, BMJ Publishing Group, Ltd.)

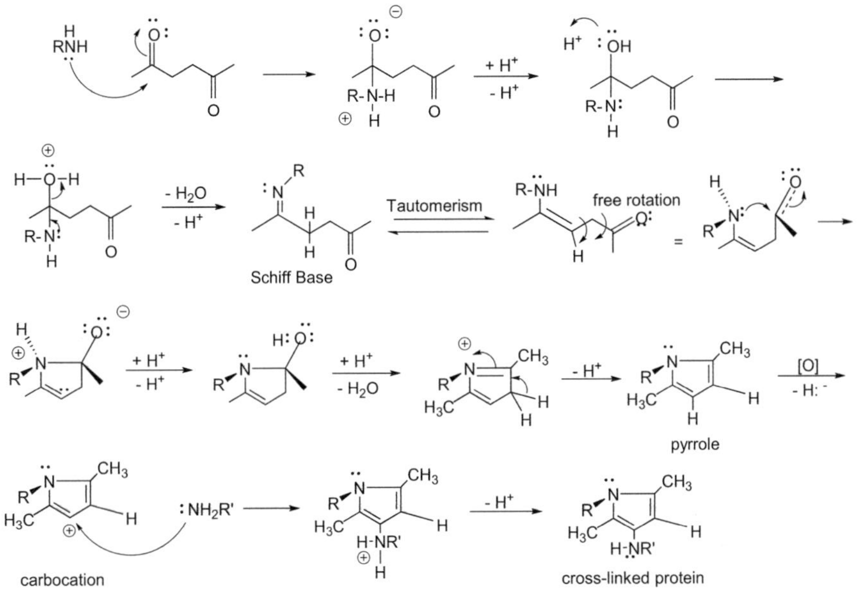

SCHEME 5.6 Reactions of hexane-2,5-dione with protein amino groups. (Reprinted with permission of M.G.B. St. Clair, V. Amarnath, M.A. Moody, et al. (1988) *Chem. Res. Toxicol.* 1:179–185. Copyright 1988, American Chemical Society.)

an eneamine, and this cyclizes to form a *pyrrole*. The pyrrole derivative is oxidized (by removal of :H⁻, the equivalent of a hydride anion) to yield a *carbocation*. The latter reacts with protein nucleophiles such as the sulfhydryl group of cysteinyl residues (R-SH) or the ε-amino groups of lysyl residues. The result is a *cross-linked protein*, in which several of the nucleophilic groups have been modified by a series of reactions, with associated loss of function, see Scheme 5.6 [20].

n-Heptane is one of the least toxic hydrocarbons [3] and does not cause damage to the peripheral nervous system. The explanation for lack of neurotoxicity was attributed to the comparatively smaller tendency to form the γ-diketone relative to n-hexane [21].

5.1.5 AROMATIC SOLVENTS

Toluene, C_7H_8, is a solvent commonly used in varnishes, thinners and (spray) paints. If inhaled, toluene causes narcosis, liver and kidney damage. It is not classified as a carcinogen (IARC Group 3) [8] but was identified as a neurotoxin [22]. The major metabolic pathway for toluene involves conversion to benzoic acid. Benzoic acid reacts with glycine to form hippuric acid which is eliminated via the kidney and urine. A minor elimination pathway involves esterification of benzoic acid with glucuronic acid, which is also eliminated via the kidney [23], see Scheme 5.7. The general theme is that adding polar oxygen atoms to a hydrophobic structure enhances solubility in water (like dissolves like) and facilitates excretion from the body.

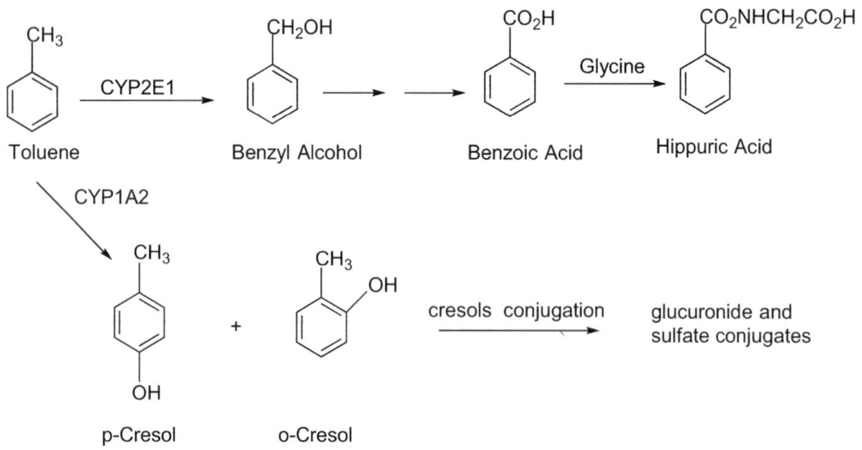

SCHEME 5.7 Metabolism of toluene. CYP2E1 and CYP1A2 are cytochrome P450 enzymes. (Modified and reprinted with permission of W. Tasseneeyakul, D.J. Birkett, J.W. Edwards, et al. (1996) *J. Pharmacol. Exp. Ther.* 276:101–108. Copyright 1996, ASPET.)

Contrast toluene with its parent compound benzene. Benzene, C_6H_6, lacks the oxidizable methyl group and is classified as an IARC Group 1 carcinogen which causes leukemia [8]. Oxidative metabolism of benzene yields hydroquinone, which is converted to reactive semiquinone radicals and reactive oxygen species (ROS) [24], see Scheme 5.8. In addition, benzene is metabolized to a six-carbon dialdehyde (muconaldehyde), which was shown to react with primary amines, peptides and guanosine *in-vitro* [25]. Muconaldehyde exerts hematopoietic toxicity (toxicity to stem cells in bone marrow, which are responsible for production of mature blood cells; white and red cells and platelets). However, this aldehyde has not been shown to cause cancer.

Xylenes, C_8H_{10}, are a mixture of ortho-, meta- and para-dimethylbenzene isomers. Around 50% of inhaled xylenes are exhaled unchanged. The remainder (<50%) is metabolized through a major pathway consisting of oxidation of a methyl group to form the benzyl alcohols, further oxidation to the corresponding methylbenzoic acids and formation of hippuric acids which are eliminated in urine. Xylene was neurotoxic in animal studies [26]. Xylenes were classified as not carcinogenic by IARC [8].

5.1.6 DIISOCYANATES

Diisocyanates are volatile organic compounds which are used to produce polyurethane polymers. The latter have many uses including fibers, flexible and rigid foams, coatings (paints and varnishes) and elastomers. In the arts, polyurethanes are used in sculpture, mold-making and theater set production. Diisocyanates are toxic; assigned by IARC to Group 2B [8]. Depending on the dosage inhaled, diisocyanates cause a variety of lung pathologies. A related compound, methyl isocyanate, was the chemical agent which killed over 2000 people because of an industrial accident in Bhopal, India in 1984 [27]. Isocyanates react with alcohols to form urethanes or carbamate esters, Scheme 5.9.

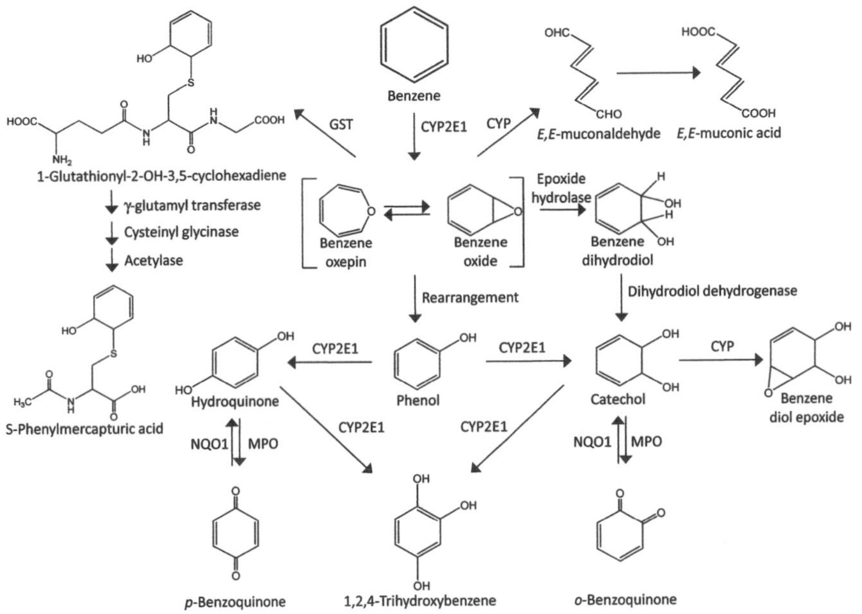

SCHEME 5.8 Metabolism of benzene. CYP, cytochrome P450; GST, glutathione S-transferase; MPO, myeloperoxidase; NQO1, NAD(P)H: quinone oxidoreductase 1. (Reprinted with permission of L. Wang, X. He, Y. Bi, Q. Ma (2012) *Chem. Res. Toxicol.* 25:1303–1315. Copyright 2012, American Chemical Society.)

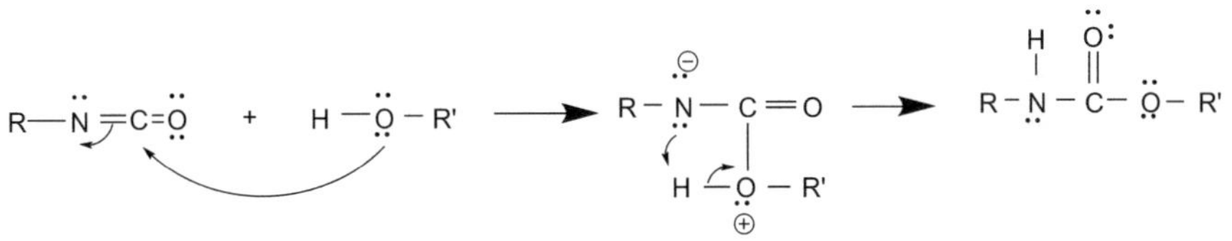

SCHEME 5.9 Urethane formation for reaction of an isocyanate and an alcohol.

Diisocyanates are *cross-linking agents* which react with diols to form polyurethanes, see Scheme 5.10.

Toluene Diisocyanate (TDI) has been identified as a causal agent for the condition known as occupational asthma. Decades ago, TDI was known to form covalent bonds with ε-amino groups of protein albumin. More recently, a new twist has been added. TDI vapor reacts first with thiol groups of glutathione to give thiocarbamates. Thiocarbamates react with ε-amino groups of albumin in a process known as *transcarbamoylation* to form urea derivatives, see Scheme 5.11.

Eight different ε-amino groups form the transcarbamoylation product. The resulting albumin-urea products show marked changes in electrophoretic mobility (suggesting conformational changes) because of cross-linking and are also recognized by immunoglobulins as "foreign" protein [28].

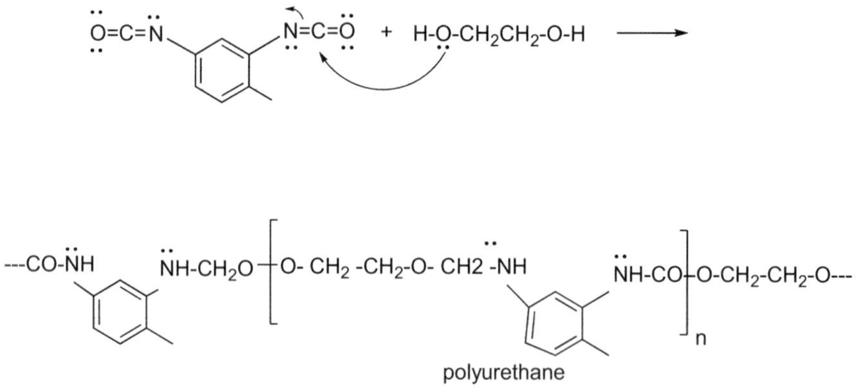

SCHEME 5.10 Reaction of toluene diisocyanate and ethylene glycol to form a polyurethane.

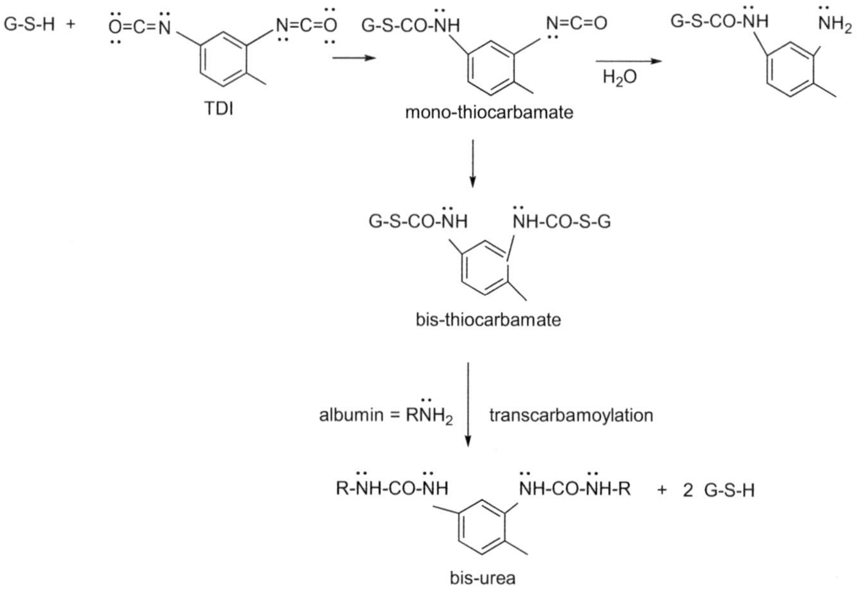

SCHEME 5.11 Reaction of glutathione and toluene diisocyanate [28].

5.1.7 N-Methylpyrrolidone and N-Ethylpyrrolidone

N-Methylpyrrolidone (NMP) is a versatile water-miscible solvent which has many uses, among them is paint stripping by art conservators. Other industrial uses include microelectronics; formulation of pigments, dyes and inks; insecticides; pharmaceuticals and cosmetics. With respect to toxicity, in 2011, the European Chemical Agency designated NMP as embryotoxic (may cause harm to the unborn child). With respect to cancer risk, NMP has not been classified by IARC [8].

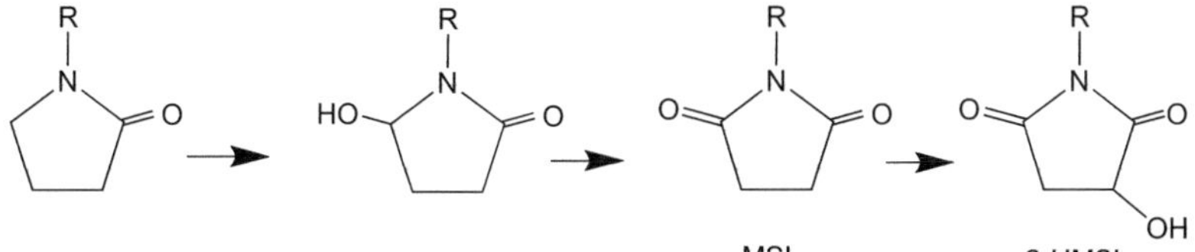

R = Me   NMP   5-HNMP   MSI   2-HMSI

R = Et   NEP   5-HNEP   ESI   2-HESI

SCHEME 5.12 Metabolism of N-methylpyrrolidone and N-ethylpyrrolidone [29,30]. Names for the methyl series: 5-HNMP, 5-hydroxy-N-methyl-2-pyrrolidone; MSI, N-methylsuccinimide; 2-HMSI, 2-hydroxy-N-methylsuccimide. (Reprinted with permission of B. Akesson, B.G. Jonsson (1997) *Drug Metab. Disp.* 25:267–269. Copyright 1997, ASPET. B.K. Schindler, S. Koslitz, S. Meier, et al. (2012) *Anal. Chem.* 84:3787–3794. Copyright 2012, American Chemical Society.)

Administration of NMP or N-ethylpyrrolidone (NEP) to humans results in a series of metabolites which appear in the urine [29,30]. The pathway, see Scheme 5.12, shows that each step introduces one additional oxygen atom into the structure. This increases molecular polarity, water solubility and facilitates excretion.

5.1.8 Alcohols, Glycols and Glycol Ethers

Alcohols are used in paint and varnish removers; lacquers, plastics, inks and dyes [31]. They enter the body through skin, ingestion or inhalation and cause inebriation [3,4]. Alcohols are metabolized through enzyme-catalyzed oxidation. Primary alcohols are converted to aldehydes and then to carboxylic acids. The enzymes involved are, respectively, alcohol dehydrogenase and aldehyde dehydrogenase. Methanol is particularly toxic because its ultimate oxidation product, formic acid, causes blindness [32,33]. Secondary alcohols are converted to ketones, see Scheme 5.13.

Glycols contain two covalently bonded hydroxyl groups. Ethylene glycol also is converted enzymatically to aldehydes and then to carboxylic acids; see Scheme 5.14 [34].

Glycol ethers are solvents which are used in resins, paints, inks, lacquers, varnishes, dyes and cleaning products. They are soluble in water and also polar organic solvents. These solvents enter the body by absorption through skin, ingestion or inhalation. General toxic effects include inebriation and kidney damage. Cellosolve and

Primary alcohols:

RCH_2OH *(alcohol dehydrogenase)* $\rightarrow$ $RCHO$ *(aldehyde dehydrogenase)* $\rightarrow$ RCO_2H

R= H, CH_3-, CH_3CH_2-, $CH_3CH_2CH_2$-, $(CH_3)_2CHCH_2CH_2$-

Secondary alcohols:

$CH_3CH(OH)CH_3$ *(alcohol dehydrogenase)* $\rightarrow$ CH_3COCH_3

SCHEME 5.13 Metabolism of primary and secondary alcohols. (Modified and reprinted with permission of J.A. Kraut, I. Kurtz (2008) *Clin. J. Amer. Soc. Nephrol* 3:208–225. Copyright 2008, American Society of Nephrology.)

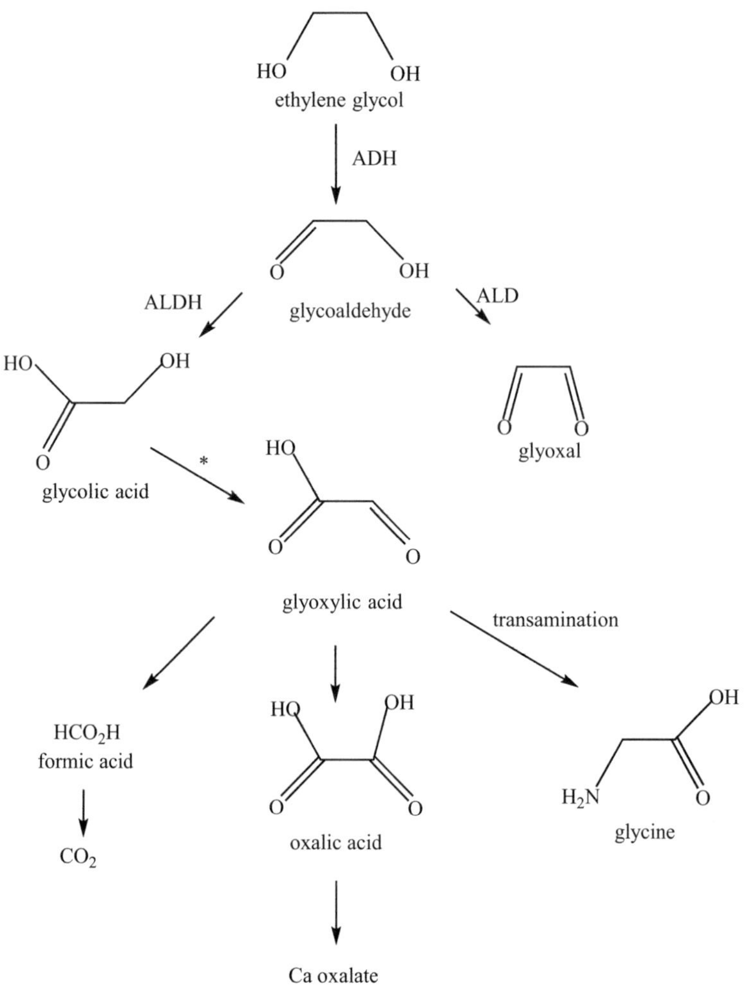

SCHEME 5.14 Metabolism of ethylene glycol. The major pathway is glycoaldehyde to glycolic acid to glyoxylic acid. *Rate determining step. ADH, alcohol dehydrogenase; ALDH, aldehyde dehydrogenase. (Reprinted with permission of E.D. Booth, O. Dofferhoff, P.J. Boogaard, W.P. Watson (2004) *Xenobiotica* 34:31–38. Copyright 2004, Taylor and Francis.)

methyl-cellosolve (ethoxyethanol and methoxyethanol, respectively) cause severe reproductive damage [3]. Butoxyethanol was classified as Group 3 carcinogen risk [8]. The metabolism of butoxyethanol is illustrated in Scheme 5.15 [35,36]. There are several pathways which are utilized to remove these solvents from the body through urinary excretion. For example, reaction of alkoxyethanol with the C-1 hydroxyl group of glucuronic acid to form a glucuronide glycoside conjugate. Alternatively, esterification with inorganic sulfate produces a sulfate conjugate. In addition, the alkoxyethanol is enzymatically oxidized to the corresponding alkoxyacetic acid, and this intermediate can be conjugated to amino acids (glycine or glutamine).

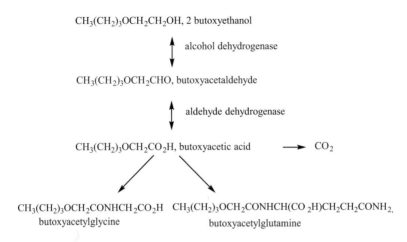

CH$_3$(CH$_2$)$_3$OCH$_2$CH$_2$OH, 2 butoxyethanol

↕ alcohol dehydrogenase

CH$_3$(CH$_2$)$_3$OCH$_2$CHO, butoxyacetaldehyde

↕ aldehyde dehydrogenase

CH$_3$(CH$_2$)$_3$OCH$_2$CO$_2$H, butoxyacetic acid ⟶ CO$_2$

CH$_3$(CH$_2$)$_3$OCH$_2$CONHCH$_2$CO$_2$H   CH$_3$(CH$_2$)$_3$OCH$_2$CONHCH(CO$_2$H)CH$_2$CH$_2$CONH$_2$,
butoxyacetylglycine   butoxyacetylglutamine

SCHEME 5.15 Metabolism of butoxyethanol in humans. (Modified and reprinted with permission of R.A. Corley, D.A. Markham, C. Banks, et al. (1997) *Fund. Appl. Toxicol.* 39:120–130. Copyright 1997, Elsevier.)

5.1.9 MINERAL SPIRITS

Mineral spirits refers to petroleum distillates with a bp range of 149°C–213°C. The composition comprises C$_8$ – C$_{13}$ alkanes (normal, iso- and cyclo-) and a lesser presence of aromatics (benzene, toluene and xylenes). Further processing results in three classes of mineral spirits, based on the aromatic content by volume: class A (8%–22%), class B (2%–8%) and class C (<2%). Uses of mineral spirits include cleaning paint brushes, thinning oil paint, solvent for aerosols, lacquers and varnishes and degreasing machine tools [2,3].

Toxicity of mineral spirits: The carcinogenicity risk is IARC Group 3 [8]. Low toxicity by oral, dermal and inhalation routes; aspiration into the lungs can be fatal; repeated exposure causes kidney damage in rats. The material is neither a reproductive nor a developmental toxicant [37]. Odorless mineral spirits (OMS) contains minimal aromatic content which removes the odor. The alkane content covers the range C$_8$ – C$_{13}$. However, it should be noted that although the material has very little odor, it retains volatiles which can enter the body by inhalation. In inhalation studies with rats, n-alkanes distribute as follows: low concentration in blood; pass the blood–brain-barrier (BBB) and deposit in the brain and in body fat [38,39].

The metabolism of normal alkanes is summarized in Scheme 5.16. One methyl terminal is hydroxylated by oxygen insertion (cytochrome P450/O$_2$) followed by oxidation to aldehyde (alcohol dehydrogenase/NAD$^+$) and then to the carboxyl stage (aldehyde dehydrogenase/NAD$^+$). The net result is a saturated fatty acid (FA) which is utilized as food. At this point, the FA can undergo β-oxidation, in which the two-carbon acetyl unit is split off, and enters the tricarboxylic acid cycle. Alternatively, the FA may be oxidized at the methyl terminal (constituting the process of *omega-* or bi-terminal oxidation) to yield a *1,ω-dicarboxylic acid*, which is then metabolized by β-oxidation [40]. Omega oxidation products can be detected in human exhaled breath by mass spectrometry [41].

$CH_3\text{-}(CH_2)_n\text{-}CH_2\text{-}CH_2\text{-}CH_3 \longrightarrow CH_3\text{-}(CH_2)_n\text{-}CH_2\text{-}CH_2\text{-}CH_2OH \longrightarrow$

$\quad\quad\quad\quad\quad\quad\quad\quad\quad\quad\quad\quad\quad\quad\quad \omega \quad\quad\quad \beta \quad\quad\quad\quad\quad \beta\text{-}$ or ω-oxidation

$CH_3\text{-}(CH_2)_n\text{-}CH_2\text{-}CH_2\text{-}CHO \longrightarrow CH_3\text{-}(CH_2)_n\text{-}CH_2\text{-}CH_2\text{-}CO_2H \longrightarrow$

β-oxidation

$CH_3\text{-}(CH_2)_n\text{-}CH_2\text{-}CH_2\text{-}CO_2H \longrightarrow CH_3\text{-}(CH_2)_n\text{-}CH_2\text{-}CH_2\text{-}COSCoA \longrightarrow$

$\quad\quad\quad\quad\quad \beta$

$CH_3\text{-}(CH_2)_n\text{-}CH=CH\text{-}COSCoA \longrightarrow CH_3\text{-}(CH_2)_n\text{-}CHOHCH_2\text{-}COSCoA \longrightarrow$

$CH_3\text{-}(CH_2)_n\text{-}COCH_2\text{-}COSCoA \longrightarrow CH_3\text{-}(CH_2)_n\text{-}CH_2\text{-}COSCoA + CH_3\text{-}COSCoA \longrightarrow$

ω-oxidation

ω

$CH_3\text{-}(CH_2)_n\text{-}CH_2\text{-}CH_2\text{-}CO_2H \longrightarrow HOCH_2\text{-}(CH_2)_n\text{-}CH_2\text{-}CH_2\text{-}CO_2H \longrightarrow$

$CHO\text{-}(CH_2)_n\text{-}CH_2\text{-}CH_2\text{-}CO_2H \longrightarrow HO_2C\text{-}(CH_2)_n\text{-}CH_2\text{-}CH_2\text{-}CO_2H \longrightarrow$

$HO_2C\text{-}(CH_2)_n\text{-}CH_2\text{-}CH_2\text{-}COSCoA \xrightarrow{\beta\text{-oxidation}} HO_2C\text{-}(CH_2)_n\text{-}COSCoA + CH_3\text{-}COSCoA \longrightarrow$

SCHEME 5.16 Metabolism of normal alkanes. n-Alkanes are hydroxylated to the corresponding primary alcohol; continued oxidation yields aldehydes and carboxylic acids. The resulting FA undergoes β-oxidation or ω-oxidation. The latter comprises functionalization of the ω-methyl carbon atom to the carboxyl stage to yield a 1,ω-dialkanoic acid. The diacid can then undergo β-oxidation. (Modified and reprinted with permission of Y. Miura (2013) *Proc. Japan Acad. Ser. B* 89:370–382. Copyright 2013, Japan Academy.)

5.1.10 TURPENTINE

Turpentine is a liquid mixture of monoterpenes, all $C_{10}H_{16}$, obtained from pine tree resin. The composition is α-pinene, 75%–85%; β-pinene, up to 3%; camphene, 4%–5%; limonene, 5%–15% and an unspecified content of δ-3-carene [42], see Figure 5.1. Turpentine is used a diluent for oil paint and varnish and also a starting material for organic synthesis.

Turpentine can enter the body by inhalation, skin absorption or oral ingestion. The monoterpenes are non-polar hydrocarbons and accumulate in loci which are lipid-rich, including nervous tissue, brain and fat deposits. Absorbed turpentine causes skin irritation and allergies. Accidental aspiration into the lungs can be fatal. Other health effects include headache, dizziness, convulsions and kidney damage [3]. Neither turpentine nor α-pinene are listed by IARC and therefore have not been investigated as cause of cancer. Limonene was designated as Group 3; not classifiable with respect to carcinogenicity in humans [8].

The metabolism of α-pinene has been studied. Oral administration of this compound to human subjects resulted in detection of these metabolites in urine/24 h

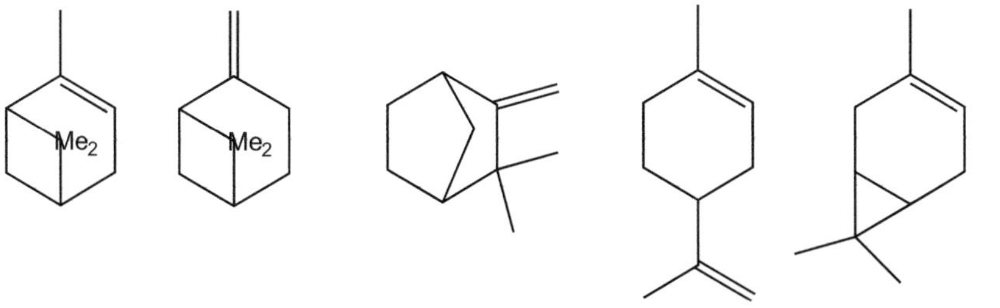

α-pinene   β-pinene   camphene   limonene   δ-3-carene
75-85%   up to 3%   4-15%   5-15%   not specified

FIGURE 5.1   Terpene composition of turpentine [42].

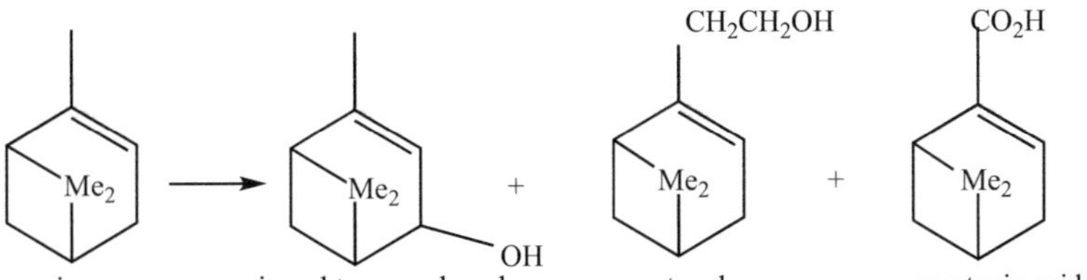

α-pinene   cis and trans verbenol   myrtenol   myrtenic acid

FIGURE 5.2   Metabolites of α-pinene. (Adapted and reprinted with permission of T.B. Adams, C.L. Gavin, M.M. McGowen, et al. (2011) *Food Chem. Toxicol.* 49:2471–2494. Copyright 2011, Elsevier.)

collection: cis-verbenol, 5.6% of original dose; trans-verbenol, 4.1%; myrtenol, 1.5% and myrtenic acid, 6.7%. In this study, ~80% of the dose was not detected. The metabolism of α-pinene in humans after oral administration is shown in Figure 5.2 [43]. The absorption, metabolism distribution, excretion and toxicology of terpenes have been reviewed [44].

5.2 INORGANIC MATERIALS

Next, we shall look at the toxicology of examples of inorganic compounds used in the production of art. The examples include compounds of lead, chromium, cadmium, mercury, silver and arsenic. In most cases, the operative word is "compound". The elemental form of these metals are less frequently encountered; such as lead in the production of stained glass windows, silver as in candlesticks and chromium as a surface coating for steel bumpers for automobiles before ~1980. Exposure to metallic dust leads to inhalation and then oxidation of the metallic atoms to ions, which are toxic. Heavy metals cause oxidative damage to biomolecules which leads to dysfunction [45]. The general toxicity pathways are illustrated in Figure 5.3.

In the context of pigments, metals are present as ions. Non-essential heavy metal ions have no biological role and are toxic to cells because they bind to proteins and this causes release of native *essential* metals (required for life) from binding sites (biological mimicry). In addition, toxic ions are responsible for production of *ROS*

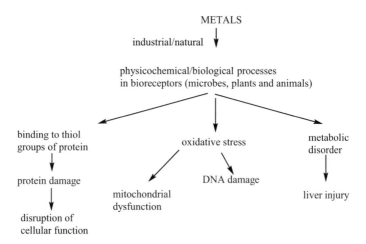

FIGURE 5.3 General metal toxicity. (Modified and reprinted with permission of S. Chatterjee, S. Sarkar, S. Bhattacharya (2014) *Chem. Res. Toxicol.* 27:1887–1900. Copyright 2014, American Chemical Society.)

(e.g., hydroxyl radicals, superoxide ion, hydrogen peroxide) which react with lipids, proteins and DNA causing malfunction. Essential metals include iron, copper, zinc, sodium, potassium, magnesium and calcium. Essential metal ions needed in trace quantities include vanadium, manganese, cobalt, nickel and tin. Chromium was once considered to be beneficial in the metabolism of glucose; however, this has been challenged [46].

5.2.1 Lead

Lead metal is toxic (IARC Group 2B). What are the discrete mechanisms and molecular targets? Lead is a metallic element that is found in the Earth's crust principally as the ore, lead (II) sulfide, PbS (galena). Metallic lead has a low melting point, and our predecessors learned how to shape objects from lead. The oldest known lead mining site is located in Turkey and dates back to 8000–6500 BC. People learned how to *reduce* the ore, adding electrons to Pb^{2+} in the mineral in order to generate the metal. Consequently, metallic lead has had many uses which have been abandoned in modern times, including jewelry, food and wine storage containers, drinking cups, children's toys and pipes to carry water. More recently, its catalytic properties were utilized as an additive for gasoline (tetraethyl lead) and as a "dryer" for linseed oil binder in oil painting. Over the past 80 years, experience has shown that lead (Pb^{2+}) is toxic, and most industrialized countries have developed laws to regulate its use. *Lead-containing pigments* including white lead, red lead, massicot and litharge were classified by IARC as Group 2A. Lead chromate is IARC Group 1 based on the carcinogenicity of Cr^{6+} [8].

What is known about the toxicity of lead on the molecular level? The principle mode of entry of lead into the human body is from water which is carried by lead pipes. Inhalation of lead is a minor mode of entry. Lead paints have a sweet taste which is associated with the eating of lead paint by children. The Romans

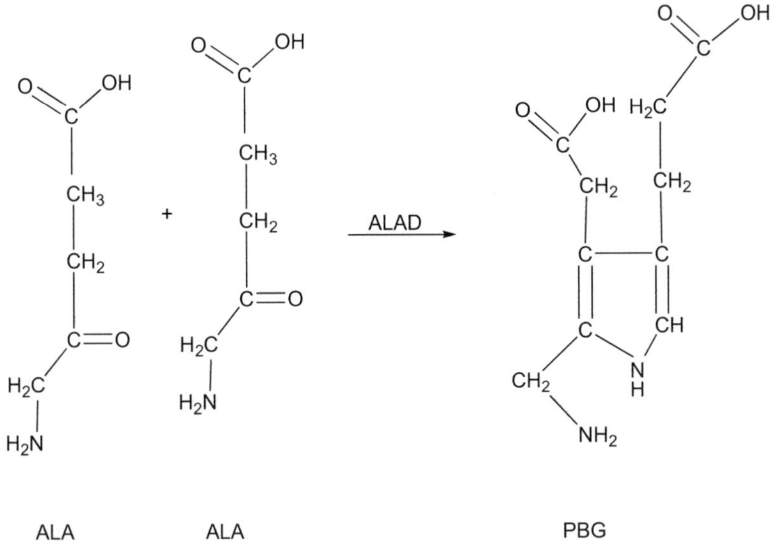

SCHEME 5.17 Biosynthesis of porphobilinogen (PBG) from δ-aminolevulinic acid (ALA) catalyzed by aminolevulinic acid dehydrase (ALAD).

sweetened their wine with lead acetate (sugar of lead). Lead poisoning is characterized by headache, poor attention span, memory loss and dullness. More advanced symptoms include muscular weakness and lack of muscle coordination. In 1840, physicians noted that lead poisoning was accompanied by *anemia* (a drop in the concentration of red blood cell concentration) [47]. This led to discovery of a *buildup of δ-aminolevulinic acid* (δ-ALA) in plasma and urine, and this, in turn, led to the understanding that Pb^{2+} somehow inhibited the enzyme, ALAD (aminolevulinic acid dehydrase), which dimerizes δ-ALA to porphobilinogen (PBG), which contains a pyrrole ring [48], see Scheme 5.17. Several additional steps are required to convert PBG into the Fe^{2+}–containing macrocycle, heme, see Figure 5.4. The protein, globin, binds four hemes by non-covalent forces to yield the oxygen-carrier, hemoglobin. We now understand broadly how Pb^{2+} can be a cause of anemia.

When Pb^{2+} is present in the body, biochemists asked, "What is so special about the enzyme ALA-dehydrase that causes it to be the target of Pb^{2+}?" The short answer is that ALA-dehydrase contains a special Zn^{2+} ion coordinated by three cysteinyl sulfhydryl groups (-SH), which are part of the polypeptide backbone of the enzyme. *Pb^{2+} displaces Zn^{2+}* from the special binding site and the resulting Pb^{2+}-ALA-dehydrase has no enzymatic activity. It has been suggested that because Pb^{2+} (1.18 Angstroms in diameter) is larger than Zn^{2+} (1.00 Å), this causes the shape of the protein to change, so that its enzymatic activity is lost. The heart of this metal ion substitution is that Pb^{2+} "loves" sulfur as a *ligand* (the species which donates electrons to the electron-deficient metal cation to form what is known as a coordination bond). What do we know about the attraction between Pb^{2+} and sulfur ligands? Actually there is a lot of evidence for it. Consider the occurrence of PbS, the major ore of lead. When the Earth's crust was cooling and solidifying, there was a "soup" (magma) which

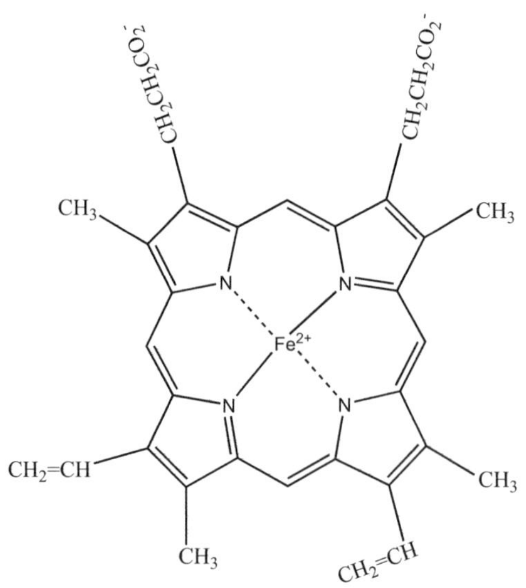

FIGURE 5.4 Structure of Heme.

contained many different kinds of cations and anions. As the crust solidified, Pb^{2+} and S^{2-} chose each other (mineralogical speed dating) and formed crystalline PbS (galena). Pb^{2+} didn't choose other available anions, e.g., chloride, bromide, oxide, cyanide, etc. True love cannot be denied, you might say. The affinity of Pb^{2+} for sulfur extends from the inorganic/mineralogical domain into the biosphere.

What other targets does Pb^{2+} seek after it enters the body? Pb^{2+} crosses the BBB. Synaptogens are a family of Ca^{2+}-binding proteins are localized in the membranes of synaptic vesicles and mediate the release of neurotransmitters in the nervous system. In these proteins, Pb^{2+} competes for the binding sites and *displaces Ca^{2+}* causing loss of biological function [49,50]. This is the basis of lead neurotoxicity.

The bulk of Pb^{2+} is stored in bone. Bone is a complex tissue which consists of a protein component, collagen and an inorganic component, hydroxyapatite, (HA). HA constitutes about 50% of the dry mass of bone and has the formula, $Ca_{10}(PO_4)_6(OH)_2$. Apatite has the general formula, $Ca_{10}(PO_4)_6X_2$, where X can be F^-, Cl^-, HO^-, $\frac{1}{2}\,CO_3^{2+}$, or $\frac{1}{2}\,O^{2-}$. Ca^{2+} can be displaced by Pb^{2+}, Sr^{2+}, or Ba^{2+} and PO_4^{3-} can be displaced by HPO_4^{2-}, AsO_4^{3-}, VO_4^{3-}, SiO_4^{2-} or CO_3^{2-} Bones contains cells which are nourished by blood vessels. Most of the Pb^{2+} in blood is carried by the red blood cells. Since the Pb^{2+} ions are in a state of dynamic equilibrium, i.e., constantly binding and unbinding to proteins, there is always a small amount of unbound Pb^{2+} ions in blood which could enter bone tissue and displace Ca^{2+} in hydroxyapatite [51].

5.2.2 Zinc, Cadmium and Mercury Familial Properties

Cadmium and mercury are toxic substances which are associated with the pigments, CdS (cadmium yellow) and HgS (cinnabar/vermilion). Zinc, cadmium and mercury comprise Group 12, and they share the analogous electron configuration, see Table 5.2.

TABLE 5.2

Electron Configurations of Group 12 Atoms and Cations

Atom	Z	EC	Ion	EC	HSAB Lewis Acid Classification
Zn	30	$[Ar]4s^24d^{10}$	Zn^{2+}	$[Ar]4d^{10}$	Borderline
Cd	48	$[Kr]5s^25d^{10}$	Cd^{2+}	$[Kr]5d^{10}$	Soft
Hg	80	$[Xe]6s^26d^{10}$	Hg^+	$[Xe]6s^16d^{10}$	Soft
			Hg^{2+}	$[Xe]6d^{10}$	Soft

The stable oxidation states for these elements are presented in Table 5.2. Zinc and cadmium have only two stable oxidation states, the element and the 2+ cation. In these cases, the electrons lost during chemical reactions are solely the outermost s electrons; the outermost d-subshell is completely filled with ten electrons, and this represents stability. Mercury has three stable oxidation states: 0, +1 and +2. The dimeric +1 cation, (+Hg-Hg+), is unique. There are no salts containing one Hg+ ion. Zn^{2+}, Cd^{2+} and Hg^{2+} share an i*soelectronic valence electron configuration* and have similar chemical properties. The toxicity of mercury and cadmium are largely *zinc-mimetic*. Because of the presence of filled outer d-subshells, the members of Group 12 are much more polarizable than the corresponding members of Group 2, calcium, barium and strontium. Hence, the Group 12 metals are classified as borderline (between hard and soft) soft Lewis acids in the HSAB Classification. Soft Lewis acids choose soft Lewis bases as bonding partners. In mineralogy, the main ores of Group 12 are sulfides, and sulfur is a soft Lewis base. In the biosphere, the cations of Group 12 analogously seek sulfur atoms of biomolecules.

Hg^{2+} and Cd^{2+} are both toxic. Neither metal has a biological function. Their primary ores are HgS and CdS, respectively, corresponding to the pigments cinnabar/ vermilion, cadmium yellow and cadmium orange. The chalcophilic tendencies (chalcophiles are metals which form sulfide minerals) of these heavy metal cations lead them to seek protein targets in the body which contain covalently bonded sulfur atoms. These proteins usually function in the transport and or buffering of Zn^{+2}. Examples include Zn-finger proteins (which bind RNA or DNA) and the enzyme thioredoxin (DNA synthesis). Organisms ranging from vertebrates to microbes have evolved thionines, small proteins whose function is to bind and hence buffer Zn^{2+}. Zinc cation is part of the structure of ~3000 proteins. In addition, in a protective role, thionines capture foreign heavy metal ions such as Hg^{2+}, Cd^{2+}, Pb^{2+} and Ag^+. Thionines contain about 30% (by mass) cysteinyl residues (sulfhydryl sidechains) and can bind up to six metal cations at each of two binding sites [52]. A related aspect of mercury toxicity is affinity for selenium-containing residues (seleno-cysteinyl and seleno-methioninyl) in seleno-proteins [53,54].

5.2.3 CADMIUM

Cadmium toxicity is associated with damage to kidneys, respiratory system, reproductive system and loss of bone mineralization. Cadmium causes kidney and liver damage; it does not cross the BBB and is not neurotoxic. Further, cadmium exposure is associated with cancer of several organs, including prostate, liver, bladder, pancreatic and stomach. IARC carcinogen risk classification for all cadmium compounds is Group 1 [8].

Cadmium occurs in nature as the sulfide ore CdS (greenockite) in deposits of ZnS, HgS and ZnS. Cadmium is a trace element in the Earth's crust (0.15 ppm) and occurs in various foods (seafood, rice and vegetables) which leads to an average intake of ~1 μg of Cd per day person. Inhalation of tobacco smoke will also increase intake of cadmium. Workers in certain fields have an increased risk of inhaling cadmium vapor, including potters, jewelers, pigment manufacturers of cadmium pigments, artists and others [55,56]. Once absorbed, Cd^{2+} is distributed throughout the body and induces the biosynthesis of thioneins. Cd^{2+} has a biological half-life of ~ 30 years, and humans do not have an efficient pathway for cadmium elimination.

Cadmium toxicity is considered to be largely *zinc-mimetic*. *Cd^{2+} causes the formation of excessive concentrations of ROS to form*. The target of Cd^{2+} has not been identified. ROS species are produced by the ETC (electron transport chain) of mitochondria, see Scheme 5.18. The function of the ETC is to pass electrons "down" a series of redox steps starting with NADH/NADH Reductase and finally passing electrons to O_2 to form water:

$$O_{2\ gas} + 4H^+_{aq} + 4e^- \rightarrow 2\ H_2O_{liq}$$

In general, metabolism is oxidative (loss of electrons) and the ultimate products of metabolism of fats or carbohydrates are carbon dioxide and water. We have accounted for the formation of water via the ETC. The formation of carbon dioxide comes from *oxidative decarboxylation* of metabolites (that is, specific carbon atoms take on two oxygen bonding partners to form a carboxyl group, $-CO_2H$, and this group is lost as carbon dioxide is released). The passage of electrons down the ETC releases chemical energy from the bonds of several metabolites, and this energy is channeled to synthesize ATP. ATP is then used as an energy source to drive "uphill" biochemical reactions, which would not proceed on their own.

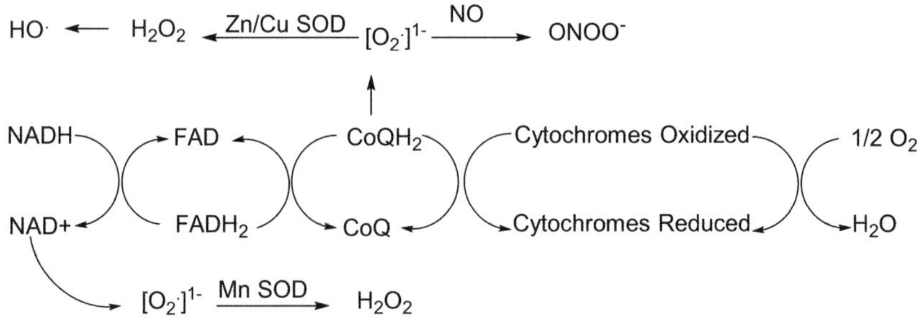

SCHEME 5.18 Mitochondrial electron transport chain. SOD, superoxide dismutase; NO, nitric oxide; NAD, nicotinamide adenine dinucleotide; FAD, flavine adenine dinucleotide; CoQ, coenzyme Q; ONOO⁻, peroxynitrite anion; symbol for superoxide is [O₂·]¹⁻, superoxide radical anion.

A very small percentage of the output of the ETC does *not* result in the formation of carbon dioxide and water. Instead, the *radical anion*, superoxide, $[O_2]^{1-}$ is produced:

$$O_2 + 1\,e^- \rightarrow [O_2^{\cdot}]^{1-}$$

Superoxide has an *odd number of valence electrons* (13 electrons), and it is therefore a free radical. The presence of the odd or unpaired electron makes free radicals extremely active. They continue to react until they obtain a valence octet of electrons around every atom in their structure. Superoxide is converted to a comparatively more stable compound, hydrogen peroxide, but a pretty reactive one at that! This reaction is catalyzed by the enzyme SOD (superoxide dismutase), a metalloenzyme, in which either of the transition metal cations, Cu, Zn or Mn function as Lewis acids, and in the case of copper and manganese, multiple oxidation states are employed.

The reaction catalyzed by SOD is a *dismutation*, (also known as a *disproportionation* reaction), in which two molecules of superoxide anion radical react; one is *oxidized* to O_2, and the other is *reduced* to hydrogen peroxide. The chemistry of the SOD reaction is illustrated in Scheme 5.19. In this scheme, M represents either Cu or Mn in the active site of SOD, where $Cu^{(n+1)+} = Cu^{2+}$ and $Mn^{(n+1)+} = Mn^{3+}$, representing the oxidized form of the enzyme. The enzyme starts out in the oxidized form, is converted to the reduced form (reaction intermediate) and re-oxidized to its initial state at the end of the sequence.

The list of ROS includes: $[O_2]^{1-}$, superoxide anion radical; H_2O_2, hydrogen peroxide; and HO, hydroxyl radical. These species react with other cellular components such as proteins, lipids and nucleic acids to produce molecules with impaired function. The cytotoxicity of free radicals is caused by reactions with cellular species which generate new free radical species. These react with other species by a *chain reaction* which is stopped when two free radicals combine to form a single bond. Free-radical reactions are characterized by the following steps: *initiation* (formation of a free radical by homolytic cleavage of a single covalent bond), *propagation*

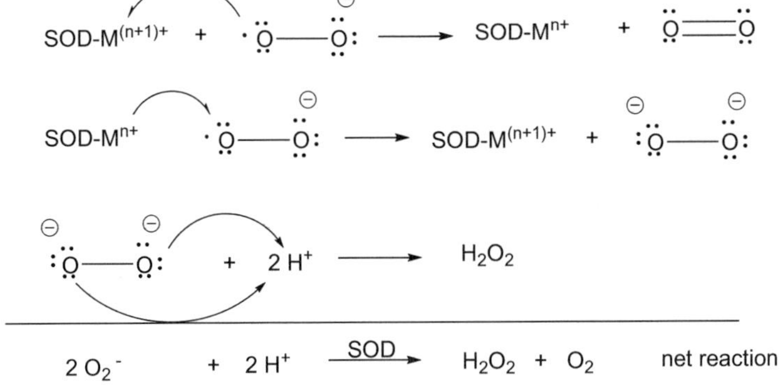

SCHEME 5.19   Enzyme-catalyzed dismutation of superoxide radical anion.

$O=O + 1 e^- \rightarrow [O_2]^{1-} + 2 H^+ + 1 e^- \underline{/SOD} \rightarrow HO\text{-}OH \quad \underline{homolysis} \rightarrow 2 HO\cdot \quad$ (initiation)

$HO\cdot + R\text{-}H \rightarrow HOH + R\cdot \qquad\qquad\qquad\qquad\qquad\qquad$ (propagation)

$2 R\cdot \rightarrow R\text{-}R \text{ dimer} \qquad\qquad\qquad\qquad\qquad\qquad\qquad\qquad$ (termination)

SCHEME 5.20   Free-radical reaction initiated by di-oxygen and catalyzed by SOD [52].

(reaction of the free radical with a non-radical to generate a new free radical and a new non-radical) and *termination* (two radicals combine to form a non-radical product via covalent bond formation), see Scheme 5.20. Propagation steps do not increase the number of radicals, but they do change the nature of the radical. Under normal conditions, ROS play a constructive role. For example, H_2O_2 is used by the immune system to destroy bacterial invaders and other ROS species are important in wound healing. However, under abnormal conditions, excess ROS have been implicated in cancer and inflammatory diseases [57].

5.2.4   MERCURY

Mercury exists in several different stable forms including: elemental, Hg°; inorganic salts of Hg^+ and Hg^{2+} (IARC Group 3) and organic mercury, (methylmercury, IARC Group 2B) [8]. This discussion will focus on the toxicity of the red polymorph, α-HgS, also known as cinnabar or vermilion. Cinnabar refers to the naturally occurring mineral and vermilion to the synthetic form. The ore has been mined since ancient times, as a source of the silvery liquid element mercury:

$$HgS_{(s)} + O_{2\,(g)}\text{heat/air} \rightarrow Hg_{(l)} + SO_{2\,(g)}.$$

This type of reaction is known as *calcination*, in which a metal cation is *reduced* to its metallic state and simultaneously liberated from its counter-ion, which combines with oxygen to form a volatile byproduct. This facilitates purification of the metal. Until recently, miners and industrial workers associated with the processing and production of HgS were exposed to toxic fumes and suffered from various forms of mercury poisoning. α-Cinnabar and vermilion are used as art pigments. The other polymorph, β-HgS, metacinnabar, is black and is not used in art.

We know about the *therapeutic* properties of α-HgS because this compound has been used medicinally to treat insomnia, irritability, sore throat, skin conditions and palpitations for over 2000 years in Traditional Chinese Medicine. Cinnabar has extremely poor solubility in water. HgS is regarded to be a network solid with the zinc blend crystal structure (sp^3 hybridization) and largely covalent bonding. Hence the very small K_{sp} value (10^{-49}, 18°C) reflects very poor solubility which is consistent with network solid structure. The structure can be represented by $-(Hg\text{-}S)-_\infty$. Therefore, a chunk of red crystalline cinnabar is one gigantic molecule. The electronegativity difference (Pauling scale) between Hg and S is 0.6, which corresponds to polar-covalent bonding. Vermilion can be synthesized by mixing aqueous solutions of Hg^{2+} and S^{2-} salts.

Cinnabar medicinals are given orally. Poor solubility translates to low bio-availability and poor absorption from the digestive tract. After absorption into the bloodstream, Hg^{2+} has a tendency to react with thiols, e.g., the amino acid cysteine, $(HSCH_2CH(NH_2)CO_2H)$, CySH:

$$HgS_{(s)} \rightarrow Hg^{2+}_{(aq)} + S^{2-}_{(aq)}$$

$$Hg^{2+}_{(aq)} + 2\,CySH_{(aq)} \rightarrow CyS-Hg-SCy_{(aq)} + 2H^+_{(aq)}$$

The bis-S-cysteinyl conjugate accumulates in the kidneys. A very small amount of Hg^{2+} is reduced to $Hg°$ which is lipophilic and crosses the BBB. In the brain, $Hg°$ is re-oxidized to Hg^{2+}. Chronic exposure to HgS leads to kidney disease. Hg^{2+} has a weak tendency to penetrate the BBB; prolonged contact will deliver Hg^{2+} to the brain. Consequently, Hg^{2+} poisoning is generally associated with kidney and liver damage, and kidney damage is a negative factor if the body is trying to eliminate Hg^{2+} [54]. HgS is much less toxic than either $Hg°$ or Hg^{2+} [58,59]. The neurotoxicity of HgS is estimated to be about one one-thousandth that of methylmercury.

The situation for CH_3Hg^+ is quite different. This agent penetrates the BBB easily and is a potent *neurotoxin*. The apparent explanation for this is that methylmercury combines with cysteine to form a product which resembles methionine, and as a "Trojan Horse", it fools the amino acid transporter which is embedded in the BBB [60].

$$CH_3Hg^+ + HSCH_2\left(NH_3^+\right)CO_2^- \rightarrow H^+ + CH_3HgSCH_2CH\left(NH_3^+\right)CO_2^-$$

methylHg$^+$ cysteine   cysteine-methylHg adduct

$$CH_3SCH_2CH_2CH\left(NH_3^+\right)CO_2^-$$

methionine

Once inside the brain, the adduct undergoes facile ligand exchange with other sulfhydryl (-SH) or selenol- (-SeH) containing molecules and causes massive dysfunction.

5.2.4.1 Does Bacterial Methylation Occur in the Human Gut?

Certain bacteria can methylate Hg^{2+} to form monomethylmercury. These bacteria inhabit sediments at the bottom of bodies of water. To determine whether or not bacterial methylation occurs in the human gut, >3500 microbial metagenomes (genetic material obtained from environmental samples) were screened for the genes which enable mercury methylation. The study included >1500 human and mammalian microbiomes. These genes were found in nearly all of the aerobic environments, but not in any anaerobic environments (including those in the gut). Consequently, there seems to be a low risk that mercury methylation occurs in the human gut [61,62].

5.2.4.2 Dimethylmercury

In ocean water, Hg^{2+} is monomethylated to (CH_3Hg^+) and again forming dimethylmercury, DMM, (CH_3HgCH_3). The second methylation is a non-biological process facilitated by adsorption to the surface of the mineral Mackinawite, $(Fe, Ni)_{1+x}$ S, where x = 0-0.11 [63]. Dimethylmercury is a deadly poison. During research, a few drops of *pure* DMM penetrated a latex glove of Professor Karen Wetterhahn in 1997, leading to her death months later [64]. Hair analysis of the deceased and earlier mice studies indicated that DMM was converted to monomethylmercury before it entered the brain and was deposited in hair. Exposure to pure DMM shows it to be a deadly neurotoxin. OSHA Hazardous Information Bulletin (March 9, 1998) provides safety and hazard information concerning DMM [65]. DMM has not been investigated by IARC [8].

5.2.5 SILVER

Silver is used as a metal (Ag°) to create art objects. In addition, Silverpoint is a drawing technique, in which a silver wire leaves a gray-blue residue of silver on surface-modified paper. In time, the silver residue darkens to brown [66].

Chronic inhalation of metallic silver dust or fumes and oral consumption of water-based "silver-tonics" (colloidal silver) can lead to an irreversible gray-blue coloration of the skin, a condition known as *argyria*. Argyria is a non-toxic and irreversible condition described by the presence of a bluish tint of the skin due to the presence of precipitated silver sulfide, Ag_2S and silver selenide, Ag_2Se. In contrast, consumption of silver nitrate ($AgNO_3$) can cause severe irritation of the GI tract [3,67]. Besides argyria, exposure to soluble silver compounds can produce toxicity in the liver, kidney and respiratory system. Ionic silver ($AgNO_3$ solution) is used routinely to treat the eyes of newborn babies (neonatal conjunctivitis prevention).

Toxicology is based partially on the inherent chemical properties of a substance. Silver is a transition metal with only two stable oxidation states, elemental (Ag°) and ionic (Ag$^+$). The cation is categorized as a "soft" Lewis acid, based on its polarizable electron cloud; and it is attracted to soft Lewis bases, particularly those based on sulfur. Hence, in-vivo, Ag$^+$ has a strong affinity for organic sulfides, such as thiols (RSH). Silver has no role in any biochemical process and is considered non-essential for life. In addition, the affinity of Ag$^+$ for chloride ion in biological fluids leads to precipitation of AgCl and hence lowers the concentration of free silver ion. These factors suggest that silver should be toxic.

What is known about the interaction of silver ion with biological molecules? In biological systems, Ag$^+$, preferentially forms bonds with the amino acid, cysteine, the tripeptide, glutathione (GSH) and cysteinyl sulfhydryl groups in thioneins and other proteins. If xenobiotic heavy metals form thiolate compounds with cellular proteins, the function of the protein is usually altered. However the combined presence of Ag$^+$ binders (sulfhydryls and chloride) in human serum reduces the concentration of ionic silver by ~250-fold.

The reaction of sulfhydryl groups with silver cation is:

$$R-S-H + H_2O \rightleftharpoons RS^- + H_3O^+$$

$$RS^- + Ag^+ \rightarrow R-S-Ag$$

In this case, "R" represents a large protein structure, which usually contains additional sulfhydryl groups. This reaction displaces a proton from a cysteinyl residue, and this proton will be buffered by the plasma, with a correspondingly tiny drop in pH. Further, Ag^+ binds to thioneins, which are small proteins present in most living organisms [54,68]. Very few bacterial species have thioneins. (For the function of thioneins, see Section 5.3.2 which covers zinc, cadmium and mercury familial properties.)

Silver cation is more toxic to bacteria than to eukaryotic cells. What are the reasons for this selective toxicity? Several factors have been proposed: bacterial systems are fooled into allowing the xenobiotic Ag^+ into the cell, probably as a Trojan horse mimic of K^+; major damage to bacterial cell membranes; lack of thioneins in most bacteria; formation of Ag^+- thiol complexes with GSH (depleting antioxidant activity) and proteins (degrading function); damage to the electron transport chain (leading to formation of ROS); and complexation of guanine bases in DNA. A mechanism for the antibacterial action of Ag^+, Zn^{2+} and Cu^{2+} is based on the action of heavy metal cation-generated ROS on bacterial membranes, while bacterial DNA was spared [69]. Concerning the antibacterial activity of silver *nanoparticles*, (clusters of silver atoms, 1–100 nm in diameter), several general mechanisms have been proposed based on Ag^+ release [70].

The established history of the use of silver as an antibacterial agent leads to a conundrum. On one hand, we have the documented bactericidal action of silver ions. Silver ions preferentially seek –SH groups in proteins in a bonding action. Sulfhydryl groups are present in essentially all proteins, in all living organisms. Consequently, Ag^+ should bind to essentially all sulfhydryl compounds, regardless of the host.

The binding of a xenobiotic metal ion such as Ag^+ usually changes the structure and hence the activity of proteins, *why then is Ag^+ harmful to bacteria, but apparently not to humans?* This question has been investigated by several groups. Ionic silver and silver nanoparticles (AgNPs, 70 nm diameter) were studied. The cytotoxicity of silver from both $AgNO_3$ solution and AgNP toward human and bacterial cells was monitored. Under specific conditions, using tissue culture media, the result was that the (*in-vitro*) *lethal dose for both forms of silver (ions and NP's) was almost the same toward both bacterial and human cells*; 0.5–5 ppm for Ag^+ and 12.5–50 ppm for AgNPs. This suggests that when silver is used to treat an infection, bacterial and minimally, some human (host) cells are killed. Some investigators question the notion of a "therapeutic window" for the antibacterial activity of silver [71–73].

The bactericidal action of silver was discovered by accident long ago. The discovery of pyrotechnology led to the development of ceramics and also to metallurgy (conversion of metallic ores to metals). The ancient Phoenicians stored water, wine and vinegar in silver containers. Dissolved oxygen gas in these aqueous fluids causes the formation of a surface layer of silver oxide.

$$O_{2\,g} + 4\,Ag_s \rightarrow 2\,Ag_2O_s$$

In this redox system, one di-oxygen molecule picks up electrons from each of four silver atoms to form two oxide anions. For this reaction, the half-reactions are:

$$4\,Ag^\circ \rightarrow 4\,Ag^+ + 4\,e^-$$

$$4\,e^- + O_2 \rightarrow 2\,O^{2-}$$

Water which is exposed to atmospheric carbon dioxide is weakly acidic (~pH 5). The presence of hydrogen ions, (H_3O^+), facilitates the release of Ag^+ into the solution.

$$2\left[Ag^+O^{2-}Ag^+\right] + 4H^+ \rightleftarrows 4Ag^+ + 2H_2O$$

In this reaction, protons displace silver ions from silver oxide to form water and aquated silver ions. This is consistent with the association of bactericidal activity of AgNPs with the formation of silver ions [74]. Therefore, the absence of oxygen therefore should prevent the oxidation of silver atoms on the surface of the nanoparticles. Silver NP's were not cytotoxic to bacteria in the absence of oxygen. This indicates that the bactericidal property of silver NP's and larger pieces of silver are due to release of silver ions. Other factors in the bactericidal activity of silver NP's include shape, size and surface area. AgNPs (<20 nm in diameter) release ~100-fold more Ag^+ compared to metallic bulk silver [75].

Currently, there are many commercial applications which place AgNPs in household products such as socks, sneakers and carpets in order to kill bacteria. This has raised concerns about possible release of silver (atoms and ions) into the environment and possible toxicological effects when these products are cleaned. Some bacterial species have developed resistance to Ag^+ based on efflux pumps which use ATP to pump silver ions out of the cell. In some situations, specific bacterial strains can transmit the genetic information for silver resistance to "naïve" species. This should be an obvious concern! Note that bacterial resistance to antibiotics was facilitated by feeding antibiotics to cattle to enhance growth [76].

5.2.6 ARSENIC

Arsenic is the 55th most common element in the Earth's crust, and there are over two hundred arsenic-containing minerals. The most common of these are arsenopyrite (FeAsS), realgar (As_4S_4) and orpiment (As_4S_6). Until the 18th century, realgar and orpiment were used as artists' pigments, but have been abandoned because of their toxicity. Ground water tends to dissolve arsenic-containing minerals which leads to the occurrence of water-soluble inorganic arsenic species, e.g., $As(OH)_3$ ("As[III]", arsenite) and $O=As(OH)_3$ ("As[V]", arsenate). (Arsenite and arsenate are the names of the conjugate bases of the corresponding acids, arsenous acid and arsenic acid.) Several countries (including Taiwan, India, Bangladesh, Chile, Mexico, Argentina and Romania) have elevated arsenic concentrations in ground water [77,78]. The World Health Organization guideline for maximum arsenic ground water concentration is 10 µg/L. Arsenic has been classified as *carcinogenic* to humans, leading to cancer of the bladder, lung and skin, and possibly to liver and kidney [79]. Arsenic and its inorganic compounds have been classified by IARC as Group 1 carcinogens [8].

Ironically, both realgar and orpiment have been used in China for more than 1500 years to treat cancer. In 2000, arsenic (III) oxide $(As_2O_3$, arsenic trioxide, ATO, arsenolite) was cleared by the USFDA as a *therapeutic agent* for acute promyelocytic leukemia (APL) [80, 81a]. Thus we have the "arsenic paradox", in which arsenicals are both cause and treatment for certain types of cancer.

The nomenclature of arsenic compounds is a bit confusing, and decoding is in order. Realgar, As_4S_4, is also known as arsenic (II) sulfide; analogously for orpiment;

As_2S_3, arsenic (III) sulfide. These are based on a nomenclature system, in which the oxidation number of sulfur is −2. In both of these arsenic sulfides, sulfur atoms are each covalently bonded to two arsenic atoms. With respect to arsenic oxides, arsenic (III) oxide, has the chemical formula, As_2O_3. When it dissolves in water, triprotic arsenous acid, $As(OH)_3$, is formed (pKa's: 9.23, 12.13 and 13.4). Arsenous acid has never been isolated. Arsenous acid and its conjugate bases are collectively known as arsenites, " As^{III}".

$$As_2O_3 + 3\ H_2O\ \rightarrow\ 2\ As(OH)_3$$

$$As(OH)_3 + \tfrac{1}{2}\ O_2 \rightarrow\ O{=}As(OH)_3$$

Arsenous acid can be oxidized to arsenic acid, $O{=}As(OH)_3$. Arsenic acid and its conjugate bases are collectively known as arsenates, "As^V". The pKa's of this triprotic acid (2.25, 6.77, 11.60) are close to those of phosphoric acid (2.12, 7.21, 12.67). Consequently, at physiological pH, As^{III} would be neutral and As^V would be present as the di- and mono-anions in a 2:1 molar ratio. Realgar is sometimes represented as AsS or more commonly, As_2S_2.

As a cancer drug used in Traditional Chinese Medicine, TCM, realgar is preferred over arsenic trioxide because the sulfide is much less water-soluble than the oxide, and hence, the dose is more controllable. The poor solubility of realgar is being addressed by the preparation of nanoparticles. The rationale is that increasing the surface area of the particles will enhance solubility.

What is known about the behavior of realgar in the human gastrointestinal (GI) tract? Pills containing *Nie Huang Jie Du Pian* were crushed and extracted (pH 1.5 or 1.8 aqueous buffer, 1 h, 37°C; simulated gastric conditions). Each pill contained 28 mg of realgar.

The extracts were filtered (0.45u) and analyzed by HPLC-ICP-MS. The extracts contained arsenate (As^V) and arsenite (As^{III}) in a 3:1 molar ratio. Approximately 4% of the total arsenic was solubilized. This shows that under simulated GI conditions, the arsenic atoms in realgar were oxidized. The fate of the sulfur atoms in realgar was not determined. In addition, realgar-containing pills were consumed by a 70 year-old man. Urine samples contained the methylated forms; monomethylarsonic acid (MMA^V) and dimethylarsinic acid (DMA^V). Peak excretion of methylated arsenicals occurred at 14 h.

[In the bioremediation or bioleaching of mining waste water, certain types of bacteria are used to convert arsenic sulfides to water-soluble arsenic oxides. For example, *Acidithiobacillus ferrooxydans* is known to oxidize realgar to arsenite and arsenate in acidified aqueous solution [82].

$$As_4S_4 + 28\ H_2O\ \text{[A. ferrooxydans, pH 1.9]}\ \rightarrow 4\ As(OH)_3$$

$$+\ 4\ HSO_4^- +\ 40H^+ +\ 36\ e^-$$

$$As(OH)_3 + H_2O\ \text{[A. ferrooxydans, pH 1.9]} \rightarrow\ O = As(OH)_3 + 2\ H^+ + 2\ e^-$$

A. ferrooxydans uses realgar as an energy source and processes the electrons released through its electron transport chain to produce ATP. In the overall process, the poorly soluble arsenic sulfide is converted to soluble arsenic oxides and hydrogen sulfate anion. From this point, the metabolism of arsenic oxides proceeds through a series of biological methylation steps.]

Arsenic compounds occur as inorganic or organic. The inorganic compounds, As^{III} and As^V, occur in drinking water and are *metabolized* in living organisms, from bacteria to mammals, by the process of methylation. Methylation results in replacing oxygen atoms with methyl groups which are covalently bonded to the arsenic atom. The process of arsenic methylation in microbes was first deciphered by Challenger and more recently has been confirmed by others [83–85]. In this process, a two-step cycle is repeated several times. One step is a two–electron reduction which comprises the addition of $2H^+$ and 2 e⁻. The other step is the capture of $[H_3C^+]$ by the nucleophilic lone pair of electrons on As. Two molecules of a thiol (glutathione) react oxidatively to form a disulfide dimer, and this releases two protons which go into solution and two electrons, which are consumed in the reduction step:

$$G-S{:}H + H{:}S-G \rightarrow G-S{:}S-G + 2H^+ + 2\,e^-.$$

The major and minor forms of inorganic arsenic in oxygenated fresh water, respectively, are As^V and As^{III}. The Challenger scheme begins with the reduction of $As^V \rightarrow As^{III}$; the electron source is a thiol. In the next step, As^{III} is methylated, the methyl source is S-adenosylmethionine (SAM), and the reaction is catalyzed by the enzyme, S-methyltransferase (SMT). This two-step sequence is repeated several times until all of the oxygen atoms have been displaced and the ultimate product, trimethylarsine, $(CH_3)_3As$, is formed, The proposed mechanism for the biomethylation of arsenic is provided in Scheme 5.21 does not take into consideration the dissociation of any of the acidic species involved.

Trimethylarsine is a volatile compound with a garlic-like odor (bp 59°C). Progressive methylation is a process which replaces strongly electronegative oxygen atoms with less electronegative carbon atoms. In microbes, the overall process converts $(HO)_3As$ to $(CH_3)_3As$, starting with a polar, water-soluble compound, and ending with a non-polar, volatile compound. The large difference in water solubility suggests that *permethylation* of arsenic is a detoxification mechanism for microbes because trimethylarsine is a gas [86]. In humans, trimethylarsine-oxide and trimethylarsine form sparingly (if at all). Bacteria metabolism in the human gut can affect the oxidation state of arsenic, methylation status and excretion [87].

In humans, arsenic metabolites are excreted via urine. The urine of 140 women from northern Argentina, where the public drinking water contained 200 µg/L of arsenic was analyzed. [In the United States, the permitted level for arsenic in drinking water is 10 µg/L.] The results, reported as percentage of total arsenic were: 7.7% monomethylated As, 11.6% unmethylated As, and 80.2% dimethylated As. This method did not permit differentiation of the oxidation state of arsenic in the metabolite. The analytical scheme consisted of HPLC/HG/ICP/MS, translation: chromatographic separation of metabolites followed by $NaBH_4$ reduction (hydride generation, replacing oxygen atoms with H:) of each peak so that the

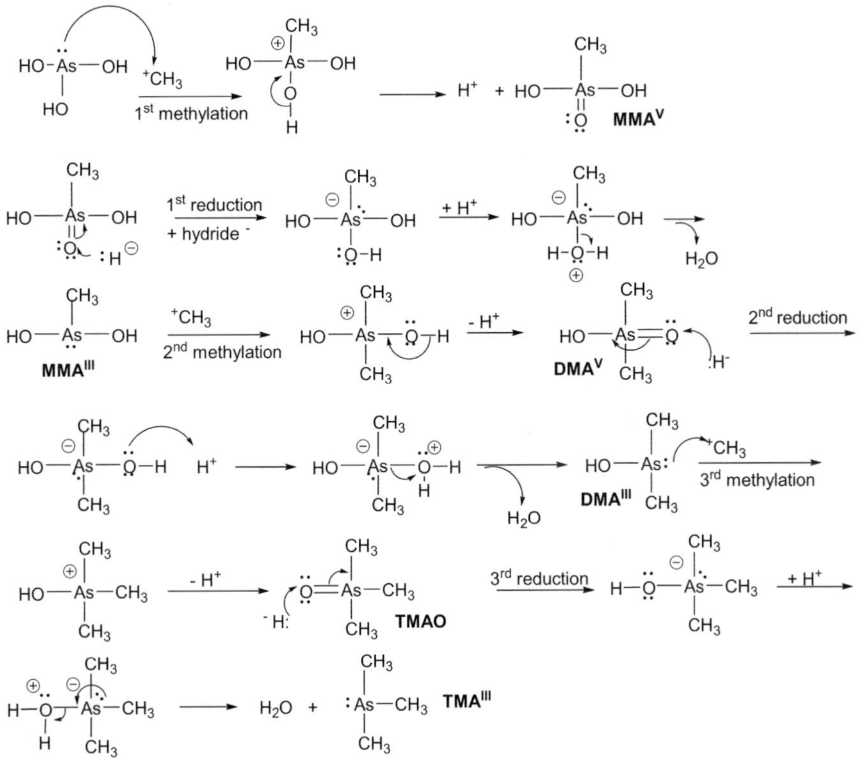

SCHEME 5.21 Arsenic metabolism, Challenger biomethylation mechanism [84]. MMA^V, monomethylarsonic acid; MMA^{III}, monomethylarsonous acid; DMA^V, dimethylarsinic acid; DMA^{III}, dimethylarsinous acid; TMAO, trimethylarsineoxide; TMA, treimethylarsine. (Adapted and reprinted with permission of W.R. Cullen, K.J. Reimer (1989) *Chem. Rev.* 89:713–764. Copyright 1989, American Chemical Society.)

product contained As^{III}. This was followed by inductively-coupled plasma mass spectrometry (ICPMS). Interaction with the plasma (He or Ar gas at ~10^4 K), strips the reduction products of all substituents and yields As$^+$. The relative concentration of each metabolite is based on the intensity of As$^+$ (m/z 75) in the mass spectrometer. It is possible to utilize HPLC to separate human urinary arsenic metabolites (HPLC/HG/ICP/MS) as follows: As^{III}, MMA^{III}, MMA^V, DMA^{III}, DMA^V, and As^V [88].

The introduction of inorganic arsenic into the metabolism therefore causes depletion of methyl groups which are needed for the normal biochemistry of the cell (methylation of DNA and RNA bases), as well as loss of sulfhydryl groups in antioxidants (glutathione and dihydrolipoic acid, in zinc-fingers of DNA repair enzymes) and interference with oxidative phosphorylation in mitochondria. These factors are responsible for the toxicity of arsenic. Arsenous acid interacts with mitochondria which results in an increase the level of ROS in the cell [89,90]. (ROS were addressed earlier in this chapter in the section dealing with cadmium toxicity.)

5.2.7 CHROMIUM

The major human exposures to chromium occur in the following industries: production and use of chromate pigments, zinc chromate primer paints, stainless steel machinery and welding, chrome plating, wood preservation, corrosion inhibition, and leather tanning. Artists can be exposed to metallic chromium and chromium compounds from pigments, minerals and pottery glazes, as well as from welding stainless steel. Pigments and minerals contain ionic chromium, either Cr^{3+} or Cr^{6+}. Stainless steel contains 10%–20% chromium metal by weight. Heating the metal above its melting point produces metallic vapor which oxidizes to form particles, which are toxic if inhaled. Some chromium compounds have been used as pigments. These include chromate salts of Ba^{2+}, Zn^{2+} and Pb^{2+}. Chromate pigments are either red, orange or yellow. Lead chromate ($PbCrO_4$, chrome yellow) was abandoned by artists in the 1880s because of instability. Specifically, chrome yellow was replaced by cadmium yellow, CdS, which was believed at that time to be more stable. However, cadmium yellow is destabilized by light contributes to discoloration of paintings. The toxicity of chromium compounds has been documented. Accordingly, both soluble and insoluble chromates and dichromates, Cr^{6+}, including Na_2CrO_4, $PbCrO_4$ and $Na_2Cr_2O_7$, have been classified as *human carcinogens*, IARC Group 1. In contrast, Cr^{3+} compounds are probably not carcinogenic, IARC Group 3 [8].

There are two types of chromium-containing pigments differentiated by oxidation state. The chromates (e.g., $PbCrO_4$, chrome yellow and $ZnCrO_4$, zinc yellow) belong to the Cr^{6+} group. The second group (Cr^{3+}) comprises Cr_2O_3, (chromium (III) oxide) and $Cr_2O_3 \cdot nH_2O$, (viridian). Chromium is a sophisticated transition metal with many oxidation states: 0, +2, +3, +4, +5, +6. Of these, +3 and +6 are the dominant naturally occurring forms.

Consider chromium (III) oxide and its hydrate. These compounds are essentially insoluble in water and other solvents, hence low toxicity is not unexpected. Continuing on to the chromates, the situation is complex. Chromate anion, Cr^{6+}, enters cells by passing through a membrane channel known as the sulfate/phosphate ion transporter. Chromate, sulfate and dihydrogen phosphate are *isoelectronic* (sharing the same valence electronic configuration around the central atom), share the same tetrahedral molecular geometry and are close in size. The respective hydrated ionic radii are 256, 258 and 238 pm [91]. It is a "Trojan horse" scenario, see Figure 5.5.

Once inside the cell, chromate reacts non-enzymatically with cellular reductants including ascorbate, cysteine or glutathione to produce the reactive intermediates, Cr^{4+} and Cr^{5+}, and the stable species, Cr^{3+} [92,93]. The structures of these chromium complexes involving biomolecules are based on X-ray spectrometry. The metabolism of chromate is summarized in Figure 5.6. Once inside the cell, chromate

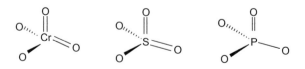

FIGURE 5.5   Isoelectronic structures: chromate, sulfate and phosphate.

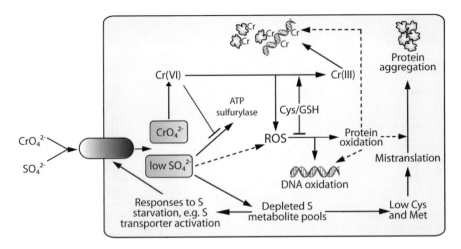

FIGURE 5.6 Metabolism of chromate. (Reprinted with permission of S.I. Holland, S.V. Avery (2011) *Metallomics* 11:1119–1123. Copyright 2011, Royal Society of Chemistry.)

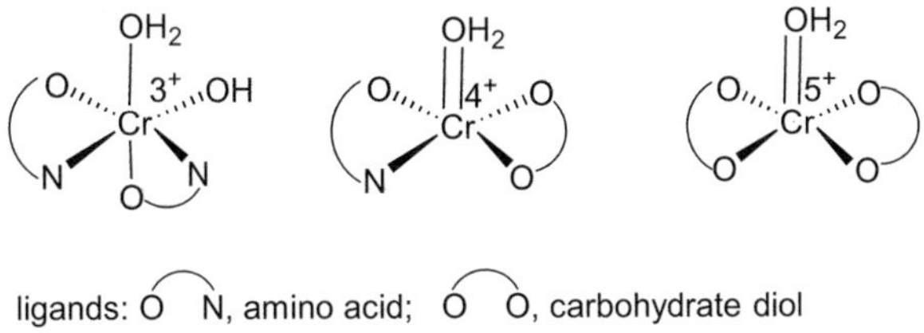

ligands: O⌢N, amino acid; O⌢O, carbohydrate diol

FIGURE 5.7 Chromium complexes, Cr^{3+}, Cr^{4+}, Cr^{5+} [93].

interacts with several biochemical systems and causes damage to proteins and DNA [94]. The safety of Cr^{3+} dietary supplements for control of blood sugar has been questioned [95].

Consistent with the Theory of Hard and Soft Acids and Bases, chromium is a hard (non-polarizable) Lewis acid and forms complexes with hard Lewis bases (oxygen and nitrogen atoms in biomolecules such as amino acids and carbohydrates), see Figure 5.7.

Inside the cell nucleus, Cr^{4+} and Cr^{5+} oxidize guanine bases in DNA thus forming 8-oxoguanine (8-oxoG). Cr^{6+} cannot oxidize guanine. Further oxidation of 8-oxoG at physiological pH, followed by enzymatic excision yields *spiroiminodihydantoin* (also known as the SP lesion), see Scheme 5.22. 8-OxoG also prefers to hydrogen bond to with thymine, thus changing the G:C base pairing to 8-oxoG:T (analogous to C:T). This change is known as a *transversion mutation*, and if not repaired by the cell, can be genotoxic.

Excess ascorbate ($pK_1 = 4.10$) at pH 7, is presented in the suggested mechanism involving Cr^{6+} and Scheme 5.23. In the first step, Cr^{6+} accepts 2 e^- from ascorbate, which is oxidized to dehydroascorbate. In the second step, the intermediate Cr^{4+} is reduced by 1 e^- to Cr^{3+} and ascorbate is converted to the neutral ascorbyl radical [96].

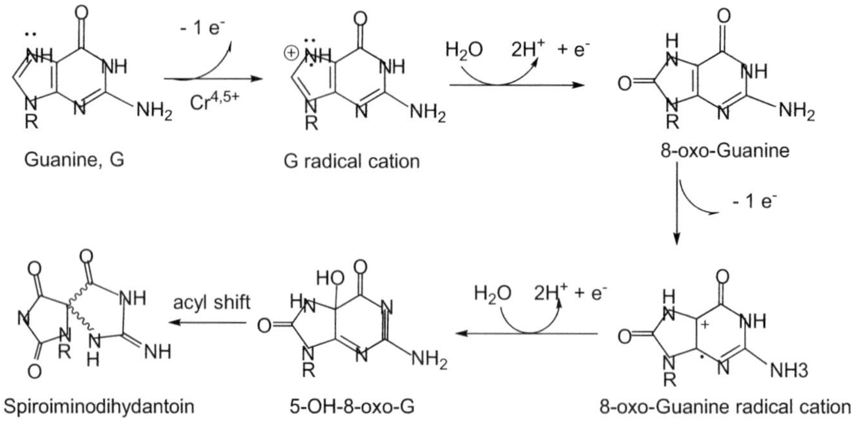

SCHEME 5.22 Chromium toxicity. $Cr^{4,5+}$ oxidation of guanine base in DNA to form spiroiminodihydantoin, the Sp lesion. (Reprinted with permission of P. Slade, M.K. Hailer, B. Martin, K.D. Sugden (2005). *Chem. Res. Toxicol.* 18:1140–1149. Copyright 2005, American Chemical Society.)

R= -CHOH-CH$_2$OH

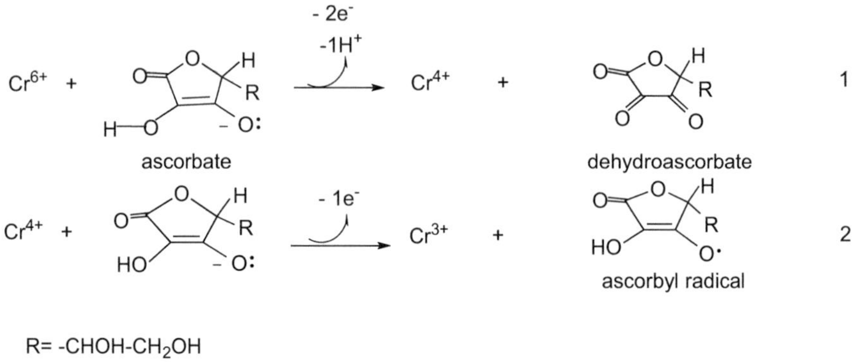

SCHEME 5.23 Reduction of Cr^{6+} to Cr^{3+} by ascorbate [96]. (Reprinted with permission of P. Slade, M.K. Hailer, B. Martin, K.D. Sugden (2005) *Chem. Res. Toxicol.* 18:1140–1149. Copyright 2005, American Chemical Society.)

5.2.8 SILICA DUST

Several art-making activities are associated with exposure to silica dust, including: grinding stone or glass, pottery and ceramics. Inhalation of silica dust can lead to silicosis and lung cancer. The causal agent of these conditions is not a soluble molecular or ionic entity, but instead is particulate matter which is inhaled into the deep region of the lung. Silicosis is a characterized by a complex series of cellular events, in which the lung becomes inelastic and dysfunctional, see Scheme 5.24 [97]. Silica dust has been classified as a Group 1 carcinogen [8,98].

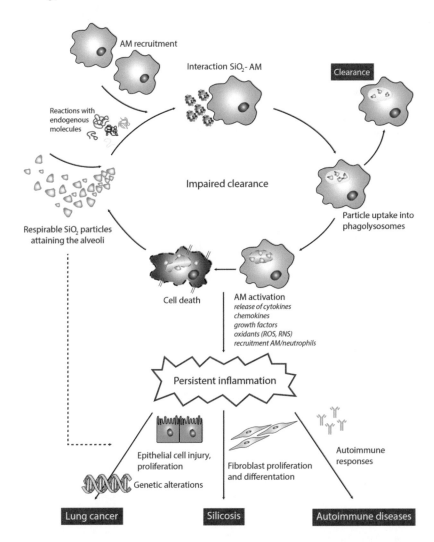

SCHEME 5.24 Proposed mechanism of toxicity of a silica particle attaining the alveolar space. The particle may directly stress the epithelium (dotted line), while the major pathway, following interaction with endogenous matter (antioxidant inactivation and surface coverage by proteins), involves recruitment of alveolar macrophages (AMs) → phagocytosis by AMs → clearance or AM activation (release of pro-inflammatory, pro-fibrotic mediators and chemotactic factors) following damage to the phagolysosome membrane → eventually cell death → release of particles and AM products → recruitment of new AMs and neutrophils. A continuous ingestion− re-ingestion cycle, AM activation, and death are established. The prolonged recruitment/activation of AM and neutrophils causes a persistent inflammation which may evoke (i) epithelial cell injury and proliferation, genetic alterations, and ultimately lung cancer; (ii) fibroblast proliferation and differentiation, collagen production and finally silicosis; (iii) autoimmune responses ending in autoimmune diseases (such as systemic lupus erythematosus, systemic sclerosis, rheumatoid arthritis, vasculitis and chronic renal disease). (Reprinted with permission of C. Pavan and B. Fubini (2017) *Chem. Res. Toxicol.* 30:469–485. Copyright 2017, American Chemical Society.)

REFERENCES

ARTISTS SELF POISONING OCCUPATIONAL HAZARD

1. Ball P, (2001) *Bright Earth*: 179–181, University Chicago Press (First published by Penguin, Great Britain).
2. Pedersen L, Permin H (1988) Rheumatic disease, heavy metal pigments, and the great masters. *Lancet* 331:1267–1269.
3. McCann M (2005) *Artists Beware*: 90–105, 127–151, 286–309. Lyons, Guilford, CT.
4. Rossel M (2001) *The Artists' Complete Health and Safety Guide*, 3rd ed: 96–103, 114–134, 150–165, Allworth, New York
5. Miller BA, Silverman DT, Hoover RN, et al. (1986) Cancer risk among artistic painters. *Amer J Indust Med* 9:281–287.
6. Guha N, Steenland NK, Merletti F, et al. (2010) Bladder cancer risk in painters: a meta-analysis. *Occup Environ Med* 67:568–573.
7. Zuskin E, Schachter EN, Mustajbegovic J, et al. (2007) Occupational health hazards of artists. *Acta Dermatovenereal Croat* 15:167–177.
8. Agents classified by IARC monographs 1–123, https://monographs.iarc.who.int>agents –classified-by-the iarc monographs, volumes 1–123. IARC, Lyon, Fr. Last updated 2 Nov 2018.

ORGANICS

Methylene chloride
9. Small entity compliance guidance for the regulation of methylene chloride. Paint and coating removal (2019). www.epa.gov/EPA-740-B-19-009. Sept 2019.
10a. Gargas M, Clewell HJ, Andersen ME (1986) Metabolism of inhaled dihalomethanes in vivo: differentiation of kinetic constants for two independent pathways. *Toxicol Appl Pharmacol* 82:211–223.
10b. Kubic VL, Anders MW (1978) Metabolism of dihalomethanes to carbon monoxide III. Studies on the mechanism of the reaction. *Biochem Pharmacol* 27:2399–2355.
11. Stewart RD, Hake CL (1976) Paint remover hazard. *J Am Med Assoc* 235:398–401.

Carbon Tetrachloride and Chloroform
12. Weber LWD, Boll M, Stampfl A (2003) Hepatotoxicity and mechanism of haloalkanes: carbon tetrachloride as a toxicological model. *Crit Res Toxicol* 33:105–136.
13. Gemma S, Vittozzi L, Testai E (2003) Metabolism of chloroform in the human liver and identification of the competent P450s. *Drug Metab Disp* 31:266–274.
14. Grandjean P, Landrigan PJ (2014) Neurobehavioral effects of developmental toxicity. *Lancet* 13:330–338.

Trichloroethylene
15. Lash LH, Fisher JW, Lipscomb JC, Parker JC (2000) Metabolism of trichloroethylene. *Env Health Perspect* 108 (Suppl 2):177–200.
16. Mayeno A, Yang RSH, Reisfeld B (2005) Biochemical reaction network modeling: predicting metabolism of organic chemical mixtures. *Env Sci Tech* 39:5363–5371.
17. Mattes TE, Alexander AK, Coleman NV (2010) Aerobic biodegradation of the chloroethenes: pathways, enzymes, ecology, and evolution. *FEMS Microbiol Rev* 34:445–475.
18. Irving RM, Brownfield MS, Elfarra AA (2011) N-biotinyl-S-(1,2-dichlorovinyl)-L-cysteine sulfoxide as a potential model for S-(1,2-dichlorovinyl)-L- cysteine sulfoxide: characterization of stability and reactivity with glutathione and kidney proteins in vitro. *Chem Res Toxicol* 24:1915–1923.

n-Hexane

19. Perbellini L, Brugnone P, Faggionato G (1981) Urinary excretion of n-hexane and its isomers during occupational exposure. *Brit J Indust Med* 38:20–26.
20. St. Clair MGB, Amarnath V, Moody MA, Anthony DC, Anderson CW, Graham DG (1988) Pyrrole oxidation and protein cross-linking as necessary steps in the development of γ-diketone neuropathy, stimulate alternative macrophage activation and eosinophilic airway inflammation. *Chem Res Toxicol* 1:179–185.
21. Perbellini L, Brugnone F, Colcheo V, DeRosa E, Bartolucci GB, (1986) Identification of n-heptane metabolites in rat and human urine. *Arch Toxicol* 58:229–234.

AROMATIC SOLVENTS

Toluene

22. Filley CM, Halliday W, Kleinschmidt-DeMasters BK (2004) The effects of toluene on the central nervous system. *J Neuropath Exp Neur* 63:1–12.
23. Tassaneeyakul W, Birkett DJ, Edwards JW, et al. (1996) Human cytochrome P450 isoform specificity in the regioselectivity metabolism of toluene and o-, m- and p-xylene. *J Pharmacol Exp Ther* 276:101–108.

Benzene

24. Wang L, He X, Bi Y, Ma Q (2012) Stem cell and benzene-induced malignancy and hematotoxicity. *Chem Res Toxicol* 25:1303–1315.
25. Harris CM, Stec DF, Christov PP, Kozekov ID, Rizzo CJ, Harris TM (2011) Deoxyguanosine forms a bis-adduct with E, E-muconaldehyde, an oxidative metabolite of benzene: implications for the carcinogenicity of benzene. *Chem Res Toxicol* 24:1944–1956 Bleasdale C, Kennedy G, MacGregor JO, Nieschalk J, et al. (1996) Chemistry of possible relevance to the toxicology of benzene. *Env Health Perspect* 104:1201–1209.

Xylenes

26. Agency for toxic substances and disease (ATSDR) (2007). *Toxicological Profile for Xylenes*. US Department of Health Human Services, Atlanta, GA. www.atsdr.cdc.gov>substances>toxsubstances

Diisothiocyanates

27. Broughton E (2005) The Bhopal disaster and its aftermath: a review. *Environ Health: A Global Access Sci Sour*, Doi: 10.1186/1476-069X-4-6.
28. Wisnewski AV, Hettick JM, Sigal PD (2011) Toluene diisothiocyanate reactivity across a vapor/liquid interface and subsequent transcarbamoylation of human albumin. *Chem Res Toxicol* 24:1686–1693.

n-Methylpyrrolidone

29. Schindler BK, Koslitz S, Meier S, et al. (2012) Quantification of for major metabolites of embryonic N-methyl- and N-ethyl-2-pyrrolidone in human urine by cooled-injection gas chromatography and isotope dilution mass spectrometry. *Anal Chem* 84:3787–3794.
30. Akesson B, Jönsson BAG (1997) Major metabolic pathway for N-methyl-2-pyrrolidone in humans. *Drug Metab Dispos* 25:267–269.

ALCOHOLS, GLYCOLS AND GLYCOL ETHERS

31. Safety Data Sheet Number WDR15-4. (2019, Feb 5) *Energel Refillable Gel Roller Pen Ink*, Pentel Co. LTD, Japan.
32. Kraut JA, Kurtz I (2008) Toxic alcohol ingestions: clinical features, diagnosis and management. *Clin J Amer Soc Nephrol* 3:208–225.

33. Jacobsen D, McMartin KE (1986) Methanol and ethylene glycol poisonings: mechanism of toxicity, clinical course, diagnosis and treatment. *Med Toxicol* 1:309–334.
34. Booth ED, Dofferhoff O, Boogaard PJ, Watson WP (2004) Comparison of the metabolism of ethylene glycol and glycolic acid *in vitro* by precision-cut tissue slices from female rat, rabbit and human liver. *Xenobio* 34:31–48.
35. ECETOC Working Group: (2005) *The Toxicology of Glycol Ethers and its Relevance to Man*, 4th ed. Tech Report 95, vol 1: 79–169, European Center for Ecotoxicology and Toxicology of Chemicals, Brussels.
36. Corley RA, Markham DA, Banks C, Delorme P, Masterman A, Houle JM (1997) Physiologically based pharmacokinetics and dermal absorption of 2-butoxyethanol vapor by humans. *Fund Appl Toxicol* 39:120–130.

MINERAL SPIRITS

37. Amoruso MA, Gamble JF, McKee RH, Rohde AM (2008) Review of the toxicology of mineral spirits. *Int J Toxicol*, 27:97–165.
38. Zahlsen K, Eide I, Nilsen AM, Nilsen OG (1992) Inhalation kinetics of C_6 to C_{10} aliphatic, aromatic and napthenic hydrocarbons in rat after repeated exposures. *Pharmacol Toxicol* 71:144–149.
39. McKee RH, Adenuga MD, Carrillo J-C (2015) Characterization of the toxicological hazards of hydrocarbon solvents. *Crit Rev Toxicol* 45:273–365.
40. Miura Y (2013) The biological significance of ω-oxidation of fatty acids. *Proc Jpn Acad, Ser B* 89:370–382. Doi: 10.2183/pjab.89.370.
41. Gaugg MT, Bruderer T, Nowak N, et al. (2017) Mass spectrometric detection of omega-oxidation products of aliphatic fatty acids in exhaled breath. *Anal Chem* 89:10329–10334.

TURPENTINE

42. Hartwig A (2019) Turpentine oil [MAK Value Documentation, 2017]. *Mak Collection for Occupational Health and Safety*. 4:128–147.
43. Schmidt L, Göen T (2017) Human metabolism of α-pinene and metabolite kinetics after oral administration. *Arch Toxicol* 91:677–687.
44. Adams TB, Gavin CL, McGowen MM, et al. (2011) The FEMA GRAS assessment of aliphatic and aromatic terpene hydrocarbons used as flavor ingredients. *Food Chem Toxicol* 49:2471–2494.

INORGANICS

45. Chatterjee S, Sarkar S, Bhattacharya S (2014) Toxic metals and autophagy. *Chem Res Toxicol* 27:1887–1900.
46. Levina A, Lay PA (2008) Chemical properties and toxicity of chromium (III) nutritional supplements. *Chem Res Toxicol* 21:563–571.

LEAD

47. Waldron HA (1966) The anaemia of lead poisoning: A review. *Brit J Indust Med* 23:83–100.
48. Jaffee EK (2016) The remarkable character of porphobilinogen synthase. *Acc Chem Res* 49:2509–2517.

49. Van Severin MC, Piquenal J, Parisel O (2010) Lead substitution in synaptotagmin: a case study. *J Phys Chem B* 114:4005–4009.
50. Godwin HA (2001) The biological chemistry of lead. *Curr Opin Chem Biol* 5:223–227.
51. Pounds JG, Long GJ, Rosen JF (1991) Cellular and molecular toxicity of lead in bone. *Environ Health Perspect* 91:17–32.

Zinc, Cadmium, Mercury Family

52. Henkel G, Krebs B (2004) Metallothioneins: zinc, cadmium, mercury and copper thiolates and selenolates mimicking protein active site features-structural aspects and biological implications. *Chem Rev* 104:801–824.
53. Krezel A, Maret W (2007) Dual nanomolar and picomolar Zn(II) binding properties of metallothionein. *J Am Chem Soc* 129:10911–10921.
54. Melnick J, Yurkerwich K, Parkin G (2010) On the chalcogenophilicity of mercury: evidence for a strong Hg-Se bond in [Tm$^{Bu t}$] HgSePh and its relevance to the toxicity of mercury. *J Am Chem Soc* 132:647–655.

Cadmium

55. Godt J, Scheidig F, Gross-Siestrup C, et al. (2006) The toxicity of cadmium and resulting hazards for human health. *J Occup Med Tox* 1:22–27. Doi: 10.1186/1745–6673-1-22.
56. Branca JJV, Fiorillo C, Carrino D, et al. (2020) Cadmium-induced oxidative stress: focus on the central nervous system. *Antioxidants* 9:492–503.
57. Schieber M, Chandel NS (2014) ROS function in redox signaling and oxidative stress. *Curr Biol* 24:R453–R462.

Mercury

58. Liu J, Shi JZ, Yu LM, Goyer R, Waalkes M (2008) Mercury in traditional medicines: is cinnabar toxicologically similar to common mercurial? *Exp Biol Med* 233:810–817.
59. Sunderman FW (1988) Perils of mercury. *Ann Clin Lab Sci* 18:89–101.
60. Hoffmeyer RE, Singh SP, Donnan CJ, et al. (2006) Molecular mimicry in mercury toxicology. *Chem Res Toxicol* 19:753–759.
61. Podar M, Gilmour CC, Brandt CC, et al. (2015) Global prevalence and distribution of genes and microorganisms involved in mercury methylation. *Sci Adv* Oct 9; 1(9):e1500675; Doi: 10.1126/sciadv.1500675.
62. Zhou X, Wang L, Sun X, et al. (2011) Cinnabar is not converted into methylmercury by human intestinal bacteria. *J Ethnopharm* 135:110–115.
63. Jonsson S, Mazrui NM, Mason RP (2016) Dimethylmercury formation mediated by inorganic or organic reduced sulfur surfaces. *Sci Rep* 6:27958. Doi: 10.1038/srep27958.
64. Nierenberg DW, Nordgren RE, Chang MB, et al. (1998) Delayed cerebellar disease and death after accidental exposure to dimethylmercury. *New Engl J Med* 338:1672–1676.
65. OSHA Hazard Information Bulletin: Dimethylmercury, March 9, 1998. www.osha.gov>dts>hib>hib_data>hib19980309.

Silver

66. Smith R (2003) *The Artists' Handbook*. Revised Edition: 97–98, DK Publishing, New York.

67. Lansdown A (2010) A pharmacological and toxicological profile of silver as an antimicrobial agent in medical devices. *Adv Pharmacol Sci* Doi: 10.1155/2010/910686.
68. Burdette S, Lippard S (2003) Meeting of the minds: metalloneurochemistry. *Proc Nat Acad Sci* 100:3506–3610.
69. Ning C, Wang Y, Li L, et al. (2015) Concentration ranges for antibacterial cations for showing the highest antibacterial efficiency but the least cytotoxicity against mammalian cells: implications for a new antibacterial mechanism. *Chem Res Toxicol* 28:1815–1822.
70. McShan D, Ray PC, Yu H (2014) Molecular toxicity mechanism of nanosilver. *J Food Drug Anal* 22:116–127.
71. Poon V, Burd A (2004) In-vitro cytotoxicity of silver: implication for clinical wound care. *Burns* 30:140–147.
72. Greulich C, Braun D, Peetsch A, et al. (2012) The toxic effect of silver ions and silver nanoparticles towards bacteria and human cells occurs in the same concentration range. *RSC Adv* 2:6981–6987.
73. Xu FF, Imlay J (2012) Silver(I), mercury(II), cadmium(II), and zinc(II) target exposed enzymic iron-sulfur clusters when they toxify *E. Coli*. *Appl Env Microbiol* 78:3614–3621.
74. Xiu Z, Zhang Q, Puppala H, Colvin V (2012) Negligible particle-specific antibacterial activity of silver nanoparticles. *Nano Lett* 12:4271–4275.
75. Burrell RE (2003) A scientific perspective on the use of topical silver preparations. *Ostomy Wound Manage* 49:(5ASuppl)19–24.
76. Foldbjerg R, Jiang X, Miclăuş T, Chen C, Autrup H, Beer C (2015) Silver nanoparticles-wolves in sheep's clothing? *Toxicol Res* 4:563–575.

ARSENIC

77. Nordstrom DK (2006) Worldwide occurrences of arsenic in ground water. *Science* 296:2143–2145.
78. Lindberg AL, Vahter M (2006) Health effects of inorganic arsenic. In: *Arsenic in Ground Water. A World Problem*: 64–81, Appelo T (ed). Proceedings Seminar Utrecht 29 Nov 2006. ISBN/EAN 978-90-808258-2-6.
79. Jomova K, Jenisova Z, Feszterova M, et al. (2011) Arsenic: toxicity, oxidative stress and human disease. *J Appl Tox* 31:95–107.
80. Chen SJ, Zhou GB, Zhang XW, Mao JH, de Thé H, Chen Z (2011) From an old remedy to a magic bullet: Molecular mechanisms underlying the therapeutic effects of arsenic in fighting leukemia. *Blood* 16:6425–6437.
81a. Liu JX, Zhou GB, Zhou SJ, Chen SJ, Chen Z (2012) Arsenic compounds: revived ancient remedies in the fight against human malignancies. *Curr Opin Chem Biol* 16:92–98.
81b. Koch I, Sylvester S, Lai V W-M, Owen A, Reimer K, Cullen W (2007) Bioaccessibility and excretion of arsenic in *Niu Huang Jie Du Pian pills*. Toxicol Appl Pharmacol 222: 357–364.
82. Chen P, Yan L, Wang Q, Li H (2013) Arsenic precipitation in the bioleaching of realgar using *A. ferrooxydans*. *J Appl Chem* Doi: 10.1155/2013/424253.
83. Challenger F (1945) Biological methylation. *Chem Rev* 36:315–361.
84. Cullen WR, Reimer KJ (1989) Arsenic speciation in the environment. *Chem Rev* 89:713–764.
85. Shen S, Li XF, Cullen W, Weinfeld M, Lee XC (2013) Arsenic binding to proteins. *Chem Rev* 113:7769–7792.
86. Azizur Rahman M, Hassler C (2014) *Aquat Tox* 146:212–219.

87. Coryell M, Roggenbeck BA, Walk ST (2019) The human gut microbiome's influence on arsenic toxicity. *Curr Pharmacol Rep* 5:491–504.

88. Le XC, Lu X, Ma M, Cullen W, Aposhian HV, Zheng B (2000) Speciation of key arsenic metabolic intermediates in human urine. *Anal Chem* 72:5172–5177.

89. Chou WC, Jie C, Kennedy A, Jones RJ, Trush M, Dang CV (2004) Role of NADPH oxidase in arsenic-induced reactive oxygen species and cytotoxicity in myeloid leukemia cells. *Proc Nat Acad Sci* 101:4578–4583.

90. Mailloux RJ, McBride S, Harper ME (2013) Unearthing the secrets of mitochondrial ROS and glutathione in bioenergetics. *Trends Biochem Sci* 38:592–602.

CHROMIUM

91. Markus Y (1988) Hydrated radii in aqueous solutions. *Chem Rev* 88:1475–1498.

92. Ortega R, Fayard B, Salomé M, et al. (2005) Chromium oxidation state imaging in mammalian cells exposed in vitro to soluble or particulate chromate compounds. *Chem Res Toxicol* 18:1512–1519.

93. Levina A, Lay PA (2008) Chemical properties and toxicity of chromium (III) nutritional supplements. *Chem Res Toxicol* 21:563–571.

94. Holland SL, Avery SV (2011) Chromate toxicity and the role of sulfur. *Metallomics* 11:1119–1123.

95. Wu LE, Levina A, Harris HH, et al. (2016) Carcinogenic chromium (VI) compounds formed by intracellular oxidation of chromium (III) dietary supplements by adipocytes. *Angew Chem Int Ed* 55:1742–1745.

96. Slade P, Hailer MK, Martin B, Sugden K (2005) Guanine-specific oxidation of double stranded DNA by Cr (VI) and ascorbic acid forms spiroiminodihydantoin and 8-oxo-2'-deoxyguanosine. *Chem Res Toxicol* 18:1140–1149.

SILICA DUST

97. Pavan C, Fubini B (2016) Unveiling the variability of "quartz hazard" in light of recent toxicological findings. *Chem Res Toxicol* 30:469–485.

98. Steenland K, Ward E (2014) Silica: A lung carcinogen. *CA: Cancer J Clin* 64:63–69. Doi: 10.3322/caac.21214.

6 Aging of Oil Paint Binder

Exposure of oil paintings to environmental factors (light, water vapor, O_2 and air pollutants) leads to "aging". Pigment degradation was the subject of Chapter 3. Binder degradation also occurs and is described by the appearance of protrusions or eruptions on the surface of paintings, see Figure 6.1 [1]. Investigation of the nature and cause of these eruptions led Boon et al. (1997) to propose a model for the aging of oil paint [2]. The model has a time domain of several hundred years, see Figure 6.2. The model provides a general framework to explore the aging of oil paint.

According to the model, fresh oil paint undergoes autoxidative chemical changes. [Autoxidation or auto-oxidation refers to oxidative processes that are driven by atmospheric oxygen.] These include covalent cross-linking between fatty acid chains and chain scission which produces low-molecular-mass products (hydrocarbons, aldehydes, ketones and acids). The drying of linseed oil catalyzed by PbO including historical recipes with associated FTIR spectra was documented by de Viguerie et al. in 2016 [3]. Hydrolysis of glycerol esters yields carboxylic acids which react with cations from catalytic "drier" compounds added to the oil or from metal-containing pigments to form metal soaps. Drier compounds include metal soaps such as linoleates of Pb^{2+} and Mn^{2+} and also stearates, palmitates, oleates and naphthenates of Al^{3+}, Ca^{2+} and Zn^{2+} [4,5].

Oil paint is produced by suspending small particles of finely ground pigment in a drying oil binder, usually linseed oil. Linseed oil is used because the composition

FIGURE 6.1 Photoimage of pustule on the surface of *Libellules blesses*, 1961 painted by K. Appel, 1961 [1]. (Reprinted with permission of I.A.T. Bronken, J.J. Boon, R. Corkery, C.C. Steindal (2019) *J. Cult. Herit.* 35: 279–287. Copyright 2019, Elsevier Masson SAS. All rights reserved.)

DOI: 10.1201/9781003053453-6

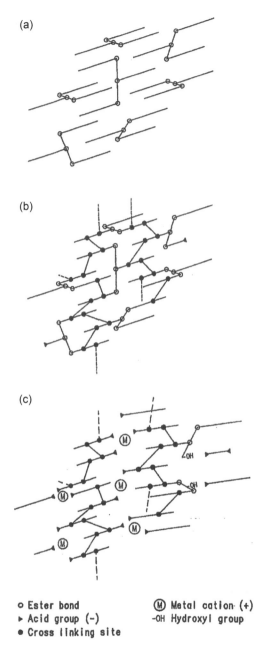

(a)

(b)

(c)

o Ester bond   Ⓜ Metal cation (+)
▸ Acid group (−)   −OH Hydroxyl group
● Cross linking site

FIGURE 6.2 Proposed model of the oil paint polymer network [2]. (a), triglyceride oil; (b), cross-linked polymer formed by autoxidation of unsaturated sites of linoleic and linolenic acids; (c), mature stage, many glyceride esters have been hydrolyzed, and carboxylate anions form electrostatic bonds with metallic cations (metal soaps). (Reprinted with permission of J.J. Boon, S.L. Peulve, O.F. van den Brink, M.C. Dursma, D. Rainford, *Symposium, Maastricht, 9-10 October 1996:* 35–56. Copyright 1997, to J.J. Boon.)

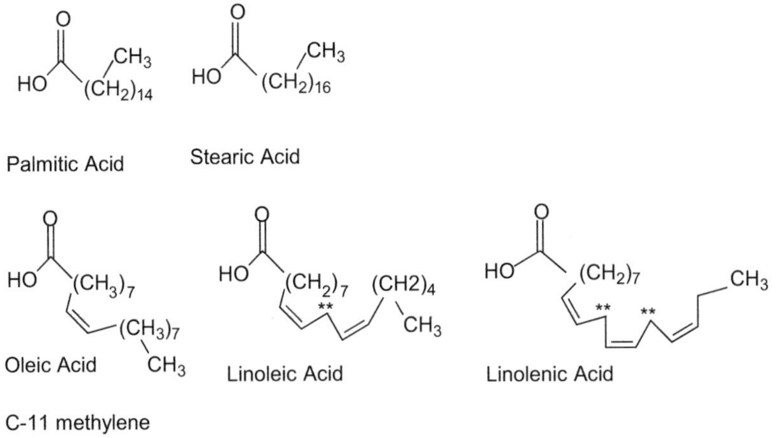

Palmitic Acid   Stearic Acid

Oleic Acid   CH₃   Linoleic Acid   Linolenic Acid

* C-11 methylene

FIGURE 6.3 Fatty acids from hydrolysis of linseed oil. Bis-allylic carbon atoms are marked with **.

contains a very high mass percentage of unsaturated fatty acids which are easily autoxidized. Mass percentages of fatty acids (FAs), released on hydrolysis: palmitic, C_{16}, (3.7–11.7), stearic, C_{18}, (2.3–8.7), oleic, $C_{18:1}$, (11.5–27.6), linoleic, $C_{18:2}$, (12.6–19.0) and linolenic, $C_{18:3}$, (34.1–59.6), see Figure 6.3 [6].

It is well established that oil paintings must stand in the studio for several months in order to "dry" before they can be exhibited. In this context, "drying" does not mean the evaporation of water, but instead, complex oxidative changes leading to a hardening of the oil matrix due to the formation of covalent cross-links [7].

6.1 MAIN FEATURES OF THE MODEL FOR AGING OIL PAINT

Initial and Curing Stage: Linolenic acid (C18:3) and linoleic acid (C18:2) – containing triglycerides auto-oxidize to yield reactive monomers (peroxides and free radicals) which form *covalent cross-links* between the hydrocarbon chains of the oil [2]. This leads to a three-dimensional polymeric structure, the "stationary phase".

Mature Stage: The oily binder contains a low concentration of water which originates from atmospheric water vapor. Hydrolysis of triglyceride esters results in the formation of carboxylic acid groups and hydroxyl groups of glycerol. The acid groups react with either pigments or driers and form metal soaps:

$$2\,RCO_2H + M(OH)_2 \rightarrow M\,(RCO_2)_2 + 2\,H_2O,$$

where M is a polyvalent metal, usually Pb^{2+} or Zn^{2+}, and $M(OH)_2$ represents a basic pigment, e.g., white lead or red lead. Massicot, a lead monoxide (MO), is also used. The metal can also be Cu^{2+} or Fe^{+2}.

α,ω-Dialkanoic carboxylic acids, $HO_2C\text{-}(CH_2)_n\text{-}CO_2H$, formed by the oxidative scission of unsaturated FA chains and hydrolysis of glyceride esters, yield double-headed metal soaps. These act as *ionic* cross-links which stabilize the "*ionomeric*"

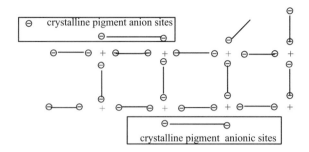

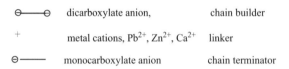

crystalline pigment anionic sites, O^{2-}, HO^-

⊖——⊖	dicarboxylate anion,	chain builder
+	metal cations, Pb^{2+}, Zn^{2+}, Ca^{2+}	linker
⊖——	monocarboxylate anion	chain terminator

FIGURE 6.4 Structure of hypothetical ionic oil paint polymer, "ionomer". In this metal-coordinated system, dicarboxylates act as ionic bridges which stabilize a three-dimensional structure. Monocarboxylates are chain terminators that limit the size of the ionomeric polymer. (Adapted from the *34th meeting of the AIC of historic and artistic works, Providence, RI, June 2006*: 16–23, ed. HM Parkin, Reprinted with permission of J.J. Boon, Hoogland F, Keune K, ed: Parkin HM. Copyright 2006 to J.J. Boon.)

structure (containing ionic and polymeric character), see Figure 6.4 [8]. Low-molecular-mass products are lost by evaporation. Free mono-FAs, di-FAs and glycerol constitute the "mobile phase" and can migrate through the paint. Components of the mobile phase can also be removed by cleaning with polar solvents.

Degradational Stage: Prolonged exposure of the polymers to light in the presence of air and metal-containing pigments leads to degradation. Paint becomes powdery and is very sensitive to mechanical cleaning.

The model is based on analysis of aged oil paint which contained white lead, obtained from a painting by J.M.E. Turner (*Dolbadern Castle*, first exhibited in 1810). A two-step derivatization scheme comprised reaction with NaOEt in EtOH (trans-esterification) followed by the reaction with the silylating agent, bis(trimethylsilyl) trifluoroamide, BSTFA, see Scheme 6.1 [9]. The first step converted all FA glyceride esters to ethyl esters. The second step converted free carboxylic acids to TMS esters. The derivatized sample was introduced into a GC/MS which separated the products and detected them by molecular mass. Consequently, this method distinguished between "bound" carboxylic acid groups (originally present as glyceride esters) from "free" carboxylic acid groups (produced by chain scission and autoxidation). The products detected included both bound and free α, ω-alkanedioic acids (suberic acid, C_8, and azelaic acid, C_9). These diacids are *not* present in linseed oil and therefore were produced by a combination of autoxidation of the unsaturated FAs and hydrolysis of the glyceride esters. Also found were palmitic and stearic acids, saturated FAs which were present as glyceride esters in linseed oil. The unsaturated FAs, oleic,

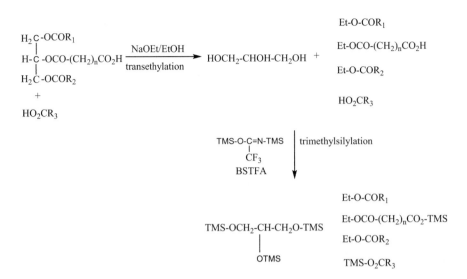

SCHEME 6.1 Two-step derivatization method to distinguish between esterified and free fatty acids in aged oil paint. TMS, trimethylsilyl; BSTFA, N,O-bis(trimethylsilyl)trifluoro-acetamide. (Adapted and reprinted with permission of J.D.J. van den Berg, K. J. van den berg, J.J. Boon (2001) *Prog. Org. Coat.* 41:143–155. Copyright, 2001, Elsevier.)

linoleic and linolenic acids, were not detected, see Figure 6.5 [2]. A subsequent study showed essentially the same pattern with more compounds detected due to improvement of the methodology [10].

6.2   IR SPECTRA OF METAL SOAPS

The IR spectrum of globular protrusions in the surface of the painting, *Libellules blesses* (Karel Appel, 1961), revealed strong absorption bands consistent with the presence of *metal soaps* at 1548, 1528, 1456 and 1398 cm^{-1}, see Figure 6.6 [1]. This spectrum also shows a medium band at 1742 cm^{-1} (ester carbonyl) which indicates that significant *hydrolysis* of the glyceride ester bonds has occurred. In addition, there is no band ~1700 cm^{-1} indicating the absence of carboxylic acid groups. For another example of degraded oil paint, consider the IR spectra of three regions of the Jackson Pollack painting, *Alchemy*, 1947, see Figure 6.7 [11]. These spectra show bands at 1540, 1450 and 1400 cm^{-1}; the spectrum of Zn stearate is included and shares these three bands.

For reference, the IR spectra of stearic acid and its Zn, Cu and Pb salts have been reported in detail [12]. Zn stearate has strong bands at 1540 cm^{-1} (asymmetric $-CO_2^-$ stretch), 1465 cm^{-1} (-CH$_2$- bend) and 1398 cm^{-1} (symmetric $-CO_2^-$ stretch) and eight weak progression bands between 1324 and 1187 cm^{-1}. Lead stearate has a doublet at 1541 and 1513 cm^{-1}, assigned to the $-CO_2^-$ asymmetric stretch. The progression bands are attributed to the wagging of transoid methylenes of the long saturated aliphatic chain in an organized raft structure [13]. For a comparison of stearic acid and Zn stearate structures and IR spectra, see Figure 6.8 [14].

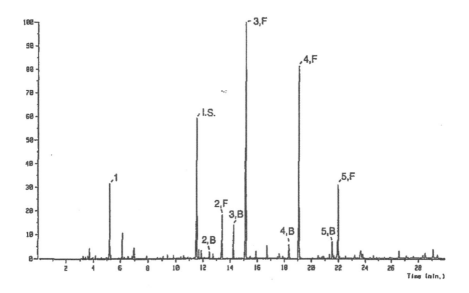

FIGURE 6.5 Total ion chromatogram of the aged paint sample. Free (F) and bound (B) fatty acids in a 19th century paint sample taken from J.M.W. Turner's painting *Dolbadern Castle* (first exhibited in 1810). The peaks are glycerol (1), suberic acid (2), azelaic acid (3), palmitic acid (4) and stearic acid (5). I.S. is the internal standard n-hexadecane [2]. (Reprinted with permission of J.J. Boon, S.L. Peulve, O.F. van den Brink, M.C. Dursma, D. Rainford *Symposium, Maastricht 9–10 October 1996*: 35–56. Copyright 1997, to J.J. Boon.)

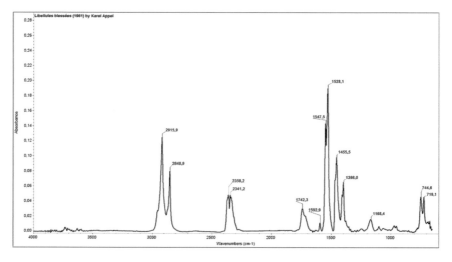

FIGURE 6.6 FTIR spectrum of globular protrusion sample from *Libellules blesses*, 1961 painted by K. Appel. Bands at 1548 and 1528 cm^{-1} are consistent with a metal soap. (Reprinted with permission of I.A.T. Bronken, J.J. Boon, R.W. Corkery, C.C. Steindal (2019) *J. Cult. Herit.* 35: 279-287. Copyright 2019, Elsevier Masson SAS. All rights reserved.)

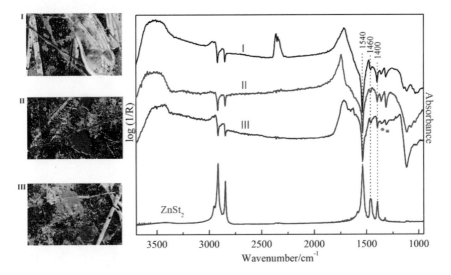

FIGURE 6.7 Details of ZnO/TiO2 white (I), phthalocyanine blue (II), and cobalt phosphate violet (III) paints from *Alchemy,* 1947, Jackson Pollard, analyzed by mid-FTIR reflection spectroscopy. Spectra acquired on the paints; sharp inverted signals at 1540, 1460 and 1400 cm^{-1} indicate the presence of zinc soaps of saturated long chain FAs (i.e., stearic acid and/or palmitic acid). Spectrum acquired in the transmission mode from a reference sample of Zn stearate (ZnSt$_2$) is also reported. Asterisk (*) indicates signals of Zn oxalates. (Reprinted with permission of F. Gabrieli, F. Rosi, A. Vichi, et al. (2017) *Anal. Chem.* 89:1283–1289. Copyright 2017, American Chemical Society.)

Figure 6.9 is a cartoon conception of the interaction of metal soaps leading to an organized, crystalline aggregate [15]. According to the model proposed by Boon et al. (1996), the dominant saturated fatty acids of linseed oil, stearic and palmitic acids, released by hydrolysis, were predicted to form single-headed metallic soaps with polyvalent cations from pigments or drier additives. These could migrate depending on the presence of water adsorbed into the paint layer, causing degradation of the paint [16].

6.3 METAL SOAP AGGREGATION: MODEL SYSTEM

Degradation of an oil painting proceeds over the course of years. A model system was constructed to follow the formation and aggregation of Pb palmitate (PbPa) soap by FTIR spectroscopy, over a period of hours [17], see Figure 6.10. In this system, "Pbpol" represents a stage where the cation has interacted with partially polymerized linseed oil. Initially, there is a *broad* band (1630 cm^{-1}) which in time changes to a *sharp* band (1510 cm^{-1}). A broad band is generally interpreted to signify that the energy-absorbing unit has more than one environment, and a sharp band signifies a single environment. In this system, the end-point spectra are consistent with crystalline Pb stearate which was cited in the references. Also, the Pb palmitate spectrum shows the –CH$_2$-progression bands in a magnification of the weak bands in the 1340–1240 cm^{-1} region. Analogous results were found for Zn palmitate.

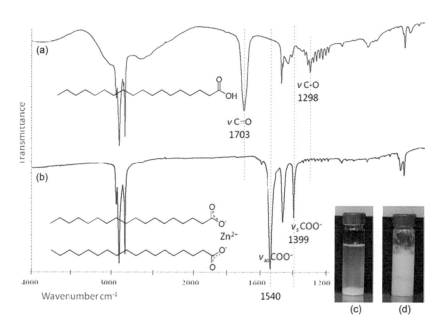

FIGURE 6.8 Transmission FTIR spectra for (a) stearic acid and (b) zinc stearate. Inset vial images show a mixture of ZnO and stearic acid 1:10 by weight (approx. 1:3 mol) in toluene after (c) 30 min and (d) 2 months showing a dramatic physical expansion of the solid phase accompanying formation of zinc stearate. (Reprinted with permission of G. Osmond (2019) *Metal Soaps in Art, Conservation and Research*: 25–46, ed F. Casadio et al. Copyright 2019, Springer.)

Metal soaps, usually those of lead or zinc, have been found in a large number of degraded paintings and their presence is recognized as a current problem in art conservation [18]. IR spectra of oil paints prepared with various artists' pigments were reviewed by van der Weerd et al. [19].

6.4 AUTOXIDATIVE REACTIONS LEADING TO CHAIN SCISSION AND CROSS-LINKING IN OIL PAINT

During the drying stage, the mass of the painting increases ~10% because of uptake of atmospheric oxygen [7]. The addition of O_2 to the unsaturated sites of the long alkyl chains leads to the formation of peroxy radicals, hydroperoxides and alkoxy-radicals, see Scheme 6.2. *Inter-chain covalent cross-links* are proposed to form from the reaction of an alkoxy radical on one chain with a double bond on another chain, see Scheme 6.3. The utility of linseed oil is due to the reactivity of linoleyl and linolenyl chains. This is because hydrogen atom abstraction (H·) at the C-11 bis-allylic methylene carbon yields a free radical which can be resonance-stabilized by allylic centers to the right and left of the unpaired electron.

In addition to the formation of cross-links, autoxidation also yields low-molecular-weight aldehydes by *chain scission*, see Scheme 6.4 [20]. Aldehydes are easily oxidized to the corresponding carboxylic acids.

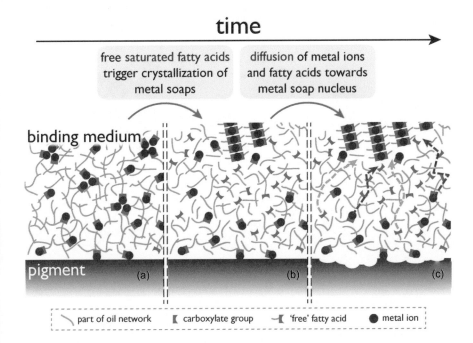

FIGURE 6.9 Illustration of metal soap-related degradation processes in ionomeric-binding media (a), triggered by the presence of free saturated fatty acids (b) and resulting in the formation of large crystalline metal soap phases (c). Dashed arrows illustrate the diffusion of metal ions (red) and free saturated FAs (blue) toward the growing crystalline metal soap aggregate. (Reprinted with permission of J.J Hermans, K. Keune, A. Van Loon, P. Iedema (2019) in *Metal Soaps in Art, Conservation and Research*: 47–68, ed. F. Casadio et al. Copyright 2019, Springer.)

6.5 METAL OXALATES IN OIL PAINT

Metal oxalate patinas have been detected on the surfaces of artworks. Numerous factors have been associated with the formation of these patinas, including microbial, pigment-varnish interactions, and photodegradation of binder [21]. Simonsen et al. showed that atmospheric CO_2 is not the source of oxalate in a model oil paint system. μ-FTIR spectroscopy (FTIR data acquired with a microscope) is frequently used to detect metal oxalates [22]. Infrared absorption bands of interest for oxalates are summarized in Table 6.1.

Samples of chrome yellow, CY, $Pb(Cr_{(1-x)}S_xO_4$, linseed oil, and fillers ($BaSO_4$ and $CaCO_3$) on glass slides were stressed under these conditions: irradiation, $\lambda > 300$ nm/30°C/1.0–1.3 y/40% RH. The CY paint was a reconstitution of Winsor and Newton CY oil paint which was used by artists such as Vincent van Gogh, Georges Seurat and A. de Souza-Cardoso [23]. The original CY paint has been associated with discoloration caused by the reduction of chromium ($Cr^{6+} \rightarrow Cr^{3+}$), see Chapter 4. The stressed samples were analyzed by several techniques: μ-FTIR, (functional groups); μ-XRD (crystal diffraction pattern), μ-XRF (qualitative metal analysis) and μ-XANES (oxidation state of the metal). In Figure 6.11, see FTIR maps constructed by scanning the sample for absorption at specific frequency ranges including:

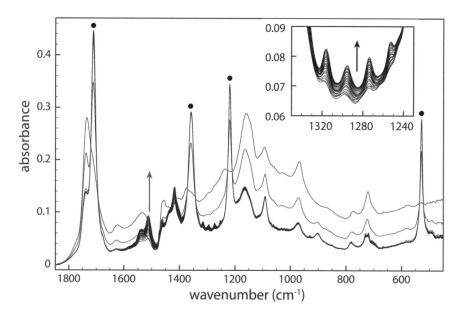

FIGURE 6.10 A baseline-corrected selection of IR spectra at 10 min intervals of Pbpol ionomer of 140–160 μm thickness, recorded during the first 200 min of exposure to a solution of palmitic acid (HPa) in acetone. Pbpol is a complex of Pb^{2+} with polymerized linseed oil. Intensity of spectra increases with time. Bands associated with acetone are marked by •. Arrows indicate the ν_{asym} stretch $-CO_2^-$ vibration of crystalline $PbPa_2$, lead palmitate, complexes. The inset in (a) shows the CH_2 progression bands of $PbPa_2$. (Reprinted with permission of L. Baij, J.J. Hermans, K. Keune, P. Iedema (2018) *Angew. Chem. Int. Ed.* 57: 7351–7354. Copyright 2018, Wiley-VCH Verlag GmbH & Co.)

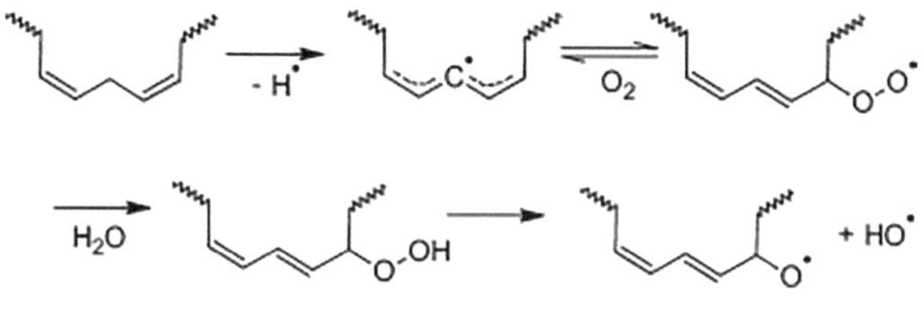

SCHEME 6.2 Mechanism for autoxidation of linoleic acid. (Reprinted with permission of S. Morsch, B.A. van Driel, K.J. van den Berg (2017) *ACS Appl. Mater. Interfaces* 9: 10169–10179. Copyright 2017, American Chemical Society.)

esters (1755–1720 cm⁻¹), carboxylic acids (1718–1700 cm⁻¹), calcium oxalate (1340–1300 cm⁻¹) and calcium carbonate (1550–1520 cm⁻¹). The maps show that calcium oxalate is present at the surface, and next is a layer containing acids, next is the bulk which contains esters and calcium carbonate. In Figure 6.12, the μ-XRD map shows calcium oxalate dihydrate near the surface and calcium carbonate below the surface. Finally, the μ-XRF map shows that Cr^{3+} is present near the surface.

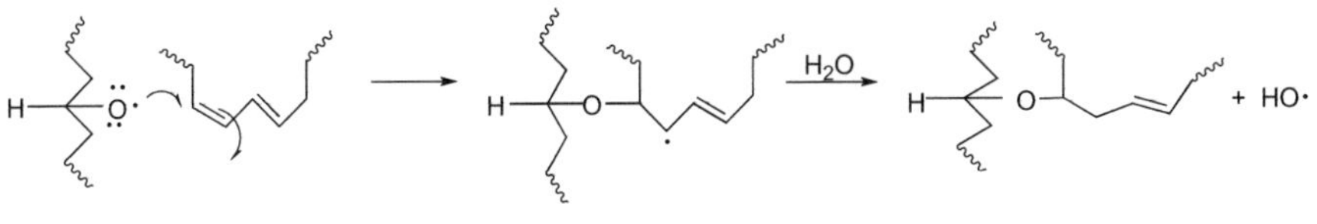

SCHEME 6.3 Formation of cross-linked oxidized linseed oil. (Adapted and reprinted with permission of I. Bonaduce, C. Duce, A. Lluveras-Tenorio, B. Ormsby, A. Burnstock, K.J. van den Berg (2019) *Acc. Chem. Res.* 52:3397–3406. Copyright 2019, American Chemical Society.)

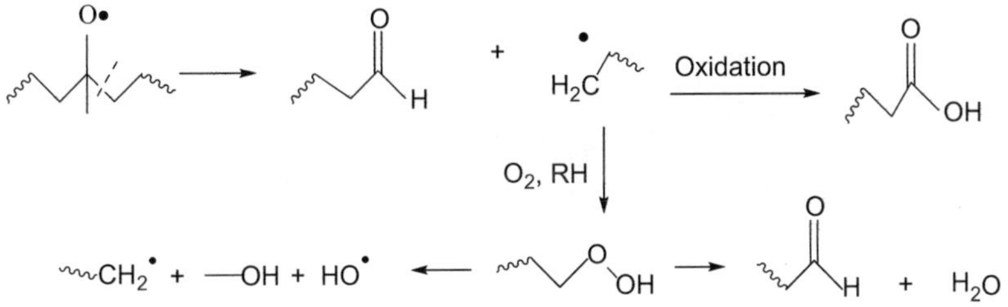

SCHEME 6.4 Mechanism for aldehyde and carboxylic acid formation during autoxidation of linseed oil. (Adapted and reprinted with permission of S. Morsch, B.A. van Driel, K.J. van den Berg (2017) *ACS Appl. Mater. Interfaces* 9: 10169–10179. Copyright 2017, American Chemical Society.)

TABLE 6.1
Infrared Frequencies, cm^{-1}, for Selected Metal Oxalates

CaO$_x$·2H$_2$O	ZnO$_x$·2H$_2$O	CdO$_x$·2H$_2$O	Band Assignments
3560, 3460	3392	3550, 3500	O-H stretch
1645	1634	1614	C=O asymmetric stretch
1329	1364, 1320	1382, 1322	C=O symmetric stretch
615	743, 611	598	H$_2$O$_{libration}$

Source: Adapted and reprinted with permission of L. Monico, F. Rosi, C. Miliani, A. Daveri, B.G. Brunetti (2013) *Spectrochim. Acta A* 116: 270–280.
Libration is hindered rotation of mutually hydrogen-bonded water molecules.

Based on these results, a mechanism was proposed, see Scheme 6.5. Hydrolysis of glyceride esters yields fatty acids and glycerol hydroxyl groups. Acids react with calcium carbonate to yield carbonic acid which dehydrates to carbon dioxide. Carbon dioxide undergoes reduction activated by light to form oxalate. Cr^{6+} in PbCrO$_4$ is reduced to Cr^{3+} by oxalate to give KCr(SO$_4$)$_2$ 12H$_2$O and CO$_2$.

Other studies suggested that coupling of oxidation of the polyunsaturated oil *binder* with reduction of pigments. Reduction of Cr^{6+} → Cr^{3+} in the degradation of chrome yellow was covered in Chapter 4. The authors of the chrome yellow

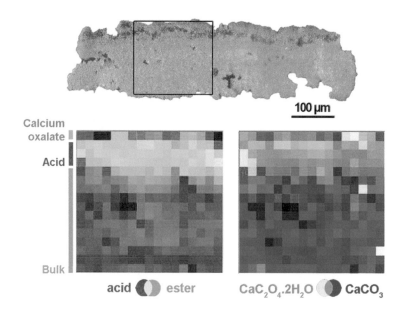

FIGURE 6.11 Optical microscopy image of a sample of chrome yellow paint (artificially aged, irradiated for 7750 h, other conditions stated in the text). Black outlined area corresponds to the SR-FTIR maps (size $160 \times 150\,\mu m^2$, with $10 \times 10\,\mu m^2$ step size). Regions of interest: acids (1718–1700 cm^{-1}), esters (1755–1720 cm^{-1}), Ca oxalate (1340–1300 cm^{-1}) and Ca carbonate (1550–1520 cm^{-1}). (Reprinted with permission of V. Otero, M. Vilarigues, L. Carlyle, M. Cotte, W. DeWolf, M.J. Melo (2018) *Photochem. Photobiol. Sci.* 17: 266–270. Copyright, 2018, Royal Society of Chemistry.)

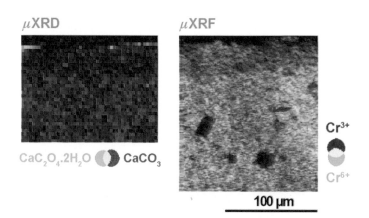

FIGURE 6.12 SR-µXRD map: red, calcite, CaCO$_3$; green, weddelite, Ca oxalate dihydrate, and SR-µXRF map at Cr K-edge showing the enrichment in Cr^{3+} in the top layer of chrome yellow paint (artificially aged 11,000 h) [23]. (Reprinted with permission of V. Otero, M. Vilarigues, L. Carlyle, M. Cotte, W. DeWolf, M.J. Melo (2018) *Photochem Photobiol. Sci.* 17: 266–270. Copyright, 2018, Royal Society of Chemistry.)

esters $\xrightarrow{\text{H}_2\text{O}}$ fatty acids

fatty acids $\xrightarrow{\text{CO}_3^{2-}}$ $H_2CO_3 \longrightarrow H_2O + CO_2$

$2 \ CO_2 \xrightarrow{+ 2 \ e^-, \ h\upsilon} C_2O_4^{2-} \xrightarrow{Ca^{2+}} Ca \ C_2O_4$

$Cr^{6+} + C_2O_4^{2-} \longrightarrow Cr^{3+} + CO_2$

SCHEME 6.5 Mechanism for the formation of calcium oxalate in oil paint. (Adapted and reprinted with permission of V. Otero, M. Vilarigues, L. Carlyle, M. Cotte, W. DeNolf, M.J. Melo (2018) *Photochem. Photobiol. Sci.* 17: 266–270.)

degradation study assumed that the oxidation of the binder was the "missing piece" in the degradation scheme [24]. Another example of this phenomenon is reduction of $Pb^{4+} \rightarrow Pb^{2+}$ in red lead coupled to oxidation of organic binder [25].

6.6 PHOTOCATALYTIC ROLE OF TiO$_2$ IN DEGRADATION OF OIL PAINT

Titanium white, TiO_2, has been recognized as a causal factor in the degradation of the binder in white oil paint. Ti White, commercialized in the 1920s was the pigment most widely used in the 20th century, thereby replacing lead white and zinc white. TiO_2 occurs principally in two crystalline forms. Anatase is a strong photocatalyst, while rutile has much weaker photocatalytic activity. Early 20th-century artists were unaware of the photocatalytic property of Ti White, and this has led to the degradation of the oil binder [26]. Currently, TiO_2 photocatalysts have been developed to remove microbes and pollutants from air and water [27].

A photocatalytic degradation cycle for TiO_2 is presented in Scheme 6.6. TiO_2 is activated by radiant energy in step 1 to generate an electron and a positively charged hole. Step 2a shows recombination which forms on TiO_2 surfaces which are coated with alumina or silica. In step 2b, hydroxyl radical and superoxide anion are formed. These free radicals attack the organic binder in step 3 to produce various intermediates (consistent with Schemes 6.2–6.4). Therefore, in contrast to other photo-semiconductor pigments (including Pb_3O_4, HgS and CdS) which are altered by interactions with humidity and radiant energy, TiO_2 is a photo-semiconductor *catalyst*, i.e., the pigment is not altered under similar conditions. Titanium soaps have not been identified in degraded Titanium White paint.

$TiO_2 + h\upsilon \longrightarrow e^- + hole^+$ 1.

$e^- + hole^+ \xrightarrow{\text{recombination}} TiO_2 + heat$ 2a.

$hole^+ \ HO^- \longrightarrow HO\cdot$ and $e^- + O_2 \longrightarrow O_2^{\cdot-}$ 2b.

$HO\cdot$ and $O_2^{\cdot-} +$ binder $\longrightarrow$ intermediates $\longrightarrow CO_2 + H_2O$ 3.

SCHEME 6.6 TiO$_2$ photocatalytic degradation cycle. (Reprinted with permission of B.A. van Driel, P.J. Kooyman, K.J. van den Berg, A. Schmidt-Ott, J. Dik (2016) *Microchem. J.* 126:162-171. Copyright 2016, Elsevier.)

REFERENCES

1. Bronken IAT, Boon JJ, Corkery RW, Steindal CC (2019) Changing surface features, weeping and metal soap formation in paintings by Karel Appel and Asger Jorn from 1946–1971. *J Cult Herit* 35:279–287.
2. Boon JJ, Peulvé SL, van den Brink OF, Duursma MC, Rainford D (1997) Molecular aspects of mobile and stationary phases in ageing tempera and oil paint films. In: *Early Italian Paintings, Techniques and Analysis, Symposium*, Maastricht, 9–10 October 1996: 35–56.
3. De Viguerie L, Payard PA, Portero E, Walter Ph, Cotte M (2016) The drying of linseed oil investigated by Fourier transform infrared spectroscopy: historical recipes and influence of lead compounds. *Prog Org Coat* 93: 46–60.
4. Tumosa C, MF Mecklenberg (2005) The influence of lead ions on the drying of oils. *Rev Conserv* 6:39–47.
5. Honzíček J (2019) Curing of air drying paints: a critical review. *Ind Eng Chem Res* 58:12485–12505.
6. Nykter M, Kymalainen HR (2006) Quality characteristics of edible linseed oil. *Agric. Food* Sci 15:402–413.
7. Tumosa CS, Mecklenberg MF (2013) Oil Paints: the chemistry of drying oils and the potential for solvent disruption. *Smithsonian Contributions to Museum Conserv* 3:51–58.
8. Boon JJ, Hoogland F, Keune K, Parkin HM (2006) Chemical processes in aged oil paints affecting metal soap migration and aggregation. *34th meeting of the AIC of historic and artistic works*, Parkin HM ed. Providence, RI, June 2006: 16–23.
9. Van den Berg JDJ, van den Berg KJ, Boon JJ (2001) Determination of the degree of hydrolysis of oil paint samples using a two-step derivatization method and on-column GC/MS. *Prog Org Coat* 41:143–155.
10. Van den Berg JDJ, van den Berg KJ, Boon JJ (2002) Identification of non-cross-linked compounds in methanolic extracts of cured and aged linseed oil-based paint films using GC/MS. *J Chromat A* 950:195–211.
11. Gabrieli F, Rosi F, Vichi A, et al. (2017) Revealing the nature and distribution of metal carboxylates in Jackson Pollack's *Alchemy* (1947) by micro-attenuated total reflection FTIR spectroscopic imaging. *Anal Chem* 89:1283–1289.
12. Robinet L, Corbeil M-C (2003) The characterization of metal soaps. *Stud Conserv* 48:23–40.
13. Barman S, Vasudevan S (2007) Mixed saturated-unsaturated alkyl-chain assemblies: solid solutions of zinc stearate and zinc oleate. *J Phys Chem B* 111:5212–5217.
14. Osmond G. (2019) Zinc soaps: an overview of zinc oxide reactivity and consequences of soap formation in oil-based paintings. In: *Metal Soaps in Art, Conservation and Research*: 25–46, ed Casadio F, et al., Springer, Cham, Switzerland.
15. Hermans JJ, Keune K, Van Loon A, Iedema P (2019) Toward a complete molecular model for the formation of metal soaps in oil paint. In: *Metal Soaps in Art, Conservation and Research*: 47–68, ed Casadio F, et al., Springer, Cham, Switzerland.
16. Bonaduce I, Duce C, Lluveras-Tenorio A, Lee J, Ormsby B, Burnstock A, van den Berg KJ (2019) Conservation issues of modern oil paintings: a molecular model on paint curing. *Acc Chem Res* 52:3397–3406.
17. Baij L, Hermans JJ, Keune K, Iedma, P (2018) Time-dependent ATR-FTIR spectroscopic studies on fatty acid diffusion and the formation of metal soaps in oil paint model systems. *Angew Chem Int Ed* 57:7351–7354.
18. Cotte M, Checroun E, De Nolf W, Taniguchi Y, De Viguerie L, Burghammer M, Walter P, Rivard C, Salome M, Janssens K, Susini J (2016) Lead soaps in paintings: friends or foes, *Stud Conserv* 62:1–22.

19. Van der Weerd J, van Loon A, Boon JJ (2005) FTIR studies of the effects of pigments on the aging of oil. *Stud Conserv* 50:3–22.

20. Morsch S, van Driel BA, van den Berg KJ, Dik J (2017) Investigating the Photocatalytic degradation of oil paint using ATR-IR and AFM-IR. *ACS Appl Mater Interfaces* 9:10169–10179.

21. Simonsen KP, Poulsen JN, Vanmeert F, Rhyl-Svendsen M, Bendix J, Sanyova J, Janssens K, Mederos-Henry F (2020) Formation of zinc oxalate from zinc white in various oil binding media: the influence of atmospheric carbon dioxide by reaction with[13] CO_2. *Herit Sci* 8:126–137.

22. Monico L, Sorace L, Cotte M, de Nolf W, Janssens K, Romani A, Miliani C (2019) Disclosing the binding medium effects and the pigment solubility in the (photo)reduction process of chrome yellows ($PbCrO_4/PbCr_{1-x}S_xO_4$). *ACS Omega* 4:6607–6619.

23. Otero V, Vilarigues M, Carlyle L, Cotte M, DeNolf W, Melo MJ (2018) A *little* key to oxalate formation in oil paints: protective patina or chemical reactor? *Photochem Photobiol Sci* 17:266–270.

24. Monico L, Rosi F, Miliani C, Daveri A, Brunetti BG (2013) Non-invasive identification of metal-oxalate complexes on polychrome artwork surfaces by reflection mid-infrared spectrometry. *Spectrochim Acta A* 116:270–280.

25. Vanmeert F, van der Snickt G, Janssens K (2015) Plumbonacrite identified by x-ray powder diffraction tomography as a missing link during degradation of red lead in a van Gogh painting. *Angew Chem Int Ed* 54:3607–3610.

26. van Driel BA, Kooyman PJ, van den Berg KJ, Schmidt-Ott A, Dik J (2016) A quick assessment of the photocatalytic activity of TiO_2 pigments–from lab to conservation studio. *Microchem J* 126:162–171.

27. Schneider J, Matsuoka M, Takeuchi M, Zhang J, Horiuchi Y, Anpo M, Bahnemann DW (2014) Understanding TiO_2 photocatalysis: mechanisms and materials. *Chem Rev* 114:9919–9986.

7 Aging of Wall Paintings

Wall paintings have been created by two different methods. In the *secco* (dry) method, colors are suspended in a non-aqueous binder such as glue, animal fat, oil or wax and applied to a dry wall. Secco paintings date back to ancient Egypt. The other method is *fresco*, in which pigments are dissolved or suspended in water and applied to the plaster while it is still wet. Fresco has been known since ancient Rome.

In the fresco technique, plaster is prepared by suspending quicklime (CaO) or slaked lime ($Ca(OH)_2$) in water and applying the slurry to a wall. Upon standing, the process of *carbonation* converts lime to calcite ($CaCO_3$) by the reaction with atmospheric carbon dioxide.

$$Ca(OH)_{2\ solid} + CO_{2\ gas} \rightarrow CaCO_{3\ solid} + H_2O_{gas}$$

The process incorporates carbon dioxide, hence "carbonation". When colors are painted on wet plaster, the process of water evaporation causes the pigments to become embedded in crystals of calcite. The wall surface is primed with three layers of plaster. The first layer of plaster, the arrichio, is made with crushed stone and sand. A preliminary drawing (the sinopia) is made on the arrichio. The second and third and third layers of plaster are the intonaco and the tonachino; these are composed of $Ca(OH)_2$, fine sand (SiO_2) and sometimes powdered marble ($CaCO_3$). The third layer is very thin and applied to small sections of the wall so that the artist can paint each section before it dries.

The application of pigments to the wet plaster layer allows the crystalline calcite mineral to surround the pigment grains, and this makes the painted layers bright and durable [1]. Note that the raw material, lime, was produced by thermal decomposition of limestone (decarbonation) ($CaCO_3$),

$$CaCO_{3\ solid} + heat \rightarrow CaO_{solid} + CO_{2\ gas}.$$

Pigments in wall paintings and easel paintings are exposed to numerous environmental factors which limit their stability. These include relative humidity (RH), air pollutants (SO_x, NO_x and H_2S), alkalis, acids and light [2]. Wall paintings are also exposed to water and aqueous salt solutions because wall construction materials are porous and also contain water-soluble ions. Consequently, water in the porous space of walls will extract these ions leading to salt deposits (efflorescence) which may interact with calcite or with pigments. Interaction of sulfate with calcite generates the more soluble gypsum, (process of *sulfation*), and facilitates erosion of the wall. Red lead is degraded by extracted salt ions [3].

DOI: 10.1201/9781003053453-7

7.1 REVERSAL OF SULFATION BY THE FERRONI-DINI METHOD

There are several causes of fresco deterioration, including atmospheric SO_2, acid rain (H_2SO_4), microbial attack, dissolution by rain water and the action of extracted salts. Although calcite is poorly soluble in water, rain will dissolve it very slowly over a long period of time. SO_2 and acid rain are more potent. SO_2 is converted to SO_3 and then H_2SO_4 by oxidation and hydration which occur within days in the atmosphere. When acid rain encounters calcite, an acid–base reaction takes place which converts calcite to gypsum:

$$CaCO_{3\ solid} + H_2SO_{4\ aq} \rightarrow CaSO_{4\ solid} + H_2O_{liquid} + CO_{2\ gas}.$$

The release of the gaseous product, CO_2, drives the reaction by entropy, (there is no way to put the genie back in the bottle). In this reaction, the anion has changed from carbonate to sulfate, in a process known as *sulfation* [4]. Industrial SO_2 emissions peaked in the 1980s, and have since been reduced. This will slow the rate of sulfation of calcite walls. Gypsum is about 100-fold more soluble in water compared to calcite, see Table 7.1. Consequently, gypsum is more easily eroded by water. A mechanism for sulfation of calcite is presented in Scheme 7.1.

Over the years, many approaches have been used with partial success to restore frescoes. For example, since 1960, commercial *organic* acrylic polymers were used to treat powdered and flaked paints. However, these methods often failed and often accelerated degradation of the artwork [5]. Hence in the current approach, the guiding principle is to use only *inorganic* materials for restorative work. Organic materials are less stable because of the tendency to air-oxidize.

In the Ferroni-Dini method, also known as the barium method, ammonium carbonate-saturated solution is applied to the damaged (sulfated) areas. In this case, ammonium carbonate is very soluble, see Table 7.1. Gypsum reacts with ammonium carbonate to produce *insoluble* calcite and *very soluble* ammonium sulfate:

$$CaSO_4\cdot 2\,H_2O_{solid} + (NH_4)_2\,CO_{3aq} \rightarrow (NH_4)_2\,SO_{4\ aq} + CaCO_{3\ solid} + 2\,H_2O_{liquid}.$$

In the second step, ammonium sulfate is removed by the reaction with barium hydroxide solution:

$$(NH_4)_2\,SO_{4\ aq} + Ba(OH)_{2\ aq} \rightarrow BaSO_{4\ solid} + 2\,NH_{3\ gas} + 2\,H_2O_{liquid}.$$

The sequence of steps yields insoluble barium sulfate, which becomes part of the solid matrix. The other two products escape into the atmosphere. Thus, calcite and barium sulfate participate in *consolidation* of the solid binder after the more soluble gypsum has been removed [6]. The Ferroni-Dini method represents a major advance in the restoration of frescoes. The consolidation process was used to reverse sulfation of a 15th-century wall painting, *Crucifixion*, by B. Angelico, see Figure 7.1. See Figure 7.2 for another example of desulfation of a wall painting from a Mesoamerican site [5].

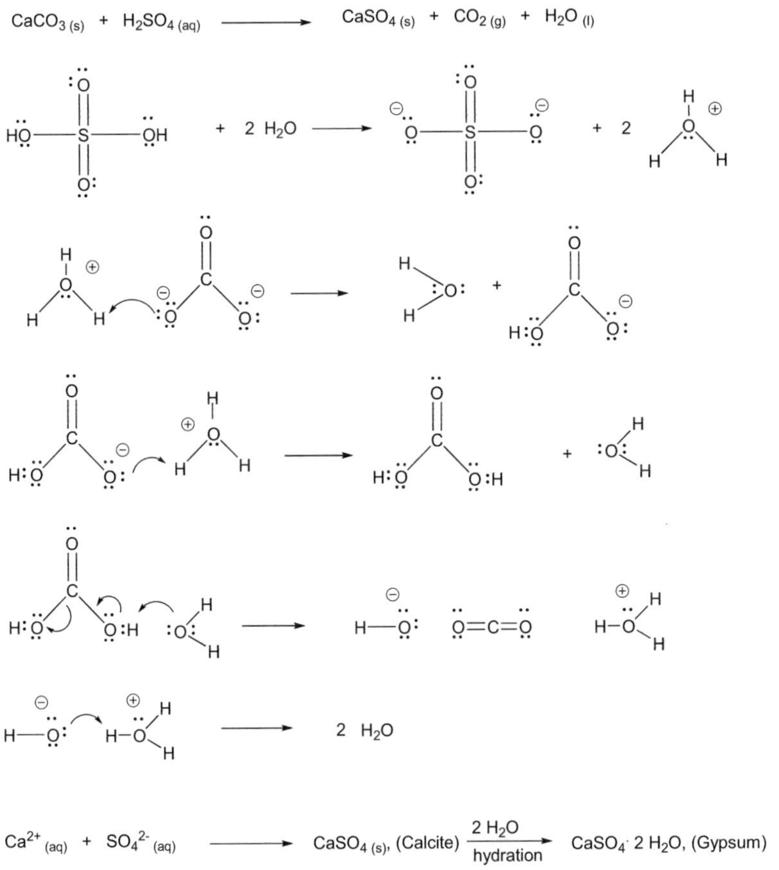

$$CaCO_{3\,(s)} + H_2SO_{4\,(aq)} \longrightarrow CaSO_{4\,(s)} + CO_{2\,(g)} + H_2O_{(l)} \qquad 1$$

2

3

4

5

6

$$Ca^{2+}_{\,(aq)} + SO_4^{2-}_{\,(aq)} \longrightarrow CaSO_{4\,(s)},\ (Calcite) \xrightarrow[\text{hydration}]{2\,H_2O} CaSO_4 \cdot 2\,H_2O,\ (Gypsum) \qquad 7$$

SCHEME 7.1 Mechanism for sulfation of calcite.

TABLE 7.1
Solubilities of Compounds Involved in Desulfation of Wall Paintings by the Ferroni-Dini Method [4]

Compound	Mole/kg Water	Compound	Mole/kg Water
$CaCO_3$	1.4×10^{-4}	$(NH_4)_2SO_4$	5.8
$CaSO_4 \cdot 2H_2O$, gypsum	1.5×10^{-2}	$Ba(OH)_2\,8H_2O$	0.12
$(NH_4)_2CO_3$	10.4	$BaSO_4$	1.0×10^{-5}

Prior to the development of the Ferroni-Dini method, the laborious detachment method was used, in which a canvas was glued to the wall painting. After the glue dried, a cut was made around the perimeter of the fresco, and the painting was rolled up onto the canvas. The painting was restored and then reinstalled on the wall [1].

FIGURE 7.1   (a and b) Desulfation of a wall painting by Beato Angelico (15th century) in the San Marco convent, Florence, Italy. Application of the Ferroni-Dini method [6]. Before (a) and after (b) treatment. (Reprinted with permission of P. Baglioni and R. Giorgi (2006) *Soft Matter* 2: 293–303. Copyright 2006, Royal Society of Chemistry.)

FIGURE 7.2   (a) Wall painting belonging to a Mesoamerican archeological site. (b) Details of a flaking surface exhibiting sulfate efflorescence. (c) The same surface after the desulfation treatment with ammonium carbonate and the application of a mixed calcium and barium hydroxide nanoparticle dispersion. (Reprinted with permission of P. Baglioni, D. Chelazzi, R. Giorgi, G. Poggi (2013) *Langmuir* 29: 5110–5122. Copyright 2013, American Chemical Society.)

7.2   INFLUENCE OF WATER-SOLUBLE SALTS

Wall construction materials (brick, mortar and cement) contain numerous salts based on water extraction of these ions: Na^+, K^+, Ca^{2+}, Mg^{2+}, NH_4^+, CO_3^{2-}, SO_4^{2-}, Cl^-, NO_3^- and $C_2O_4^{2-}$ from common burnt red bricks and sand from a sand-pit, see Table 7.2 [3].

TABLE 7.2
Extractable Ions from Burnt Brick and Sand [3]

Ion	Extracted from Burnt Brick, mg/kg	Extracted from Sand, mg/kg
SO_4^{2-}	520	32
Cl^-	260	19
HCO_3^-	240	460
NO_3^-	10	11
Ca^{2+}	280	150
Na^+	31	23
K^+	25	28
Mg^{2+}	0	96

20 grams of crushed solid was stirred with 200 ml of distilled water; the filtrate was analyzed spectroscopically.

Red lead is known to darken in wall paintings [7]. A darkened wall painting, approximately 100 years old in the Church of St. George in Kostol'any pod tribečom, Slovakia was analyzed by X-ray diffraction (XRD). The diffractogram shows peaks corresponding to plattnerite (PbO_2), cerrusite ($PbCO_3$) and magnesium lead (II) carbonate [$MgPb(CO_3)_2$], see Figure 7.3. An experimental test sample of red lead applied to the plaster coated on brick (fresco style) was stored for 6 months in a plastic container with aqueous 0.2M $MgCO_3$ so that the solution was soaked into the brick. The surface was then analyzed by XRD. The diffractogram has peaks corresponding to red lead (minimum), plattnerite, cerrusite and magnesium lead (II) carbonate. On the basis of this data, the conclusion was that red lead in the wall painting degraded due to contact with Mg^{2+} and CO_3^{2-} which likely originated from efflorescence of extracted salt [3]. Degradation of lead-based pigments by salt solutions was addressed by Kotulanova et al. [8].

7.3 DEGRADATION OF OIL BINDER

Another type of wall painting degradation involves the oil binder used in the secco technique, see Figure 7.4. In this example, the sample is a paint fragment obtained from a Greek Orthodox church near Triste, Italy, which was decorated in 1819. The paint fragment layers with associated pigments are presented in Table 7.3 and Figure 7.4a. Accordingly, the fourth layer of paint contains white lead and its FTIR spectrum shows the frequency of bands, cm^{-1}, assigned to the oil binder: (2930, 2850, C-H); ester carbonyl (1738); free fatty acid $-CO_2H$ (1711); δC-H (1460); metal soap (ν_{asym} and ν_{sym} $-CO_2^-$, 1570 and 1414) and metal oxalate (ν_{asym} and ν_{sym} $-CO_2^-$, 1640, 1319). [The bands at 1570 and 1414 cm^{-1} were labeled as cx for carboxylate which might be confused for ox, oxalate.] Figures 7.4d–i are false color maps which show the locations of drying oil, fatty acids, metal soaps, metal oxalates and white lead

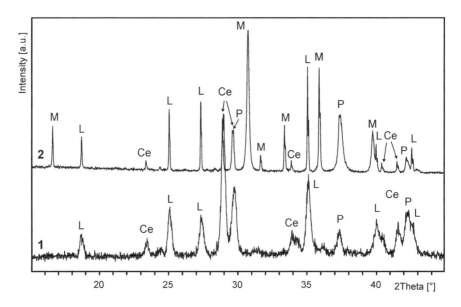

FIGURE 7.3 Comparison of X-ray diffractograms. **1**- a fragment from Kostol'any wall painting. **2**- a reaction product of red lead, Pb_3O_4, with an aqueous solution of $MgCO_3$ after 6 months of contact. Phase abbreviations: M – minimum, Pb_3O_4; Ce- cerrusite, $PbCO_3$; L-lead magnesium carbonate $PbMg(CO_3)_2$; P- plattnerite, PbO_2. 2θ, the detection angle, is characteristic of the unit cell of specific compounds. (Reprinted with permission of E. Kotulanova, J. Schweigstillova, S. Svarcova, D. Hradil, P. Bezdicka, T. Grygar (2009). *Acta Res. Rep.* 18: 27–31. Copyright 2009, Academy of Science, Czech Republic.)

TABLE 7.3
Pigments Identified in Paint Fragment from Greek Orthodox Church Near Trieste, Italy [9]

Paint Layer	Pigments Identified
1st	Calcite
2nd	Prussian blue, white lead
3rd	White lead, yellow ochre, red lead
4th	White lead
5th	Red ochre

in the various layers based on FTIR data [9]. These results are consistent with the autoxidation and hydrolysis of the oil binder, as described in Chapter 6.

The stability of "medieval pigments", available from about 400 to 1400 AD was reviewed [2]. The list includes whites (lead white, calcium carbonate), yellows (ochres, orpiment, massicot, lead-tin yellows), orange-reds (ochres, realgar, vermilion, litharge, red lead), blues (ultramarine, blue ochre, smalt, azurite, Egyptian blue), greens (green earths, malachite, verdigris), brown (umbers) and black (carbon black). Despite known instability issues, many of these pigments were used in wall paintings

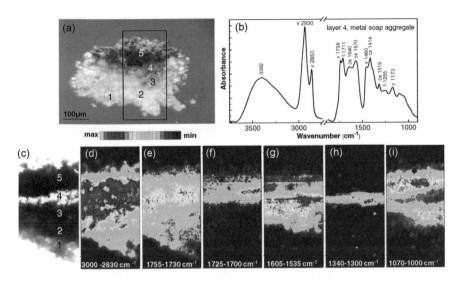

FIGURE 7.4 Analysis of paint fragment from a Greek Orthodox church near Trieste, Italy. (a) Photomicrographs in white reflected light, of the C2 section preserving the order of its stratigraphy, after being compressed in a diamond anvil cell device. The different layers are clearly observed and numbered, whereas the black outline indicates the region of interest (ROI) selected for FTIR. (b) FTIR spectrum taken from the data corresponding to layer 4 (magenta false color in (h)). The bands of drying oil (**v**), fatty acids (**f**), metal carboxylates (**c x**) and metal oxalates (**o x**) are indicated. (c) Photomicrograph of the ROI of the thin section selected for FTIR. FTIR images, representing the spatial distribution of: (d) aliphatic compounds, (e) triglycerides of drying oil, (f) fatty acids, (g) metal carboxylates, (h) metal oxalates, and (i) lead white. The size of the FTIR images is $340 \times 170\,\mu m^2$. (Reprinted with permission of S. Sotiropoulou, Z.E. Papliaka, L. Vaccari (2016) *Microchem. J.* 124: 559–567. Copyright 2016, Elsevier.)

because of the quality of their color and cost of material. To be suitable for fresco wall painting, pigments must be stable to alkali and lightfast. The following palette of pigments satisfies these requirements and were recommended for permanent frescoes: white, $BaSO_4$; black, Mars Black; red, Indian red; blue, cobalt blue or Cerulean blue; green, chromium (III) oxide or hydrated chromium oxide (viridian); yellow, Mars yellow, and violet, Mars violet [10]. Mars pigments are hydrates of iron (III) oxide (-yellow, $FeO(OH)$; and -red, -orange and -brown are hydrates of Fe_2O_3). Mars black is based on Fe_3O_4, which contains Fe^{2+} and Fe^{3+} [11,12].

REFERENCES

1. Fuga A (2006) *Artists' Techniques and Materials*: 99–107, J. Paul Getty Museum, Los Angeles, CA.
2. Coccato A, Moens L, Vandenabeele P (2017) On the stability of medieval pigments : a literature review of the effect of climate, material selection, biological activity, analysis and conservation treatments. *Herit Sci* 5:12–37.
3. Kotulanova E, Schweigstillova J, Svarcova S, Hradil D, Bezdička P, Grygar T (2009) Wall painting damage by salts: causes and mechanisms. *Acta Res Rep* 18: 27–31.